BUILDING LONDON'S UNDERGROUND

Antony Badsey-Ellis

Capital Transport

Published by Capital Transport Publishing Ltd
www.capitaltransport.com

Printed by Parksons Graphics

Contents

Abbreviations

AC	Alternating current
B&PCR	Brompton & Piccadilly Circus Railway
BAA	British Airports Authority
BoT	Board of Trade
BS&WR	Baker Street & Waterloo Railway
C&SLR	City & South London Railway
CCE&HR	Charing Cross, Euston & Hampstead Railway
CLR	Central London Railway
DC	Direct current
DLR	Docklands Light Railway
ELL	East London Line
EPBM	Earth Pressure Balance Machine
GN&CR	Great Northern & City Railway
GN&SR	Great Northern & Strand Railway
GNP&BR	Great Northern, Piccadilly & Brompton Railway
GNR	Great Northern Railway
GWR	Great Western Railway
h.p.	horsepower
JLE	Jubilee Line Extension
JV	Joint Venture
LCC	London County Council
LER	London Electric Railway
L&NER	London & North Eastern Railway
LPTB	London Passenger Transport Board
L&SWR	London & South Western Railway
LT	London Transport
LTM	London Transport Museum
LUL	London Underground Ltd
M&SJWR	Metropolitan & St John's Wood Railway
MDR	Metropolitan District Railway
MHA	Mott, Hay & Anderson
MR	Metropolitan Railway
NATM	New Austrian Tunnelling Method
NLR	North London Railway
p.s.i.	Pounds per square inch
r.p.m.	Revolutions per minute
SCL	Sprayed Concrete Lining
SGI	Spheroidal Graphite Iron
TBM	Tunnel Boring Machine
TfL	Transport for London
UERL	Underground Electric Railways Company of London
W&CR	Waterloo & City Railway

Preface and acknowledgements

This book is intended for anyone who is interested in how the London Underground was made, but is not written as a detailed technical work. I wrote it after realizing that despite the large number of books that have been written about the London Underground and its history, none of them could really be considered as an engineering history. I wanted to explain how developments in engineering technology enabled the Underground to be built, and how the building of the tunnels drove innovation in the technology.

I have not attempted to describe the building of every part of the Underground, but instead focused on the areas that were innovative, or that had particularly interesting features. For those who want to know more, there is a list of references at the end of the book.

I am very grateful, as ever, to Mike Horne for reviewing the draft text and suggesting improvements. At Crossrail, Mike Black, the Head of Geotechnics, and Rana Alakus both read the chapter on the newest railway to be built in London and provided help with getting the facts straight. I also extend my thanks to the staff of The National Archives, the London Metropolitan Archives, the reference libraries of the London Transport Museum and the Institution of Civil Engineers, all of whom have facilitated my research, and to Brian Hardy, Kim Rennie, Printz Holman, Nick Catford, Simon Lewis, John Bull (and others at London Reconnections), the London Underground Railway Society, and Herrenknecht AG for providing photos and illustrations. My final thanks must go to my wife Wendy, who has read through the book and helped with improving the style and clarity, as well as acting as a sounding-board for my thoughts. As always, responsibility for any mistakes and errors rests with me.

Antony Badsey-Ellis
Amersham
January 2016

Introduction

This book is about the civil engineering that created the London Underground, and mostly about the amazing feats of tunnelling that created the network of tunnels beneath the capital. The work started a little over 150 years ago, and continues today, but on a scale and with machinery that would be unrecognizable to the navvies who dug the Metropolitan Railway with picks and shovels. In the chapters that follow, the stories of how the tunnels and stations were made are presented, roughly in chronological order. The aim is to trace the history of building the subterranean parts of the Underground, and the focus is on the innovation that occurred with each subsequent line or extension that opened, and so not every engineering event is included. There is little about the parts of the Underground that are on the surface: these were built using methods that were tried and tested by the time that these lines were made. But those who wonder just how engineers in late Victorian times managed to carve out tunnels through the London clay and make them meet to within an inch or so, using little more than plumb-lines, theodolites, and pick-axes should find the answers in these pages.

A nineteenth century map showing the proposed Thames Archway tunnel and the drift tunnel which was constructed. The curved access roads, which were never made, are also marked.

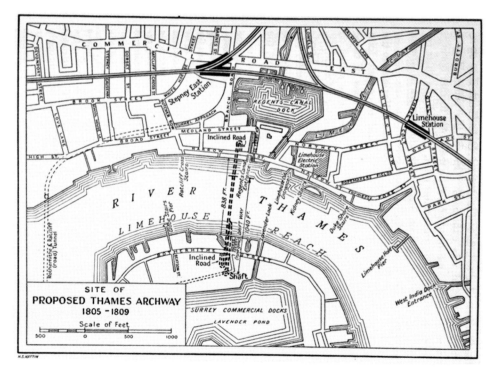

Railway tunnels

The oldest railway tunnel in the world is believed to have opened in 1793, on a tramroad used to move limestone from a Derbyshire quarry to a canal. It was a modest 32 yds (29 m) long, and was constructed with a masonry arch lining. This is where railway tunnelling began.[1] The techniques used to construct it were becoming established for building canal tunnels, which dated back about 25 years earlier.

As Britain's railway network developed in the mid-1800s, it became necessary to build longer and longer tunnels. Engineers sought to keep the tracks as level as possible, and where natural obstacles such as hills and mountains were encountered, cuttings and then tunnels were built. Through the nineteenth century the techniques and technology to build tunnels developed as different types of geology were encountered and new machinery was invented; however, it remained an intensively manual process, often fraught with danger. In order to make the best progress, but also to provide ventilation for the steam locomotives that would pass through upon completion, shafts were sunk along the line of the hill and miners would start additional tunnel faces from the foot of these. They worked by candle-light: awkward enough when picks and shovels were being wielded, but positively dangerous for those tunnels that required gunpowder to blast through rock. Injury and death were common; the death-rate on the Woodhead Tunnel beneath the Pennines was higher than that at the battle of Waterloo. It was the men who worked on these tunnels who, in the 1860s, would help excavate beneath London's streets.

Tunnelling under water

The tunnels built by the railways as they developed from the 1830s were made through developments of existing mining techniques, as for the most part they went through solid ground. Tunnelling through soft ground was a different challenge, and amazingly it was one that was taken up at the beginning of the nineteenth century.

Not only was the Thames Archway tunnel to cut through soft clay, it was also to be the first under-river tunnel in London. The famous Cornish engineer, Richard Trevithick, was part of the Thames Archway Company that was founded in 1805 for the purpose of making the tunnel. It was to link the Rotherhithe peninsula with the Limehouse area on the north bank. On both sides of the river inclined access roads descended away from the river before curving back round through 180°; this avoided the need to acquire long narrow sites for the ramps. A shaft 11 ft in diameter was sunk by the original engineer, Robert Vazie, to a depth of 42 ft but with money running low the diameter was reduced to 8 ft for the next 34 ft. Vazie struggled to cope with the water that leaked into the shaft, and in August 1807 Trevithick was brought in by the company to complete the job, being promised £1,000 if the tunnel was successfully finished; initially working with Vazie, he was given complete control from October after the two men fell out. He expected to complete the work in 9 months, and thought that he would "be making [£]1000 very easily, and without any risk of loss on my side".[2]

A steam pumping engine of insufficient capacity was installed and then upgraded to deal with the water. A single 'pilot' tunnel (known as the Thames Drift Tunnel, or driftway) was bored from Rotherhithe towards Limehouse. The miners would have been very cramped: it was 1·52 m high, and between 76 and 91 cm wide. Three men worked at a time, in six-hour shifts, kneeling in the wet mud as they excavated the tunnel face in front of them.[3] It was intended that this would form the drain for the larger tunnel that was to be excavated subsequently. However, the soft clay beneath the river bed what not like the rock that the Cornish miners were used to, and the timbers used to support the tunnel roof and sides were of little use; water broke into the workings on two occasions. The first, on 23 December 1807, was fixed by placing clay over the quicksand layer and then draining off the water through a pipe. The second, on 26 January 1908, was more serious and the tunnel was flooded. Trevithick nearly drowned in this inundation.[4] The pilot tunnel had almost crossed beneath the river and was 1,040 ft long, but the company directors were not happy and work ceased.

After prevarication over what should be done with the tunnel, a competition was held inviting suggestions from the public. One idea that was investigated in detail was for the creation of the tunnel in prefabricated sections sunk into a trench cut across the bed of the river. This was suggested by Charles Wyatt, who proposed that the sections be 50 ft lengths of brick tunnel, sealed at each end. Once in the trench they would be covered by 6 ft of clay (to prevent damage by ships' anchors) and the temporary brickwork at each end would be removed and the tunnels joined together. A manhole in the upper surface of each tube would allow access for the work. In this way the risk of excavating in the treacherous soil below the river would be greatly diminished.

The Thames Archway Company liked the idea, and appointed John Isaac Hawkins to test the concept on a half-scale model. In particular they wanted to know if the method of joining the tubes was practical, and how disruptive the construction would be to river traffic (an important consideration in the 1800s). Hawkins made two tubes, each 25 ft long and 9 ft in diameter, with 13½ inch thick walls, and attempted the process in shallow water in the Thames.

The brick tubes were floated into position above the trenches on barges that were designed to be sunk during the process. Scaffolding was used to guide the tubes into position; experience found that this was often damaged from boats colliding with it. The experiment was ultimately deemed successful, but the costs put off the company from proceeding with the idea for their main tunnel.[5] As a result, the tunnel was abandoned and the company was dissolved.

Brunel and the tunnelling shield
The next attempt to build a tunnel under the Thames was just over 1 km upstream, linking Rotherhithe and Wapping, and started in 1825. This was the Thames Tunnel, and it was the work of Sir Marc Brunel and his son, Isambard Kingdom Brunel. The construction cost far more and took far longer than had been planned, but it was ultimately successful. It has been well-documented in some considerable detail elsewhere, and it is not proposed to give a detailed history here. The important point is that its success in the poor ground beneath the Thames was a result of Marc Brunel's invention: the tunnelling shield. This was a device to provide a protective compartment around the miners excavating the tunnel, and the workers erecting the permanent tunnel lining behind.

Brunel's shield was a set of twelve rectangular iron frames placed side by side, each with three rows of compartments one above the other. Each frame was 22 ft high and about 3 ft wide. The tunnel face was covered over by wooden 'poling' boards in each compartment, which were removed in turn by the miner in each of the compartments. He would then excavate the soil behind the board to a depth of 4½ inches, and then replace the board. The process would then be repeated for each board until the frame could be pushed forward using large screw jacks fitted to its rear, and pressing against the brickwork behind. In this way the whole set of frames slowly advanced into the soil, forming a large rectangular tunnel almost 38 ft wide and 22 ft 6 ins high. To the rear, bricklayers created a mass of brickwork that filled the space but for the two parallel tunnel bores that remained, each in the shape of an arch 16 ft 4 ins at their highest points, and 13 ft 9 ins wide. The design of the tunnels meant that they were protected by at least 2 ft 6 ins of brickwork from the clay, silt, gravel, and other sediment through which they were cut.

The work was difficult and dangerous, and the tunnel took just over 18 years to complete. The sinking of the Rotherhithe shaft began in February 1825, and the excavation of the tunnel 63 ft below the surface started in November of that year. After just over two years of tunnelling a length of 600 ft had been excavated, and the miners had already coped with one flood from the river above them. On 12 January 1828 the waters burst in again, killing six miners. The tunnel face was bricked up for seven years before work started again.

Work restarted in 1835 after the Government provided a loan, and an improved shield was constructed. The tunnel was completed in November 1841, and opened to the public sixteen months later.

A cross-section of the Thames Tunnel during one of the inundations, showing the shield at the left. (LTM)

The Geology of London

The most notable feature of London's geology is the London Basin, which is composed of a thick layer of chalk forming a syncline (curved depression) beneath the capital. The chalk was deposited in the late Cretaceous period (65 – 100 million years ago). The axis of this depression is roughly east-west, and it descends towards the east. This accounts for the chalk hills found to the north-west (Chilterns) and south (North Downs) of London. The chalk is overlain by younger rocks that are grouped together as the Thanet Beds, which are marine sands deposited 55 – 57 million years ago. These are in turn covered by the Lambeth Group of sediments (also known as the Woolwich and Reading beds). These are a mix of sands, gravels, clays, and sandstones.

Above the Lambeth Group is found the London Clay, without which the tube railways of London would not have developed. The clay was deposited as a very fluid mud on the borders of a tropical sea between 49 and 56 million years ago, and forms a layer around 20 – 32 m thick, although this increases to several hundred feet outside central London. It is composed of very small mineral particles which together form a material that can act plastically when water is present, but can dry out to have a hard, crumbly texture. It contains a variety of fossils as well as large round mineralized masses (called septarian nodules). Five divisions of the clay are recognized, the first being the oldest and therefore deepest. London clay has a bluish colour when freshly excavated, but this soon becomes brown as it dries out. Most importantly for tunnellers, it has a reasonable stand-up time: in other words, a tunnel cut through it will remain without collapsing immediately, giving time for permanent support to be installed. However, as the clay is under pressure, it will expand into any cavity made in it. This can benefit a tunnel, as it will fill the space left between the cut clay surface and the tunnel structure, but this cannot be relied upon completely. It is therefore important to fill this space with some other substance, such as a grout. The expansion of the clay caused problems when Primrose Hill tunnel was bored by the London & Birmingham Railway in the mid-1830s. A masonry lining was constructed using London stock bricks. The pressure of the clay was such that the mortar was squeezed out from the joints and the bricks were then crushed. The work was quickly altered to use a thicker lining and harder engineering bricks laid with quick-setting Roman cement.[6] Aside from this, the clay is an ideal medium for making tunnels.

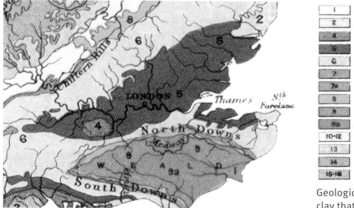

1	Alluvial
2	Pleistocene 'Crag'
4	Bagshot Beds etc
5	London Clay
6	Chalk
7	Upper Greensand
7a	Gault
8	Lower Greensand
9	Weald Clay
9a	Hastings Sand
10-12	Middle & Upper Oolite
13	Lower Oolite
14	Lias
15-16	Trias

Geological map showing the clay that underlies London.

The London Clay has beds of sandier material above it, called the Bagshot Beds. The distinction between the two is often poor, but the Lower Bagshot Beds consist of sand and loam with some clay and flints. Tunnels being made near the boundary must take care because of the risk of running into areas of wet sand and gravel. South of the Thames the London clay is deeper, and this has made construction of tube railways more difficult as the Bagshot Beds are at the normal depth for building tunnels, and these are very waterlogged. It is possible to tunnel through water-bearing sand and gravel (see Chapter 5 for how this was done for the first tube railway) but it is more expensive and slower than through clay.*

Way-leaves and easements

In order to better understand why the Underground system has developed in the way that it has, a little explanation of property law is required, and in particular the concept of easements. An easement is a right of one party over the land of another party. They are a form of licence that usually form part of the deeds to the land, and are registered at the Land Registry; because of this they remain with the land even if it is sold. They are often confused with way-leaves; however, a way-leave is a simpler form of agreement that usually lasts for a fixed period of time and does not transfer with the sale of the land. In the UK, ownership of a piece of land includes the subsoil beneath the land, with certain exceptions relating to mineral rights. To pass beneath the land of another party, an easement will be required, as that party owns the subsoil. The easement can be purchased by agreement, or the legal powers to compulsorily purchase an easement can be sought in an Act of Parliament. Each easement required the drawing up of documents by lawyers and the paying of compensation to the landowner, so in urban areas with a dense patchwork of property ownership this had the potential to be expensive.

The Metropolitan Railway (MR) followed the line of the New Road because it avoided the need to demolish property. As chapter 2 shows, it was extremely disruptive, even in an age before the complex tangle of utility pipes and cables that exist beneath road surfaces today. Local authorities who opposed the construction of a tunnel beneath their streets were won over by the argument that the lessened street traffic resulting from the railway would reduce the costs of maintenance to their ratepayers.[7] The matter was complicated by the legal position of public highways though. The maintainer of the highway did not own the subsoil; they only owned their road to a sufficient depth for its construction and maintenance. The subsoil below this was owned by the freeholders of the properties that bordered the road, which is why many older properties in London had cellars or vaults extending out beneath the street, sometimes meeting those of the property opposite at a subterranean party wall.[8] However, this was not the case with the New Road, possibly because it had only been created in 1756 and therefore the land and its subsoil was owned by the turnpike trusts that administered it. This would certainly have made it easier to negotiate an easement.

---

*   The other reason for the lack of tube railways south of the Thames is the opposition from the main-line companies who operated an extensive network of overground routes and tried to block any attempt to extend the Underground in what they regarded as being 'their' territory.

As the sub-surface railways of the Metropolitan and Metropolitan District were extended, they began to cut across the street pattern. Property had to be purchased, sometimes at great expense. The Land Clauses Consolidation Act of 1845 sought to clarify the law around land purchase powers, but significantly included a section that stated 'that no party shall at any time be required to sell or convey to the promoters of the undertaking a part only of any house or other building or manufactory, if such party be willing and able to sell and convey the whole thereof.'[9]

In other words, a property owner could insist that the railway company purchased the whole of the property under a compulsory purchase order, even if the company only needed a fraction of the land. This made railway construction expensive, particularly in urban areas where there was a dense patchwork of properties. For example, the extension of the MR from Aldgate to the temporary station at The Tower of London in 1882 was 631 yards long. The works cost £78,000, including the station, but the total cost of the extension including property purchase came to £512,949.[10] The completion of the Inner Circle in 1884 came at a cost of £1 million per mile for works and property purchase.[11]

The City & South London Railway of 1890 followed the same principle of tunnelling below streets wherever possible to keep the cost of property purchase to a minimum, as it had specifically negotiated free use of the subsoil beneath the roads in its Act of Parliament in 1884. Compulsory purchase powers were included in its Act to allow it to obtain the necessary easements beneath other land. However, two years after it opened Parliament appointed the Joint Select Committee of the House of Lords and the House of Commons on the Electric and Cable Railways (Metropolis) to consider the surge in Bills being deposited to construct tube railways. The Committee made a number of recommendations. The most relevant here were:

- As to the terms and conditions under which the sub-soil should be appropriated, the Committee report that in the case of private property, not under the public streets, it appears to them to be desirable that the companies should be allowed to acquire a way-leave, instead of purchasing the freehold of the land, subject to the terms of the Land Clauses Acts as to compensation.

- In the case of public streets the Committee think it expedient that the companies should be empowered to pass under the streets at sufficient depth without payment of compensation for the way-leave. In consideration of such free passage the Committee advise that the companies should be put under obligation to furnish an adequate number of cheap and convenient trains.[12]

The fact that gas and water companies received free easements beneath public highways, as they were a public benefit, helped the case for the tube railways. The clause about "cheap and convenient trains" was to ensure that railways taking advantage of such easements were also a public benefit.

This helped the tube railways, but it still meant that it would be cheaper to follow the streets than to pass under private property, even though the vast majority of the tunnels being planned would cause no problem for the landowners above. (Damage caused by ground settlement would, of course, still have to be paid for via compensation). However, they tended in their Acts to vary the terms of Section 92 of the 1845 Act to allow them to just purchase their easements below the land that was required, rather than the entire property, in line with the Committee's recommendations.

The Great Northern & Strand Railway (which formed the eastern part of the Piccadilly line) was arranged to run beneath the tracks of the Great Northern Railway between Finsbury Park and King's Cross, which would have simplified the negotiation of an easement for a long stretch of tunnel. South of King's Cross, however, it cut across the street layout beneath many properties; there was no easy way for it to reach Southampton Row otherwise, unless it followed the Euston Road and then turned through a sharp curve into Upper Woburn Place. Presumably the company felt that the cost of purchasing the necessary easements outweighed the extra length of tunnel and the speed restriction that the curve would have necessitated. A different approach was taken by the Brompton & Piccadilly Circus Railway (which formed the western part of the Piccadilly line): near South Kensington it follows a series of reverse curves in an attempt to maximize its use of the free easement beneath the roads, but at the expense of speed restrictions and greater track and wheel wear that continues today.

It will be seen in Chapter 19 that the Victoria line was granted specific powers to take the subsoil beneath property, with only the payment of compensation. Since the line was being built with public money, the only reason for its construction was that it would be to the benefit of the public (it was not going to make a profit), and as the majority of property-owners beneath whose land it would pass would never be inconvenienced by it, this seemed to be a sensible way forward.

Tunnels and covered ways
There are three distinct types of tunnel on the London Underground, with different techniques used for their construction.

- A **tunnel** is built from each end by miners excavating the soil and constructing a lining behind. In the case of long tunnels, shafts might be sunk from the surface to intersect the line of the tunnel, with additional tunnelling faces being started in both directions from the base of the shaft. The cross-section of such tunnels is often a horse-shoe shaped, and on the Underground they are lined with brick.
- A **covered way** is built by excavating the ground along the line of the route down to below track level, and then constructing the tunnel walls and roof (and usually the invert), before covering over the structure and reinstating the ground above, which was often a road. Early covered ways on the Underground usually had flat side walls with an arched roof above, most often built of brick. More recent covered ways tend to have rectangular cross-sections and are made of concrete.
- A **tube tunnel** is built from within a cylindrical tunnelling shield, with the shield being driven forward by pressing against the section of completed tunnel lining. They are circular in cross-section when made (some were subsequently enlarged to have different cross-sections), and are lined with cast-iron, steel, or concrete segments which fit together to form rings. Modern tube tunnels are excavated using tunnel boring machines, but the resultant tunnel and lining is broadly similar to the traditional tube tunnels.

Cut and cover

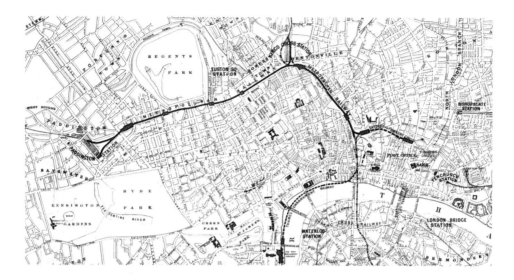

The Metropolitan Railway

It is not proposed to dwell on the legal and Parliamentary origins of the Metropolitan Railway (MR), beyond stating that it began with an idea for a railway linking Paddington and King's Cross station beneath the streets in 1850. Charles Pearson, whose idea it was, determinedly pushed forward despite criticism and rejection. Parliamentary authority for a line between Edgware Road and King's Cross was received in 1853, and the following year a new Act received Royal Assent for the creation of the Metropolitan Railway from Paddington to Farringdon Street. Difficulties in raising the necessary finance led to the scheme remaining moribund until both the Great Western Railway (GWR) and the Corporation of the City of London bought almost half the company's shares between them.

By amending the route slightly through their Act of 1859 the costs were reduced and work was able to start. The railway was to follow beneath the line of the Marylebone and Euston Roads in a covered way* from Paddington as far as King's Cross, beyond which it would then pass through open cutting to the east of Gray's Inn Road. A conventional railway tunnel would take the line through the higher ground at Clerkenwell, before it emerged shortly before the terminus at Farringdon Street.**

---

*   Although most of the MR was built using cut and cover, and therefore comprises covered ways rather than tunnels, the latter term is often used in this chapter. The description of the work will make clear the method of construction.

**   The terminus was often referred to as 'Victoria Street', this being the name of the road bordering the western edge of the station site, and which was renamed Farringdon Road in 1863.

Contracts were signed in early December, with work to begin in the new year, under the supervision of the MR Chief Engineer, John Fowler. The contractors would start at Paddington and King's Cross so that the connections to the main-line railways here could be used straight away to remove the massive amounts of earth.[13] The use of broad gauge tracks by the GWR increased the width of the tunnel and thus the amount of soil to be excavated.

John Fowler (1817–1898)

Fowler was one of the great Victorian railway engineers. His first railway work was on the line between London and Brighton, and he then moved on to become the resident engineer on the Stockton & Hartlepool Railway. At the age of 26 he started his own engineering practice, advising railways in the Sheffield area at first. The Railway Mania of the 1840s kept him very busy, and the following decade he became the engineer of the Metropolitan Railway.

The underground engineering of the Metropolitan Railway and its fellow company, the Metropolitan District Railway, occupied Fowler for the rest of his life. He continued to work on other projects alongside this, and although he semi-retired in 1890 at the age of 73, he continued to be consulted until his death eight years later. He was knighted by Queen Victoria in 1890, after the opening of the Forth Bridge which he had designed with Benjamin Baker.

Building the tunnels

Two contractors were appointed to build the railway. Smith & Knight were to construct the section between the connection with the GWR at Paddington and the western side of Euston Square, and John Jay took the line from Euston Square to Farringdon Street. The latter took the lead, and the first shafts were sunk at Euston Square (the area in front of Euston main-line station, rather than the Metropolitan Railway station), and on a plot of vacant land at King's Cross. Smith & Knight were not far behind, and at the start of February both contractors were reported as being on site (despite the company expecting the work to start in March). The first work was to reroute the utilities that lay below the streets, fortunately an easier task in 1860 than it is today with the plethora of pipes, wires, and tunnels that have been installed under the streets. Meanwhile the railway company was busy acquiring the properties that would be directly affected by the works.

The MR contractors

The contractors who built the early railways are generally less well remembered than the engineers. John Smith and George Knight were an established firm of railway contractors that had constructed a number of lines around the country in the 1850s. In 1859 they had started work on the Lyttelton railway tunnel in New Zealand, but withdrew from the contract after finding that the volcanic rock was harder to excavate than they had been led to believe, but that the local authority was not willing to pay more for the work as a consequence. This was around the time that they were awarded the MR contract which, like many of their works in Britain, was of a good standard. They continued in business with contracts in the UK and overseas until the company failed in the 1866 financial crash.

John Jay started as a building contractor and moved into railway work in the late 1830s when he constructed some GWR viaducts near London. In the 1840s he worked on construction contracts for the GNR in the King's Cross area, including that for the main-line station which remains in use today. He invested in the MR in the late 1850s, which probably accounts for him being given one of the two contracts (and in particular, that which linked with the GNR). His company survived the 1866 crash, and continued until his death in 1872.

The work to construct the tunnel was almost entirely manual. The contractors employed navvies to use pick-axes and shovels to remove the soil. One section at a time the road was closed to all traffic but pedestrians and the surface was torn up. The soil was excavated and carried away in barrows, and then piled into large heaps for later removal. The work continued day and night, in all weathers, with perhaps 2,000 navvies on site at the peak of the work. Braziers would be lit at dusk to light the workings and perhaps to provide some warmth, although the navvies were a notoriously hardy group of men who seemed to need little by way of home comforts so long as they could easily obtain sufficient beer once their shift was over. As the cuttings deepened large timber props were installed to hold up the sides prior to the construction of the brickwork. Horses were used to pull cartloads of soil away from the worksites. Some of this was removed to Stamford Bridge in west London, and today lies beneath the stands of Chelsea Football Club.

South Wharf Road in Paddington had to remain open to traffic during the tunnelling work. A very sturdy wooden framework was built across the workings, upon which a surface consisting of two layers of planks was provided for traffic. This was supported on wooden beams 43 ft long and 16 ins square placed across the road every 5 ft and supported from below by extensive wooden scaffolding. Much of the excavation was through gravel, which probably speeded up the work, being easier to cut and remove than clay.

In the clay soil beneath the Marylebone Road, the excavation took place in three stages, each of which was to the full width of the cutting. The first used 21 men to remove the soil to a depth of 5 ft for a length of 37 ft along the road. The material removed consisted mainly of the road surface and then clayey gravel. In the second stage 16 men removed a further 6 ft of loam soil for a length of 27 ft, and in the final stage 21 men took the cutting down to its full depth of 22 ft 3 ins and removed a mix of gravel and sand, and finally clay at the lowest level. The cost of the digging and scaffolding the trench, including timber, averaged 12½d per cubic yard. A further 2s 3d per cubic yard was spent on carting away the spoil (more than twice the cost of the excavation). The gravel removed from the workings was either retained for making concrete or use as ballast, or was sold, fetching 2s 9d per cubic yard. Further east, where the gravel and sand beds were absent and the entire work was through clay the excavation costs were around four times greater – and there was no gravel to be sold to offset the cost.

Once the street had been dug down to the required depth, typically around 20 ft, and to a width of 33 ft 6 ins, the 4-ft-wide footings for the side walls were constructed from brick, to a depth of 5 feet, and at a distance apart of 28 ft 6 ins. No invert (i.e., the tunnel 'floor', joining the two sides together) was constructed, which caused problems in later years for the railway.* On these footings the side walls were constructed, three bricks (2 ft 5 ins) deep, and 11 ft high. All of the brickwork was made from regular stock bricks, cemented with either blue lias or greystone lime mortar. Recesses were constructed about every 50 ft on alternative sides of the tunnel, into which track workers could stand if a train passed. These had gas lights installed in them. An 18-inch drain was installed beneath the centre of the tunnel throughout its length, carrying water to sewer connections or pumps.

Wooden frameworks called 'centrings' were built between the walls, and on their curved upper surfaces shallow elliptical arches were formed from between six and eight layers of brickwork, usually rising to a height of 17 ft from the floor of the tunnel. Where the tunnel was deeper below the surface the arch was made taller to give it greater strength, making the tunnel a maximum height of 19 ft. The spaces behind the side walls and over the arches were then back-filled with concrete and the roadway replaced on top. For some sections of the tunnel it was not possible to make it sufficiently deep to accommodate an arched roof of brickwork. In these areas, girders made of cast iron spanned between the side walls, between which small brick jack arches running across the tunnel were built. The road surface was reinstated above this tunnel roof. The main girders were 30 ft long and either 18 or 30 inches deep. When supported at their ends they could withstand loads of 35 tons and 45 tons respectively at their centres. The 30-inch girders were the standard form of construction, weighing 4½ tons each and being placed every 8 feet, but where headroom was constrained the shallower type of girder was used every 6 feet.

The tunnels were built in lengths of 12 ft, each of these taking around a day to complete on average, thus taking the tunnel forward at a rate of 72 feet every six-day working week. The pace slowed when the tunnel passed close to churches and other heavy buildings, and navvies skilled in mining techniques advanced the tunnel in these places in lengths of four feet at a time.

One slight complication was where the line passed between Park Square and Park Crescent. These were (and still are) private gardens maintained for the use of the

---

*   A short length of the walls near Gower Street station slipped forward some years later, as a result of the pounding of the clay from passing trains and the lack of a tunnel invert. An invert was added to this section as part of the reconstruction. (*The Railway News*, 15 January 1916).

householders. In 1821, to provide a safe passage between the two gardens, avoiding the traffic on the Marylebone Road, a tunnel was constructed with ramps at either side. This was called Nursemaids' Tunnel, as it was used by nursemaids pushing their charges in perambulators. Under the terms of its Act of 1854 the MR had to retain this tunnel, and so the MR had to dip slightly to pass beneath. To avoid excessive excavation the crown of the railway tunnel cut through the lower part of Nursemaids' Tunnel. A new floor was installed, with riveted iron cheek plates filling the spaces at the side.

Less than 100 m to the east, on the approach to Portland Road station, the line needed to cut beneath the two houses at the north-east end of Portland Crescent. The MR had to purchase both houses, which they carefully demolished, in order to build the tunnel beneath. As they were advised that future occupiers would insist upon having basements, girders were used to maximize the tunnel headroom whilst giving space for basements 8 ft high beneath the replacement houses, which were constructed to be identical to those that had stood there previously. The company paid £150 for plans to be drawn up prior to the demolition so that this could be done.[14]

The construction of the single-track tunnels for the connections with the Great Northern Railway (GNR) at King's Cross was similar to the other tunnels, except that they were narrower. By April 1860 the work on at least one of these tunnels was well under way, as shown by the drawing in the *Illustrated London News*. This depicts

At the mid-point of Nursemaids' Tunnel the crown of the Metropolitan Railway cut through. This photograph shows the brick arch (six rings of brickwork thick) and metal cheek plates installed where the tunnel passes beneath. *(Author)*

the start of the tunnel walls being erected; above these, planks support the soil, and these are held in place by massive timber props. The navvies access the worksite via a wooden ladder from the surface, and a foreman seems to be directing a group of them. Once these tunnels were completed works trains could be run from the GNR down to the MR to collect excavated spoil in large quantities. This was removed by railway wagon and deposited on the east side of the railway line between Hornsey and Wood Green.

The tunnels around King's Cross were made more complex by the presence of the Fleet River, which was used as a sewer and had been covered over in the early 1800s. It ran in a culvert beneath Pancras Road, following the original curved line of the road around the Great Northern Hotel and across the open area in front of King's Cross station. The single-track tunnel beneath Maiden Lane (now York Way), connecting the east side of the GNR station with the MR facing to the west had to pass beneath the Fleet. Iron tubes were incorporated into the crown of the tunnel arch as it was built, and the Fleet was diverted into these so that it could pass over the tunnel. A similar crossing of the tunnel to the west side of the main-line station was also needed.

Between the station at King's Cross and the 728-yard-long Clerkenwell Tunnel the railway was built in a deep cutting. The walls for this were of brick with concrete behind, and angled backwards so that more light would enter the cuttings, and strong metal braces were placed between the walls at regular intervals to withstand the pressure of the earth behind. The walls were of a standard design in all MR cuttings, having piers 3 ft thick with 8 ft wide recesses in between.

The Clerkenwell Tunnel was bored conventionally from each end through the clay, as well as from twelve shafts dug down from the surface; although the tunnel

Construction work at King's Cross. *(Illustrated London News)*

was not deep, the complication here was that the shafts had to pass through layers of wet gravel to reach the clay. Eleven of these were temporary and backfilled once the tunnel was completed. The lining of the tunnel has a semi-circular arch six rings of brickwork thick to resist the superincumbent pressure of the soil, and the side walls below the arch were seven bricks thick. Work started on the tunnel in November 1860, and it was driven forward from each face in lengths of 9 ft until it was completed in May 1862. Each 9 ft length would be dug by 16 miners and labourers over the course of nine shifts. Twelve bricklayers and labourers would then build the lining over the course of seven shifts.

The tunnel was more expensive to construct than the cut and cover tunnels. The labour cost alone was £33 for each 9 ft length. With 270 cubic yards of clay to be mined out of a length, this was 2s 6d per cubic yard – not a great deal of money when a cubic yard of dry clay weighs 2,970 lbs. When the additional excavation costs were included – shafts, hoists, carting away, profit for the contractor and the miners – it came to around 7s 6d per cubic yard. Then there was the cost of the tunnel lining. Each 9 ft of tunnel required 34,000 bricks and 14 cubic yards of mortar, working out at 30s per cubic yard.

Stations and junctions

Despite being an underground railway, only three of the seven* stations were made in tunnels beneath the street. At Paddington, the station was alongside the GWR terminus with its platforms at the same level. Edgware Road station was in the open air, part of a large two-acre site excavated down below street level to accommodate the station as well as the engine and carriage depot for the MR. To the east the line entered the tunnel beneath the Marylebone Road. The next three stations, at Baker Street, Portland Road (now Great Portland Street), and Gower Street (now Euston Square) were all in tunnel directly beneath the surface, with 45 ft 1 in wide arches spanning the tracks and side platforms. The arches were six layers of bricks thick at the crown, increasing to twelve at the springing, and had a rise of 10 ft 4 ins. Baker Street and Gower Street had regularly spaced shafts to the surface, lined with glazed white tiles and with glazing at the top to let in light. Portland Road had two glass domes in the station building but otherwise relied on gas lamps for illumination. Stairs placed behind the retaining walls led down from the station buildings to the platforms within the tunnel stations.

King's Cross was a large station with three platforms and three tracks: one pair of each for the MR from Paddington, and one track with a platform on the northern side for the main-line connections with the GNR. The line emerged from tunnel at the western end of the station, which was situated in a wide cutting and covered over by a large arched glass roof. Farringdon Street was also in a wide cutting, excavated down on vacant land that had been owned by the City Corporation.

The most complicated part of the railway to construct was in the King's Cross area,

---

* Although the line opened with seven stations from Paddington (Bishop's Road) to Farringdon Street, it was the intention to construct a short branch to a station at Paddington (Praed Street) – today's Circle and District line station. This plan was abandoned in 1862, although the junction tunnel at Praed Street was constructed, saving some difficulties when the line through Praed Street was constructed three years later.

The massive timber centring in use at Portland Road station c.1862. *(LTM)*

A cross-section of the platforms at Baker Street, drawn from the plans in 1860 before they were constructed. *(Illustrated London News)*

PROPOSED STATION AT BAKER STREET.

where three connections were made with the Great Northern Railway (GNR) near to its main-line station. Two single-line connections faced eastwards, towards the city, and a single connection faced westwards. Large junction tunnels were formed at the points of connection with the MR, wide enough for both tunnels to stand side-by-side at the end. These needed greater height for their arches, and so at these points the tunnels had to be excavated deeper beneath the street. The junction tunnels tapered back to a single tunnel at the far end, and because of this shape were referred to as 'bell-mouth' tunnels. The single westward facing connection was called the Maiden Lane Curve, because of the road beneath which it lay. Just south of the tunnel portal adjacent to the main-line station the track split, with the Maiden Lane Curve heading westwards and the York Road Curve heading east. Shortly before the former met the main route of the MR it crossed the eastward connection to the west side of King's Cross station (the Hotel Curve) at a flat junction in tunnel. This led to the creation of a subterranean signal cabin in the space between the three tunnels. The openings into this can just be seen in the drawing made in February 1861.

The other junction on the line was at Praed Street, where the MR had hopes of extending round to Kensington. Unlike the other junctions, the roof above the brick retaining walls consisted of a large, curved structure of wrought iron. Its eastern end was an arch of 28 ft 6 ins to match the adjacent brick tunnel. At the west, so that

The junction at King's Cross of the main Metropolitan Railway (to the left) and the Hotel Curve (to the right), looking westwards. *(Illustrated London News)*

two double track tunnels could be spanned, it had an arch of 60 ft span. This was described as "resembling the inverted hull of a large iron ship".[15]

Progress and disruption

The eastern end of the line, being built by John Jay, was predominantly through clay. He seemed keen to demonstrate progress to the company as quickly as possible, and at a directors' meeting in April 1860 stated that he would have a 100-yard section of tunnel completed by the end of May and ready for inspection. Charles Pearson wanted to make this a public festival for shareholders to attend, but the rest of the board was reluctant to spend any of the company's money on an event.

The western section being made by Smith & Knight had to contend with more sand and gravel, to the extent that in March 1860 the MR's Chief Engineer was suggesting that it could be used to form a bed to the Serpentine lake in Hyde Park. Concerns had been raised for a few years about deep holes in the lake bed, and the need to filter the water which was regarded as rather polluted. The engineer, John Fowler, reckoned that the contractor would probably supply the gravel free of charge as it would save having to otherwise pay for its transport and disposal.[16] Springs found in the gravel layer could also supply clean water to the lake, rather than water companies being paid for this service.[17] Over the course of the work the gravel was sold on, bringing a useful profit to Smith & Knight. Of three shafts dug on the site of Baker Street station, adjacent to the Marylebone Workhouse, two revealed a stream at the bottom. Pumps were brought in to remove the water; like almost all the work on the line these were manually operated.[18] Pipes were installed to channel the water into low-level sewers and drains where these were available. Beneath Stafford Street (now Cosway Street), at the east end of Edgware Road station, a 3-ft diameter siphon had to be constructed beneath the railway tunnel

In early May 1860 the newspapers estimated that two-thirds of the length of the route between Paddington and King's Cross was being worked on. The traffic disruption and chaos caused to those with a need to use the Marylebone and Euston Roads would have been immense. Almost the entire width of the street had to be dug up, although not all at once. The railway tunnel would be formed along the centre, 33 ft 6 ins wide, but firstly the street either side of this was dug up so that new sewers could be built to replace those which were subsequently removed for the railway tunnel. It did not take long for the residents and shopkeepers to lose patience: on 4 May a meeting was held at Frampton's Music Hall in St Pancras. The shopkeepers were especially concerned about the loss of trade, as unsurprisingly potential customers were disinclined to walk through the mud churned up by the works to reach their shops. A Trade Protection Association was formed, and the attendees subscribed money to help their cause. It was also agreed to send a deputation to the next meeting of the St Pancras Vestry to enlist their assistance. This was duly done, and the vestry decided that their chief surveyor and solicitor should "take immediate measures ... to protect the inhabitants of this parish".[19]

Williams described the disruption caused by the work very well:

A few wooden houses on wheels first made their appearance, and planted themselves by the gutter; then came some wagons loaded with timber, and accompanied by sundry gravel-coloured men with picks and shovels. A day or two afterwards a few hundred yards of roadway were enclosed, the ordinary traffic being, of course, driven into the side streets; then followed troops of navvies, horses, and engines arrived, who soon disappeared within the enclosure and down the shafts.[20]

Property owners would suddenly find the men installing timber props against their houses and shops to guard against collapse; not the most reassuring sight. Whilst the sewers were being reconstructed access to houses was across the works, and the owner would find "a temporary way of wet planks, erected for his use and the use of the passers-by, over a yawning cavern underneath the pavement".[21]

Publicans seemed particularly keen to make claims against the railway for damage to their properties. In Chapel Street, near Edgware Road station, the publican owner of No. 1 was awarded £120 after the loss of part of an external wall to the railway caused his lodgers to move out. At the other end of the railway the owner of a pub called the Pickled Egg gained £100 after claiming that the foundations of his building were shaken.[22] The cellars of the Queen's Arms pub in the New Road were flooded after a water main burst following a landslip caused by the railway works, and a large crack appeared between the original building and a newer building constructed closer to the road. However, the lawyers for the MR asserted that the flooding took place two months after the water pipe burst, and that the crack was due to faulty construction. They then noted that the newer building had been constructed in contravention of an Act of Parliament, and it was therefore a 'common nuisance' and the owner had no right to compensation. The court agreed.[23]

The first fatal accident to be recorded during the construction of the line occurred at this time. An eight-year-old boy was playing with his friends on one of the many mounds of excavated soil, probably between Euston and King's Cross. The mound slipped and he fell under the wheels of a passing omnibus, dying within minutes. At the inquest it was determined that the company and contractor (John Jay) had left the site "in a careless, unguarded manner, and in a way calculated to endanger human life".[24] The vestry surveyor was also criticised for not enforcing the law by making the companies improve their worksites. It was surprising to see that *The Daily News* reported in July that the sewer diversion work had been completed in the King's Cross area without an accident.

In the same month the sites for the stations were being cleared of their existing buildings. Negotiations with the City Corporation had completed for the site at Farringdon Street; the company was to pay just one-third of the agreed price, and the rest via a rent charge with 4½% interest over the next 40 years.

Perhaps the concerns of the local population raised in May, together with the death of the child caused a change in construction technique. As John Jay's men worked west from King's Cross it was decided to build the railway tunnel with less surface disruption by tunnelling below the surface, rather than using cut and cover. A large opening was created opposite the GNR main-line station, and four separate shafts (in two pairs) were placed along the line of the tunnel to the west. Each of the pair of shafts was equipped with a powerful steam engine, possibly for pumping water, although this was not clear from the report.[25] Tracks were laid along the tunnels from the main-line connection, and the excavated soil loaded directly into wagons. The workings were illuminated by burning gas jets, supplied via a metal pipe led along the tunnel.

August 1860 saw the block of buildings between Pentonville Road and Gray's Inn Road demolished, so that the MR station at King's Cross could be constructed. The final connection with the GNR, linking to the western side of the main-line station, was being constructed. This was later to be known as the Hotel Curve. This was still being worked on in early 1861, as shown in the drawing from the *Illustrated London News* which depicts the timber framework for the tunnel arch still in position just beyond the flat junction with the Maiden Lane tunnel. The Hotel Curve was not completed until August 1862.

On 4 September 1860 Smith & Knight's workmen closed the Marylebone Road between the junction with Marylebone High Street and Portland Road (today's Great Portland Street). All traffic was diverted via the parallel Devonshire Street whilst the full width of the road was excavated to build the next section of tunnel. Disruption had occurred here since March or April so that the sewers could be diverted, but this was the main piece of work. Further west, houses were being pulled down on the borders of the site for Edgware Road station.

The next reported accident on the line was on 12 October, when those living and working near Belgrave Road, almost opposite King's Cross main-line station, were rocked by a "loud report, resembling the simultaneous discharge of a park of artillery, which shook the neighbouring houses to their foundations".[26] A leak had occurred in the pipe supplying the gas lighting in the tunnel workings, and the pocket of gas thus formed had ignited. The wooden frameworks supporting the brick-work of the tunnel arch were displaced, and some of the timber frameworks caught fire. Fortunately both the GNR and the London & North Western Railway at Euston station were able to send fire tenders to the site quickly; the burning woodwork was soon put out, but it was soon found that two of the workmen were seriously injured, one later dying from his injuries.

Less than one month later the area was rocked by another explosion. On the morning of 1 November *The Albion*, a locomotive working for the contractor was waiting to enter the tunnel leading to the Maiden Lane and York Road connections adjacent to King's Cross main-line station, and thereby to the workings. Without warning its boiler exploded, killing its driver and fireman and seriously injuring three other men working nearby. The station entrance from York Road had to be guarded by police to prevent numerous bystanders from gaining access to the site whilst the investigation into the accident took place. The inquest sat for several sessions over a period of almost three weeks in order to allow adequate investigation of the engine. The final conclusion was that the engine's firebox had been poorly constructed; it was about nine years old, and had been fitted as a replacement for the original by the Eastern Counties Railway at their works. No blame for the accident was attached to either the contractor nor the engine's crew.[27]

A view from the site of King's Cross station made in February 1861 shows the completed tunnel in front of the main-line station with five layers of brick in its archway. Work in the foreground is rather less advanced; the cutting for the tunnel has been dug and is propped using a series of stout timbers. Planks across these form walkways for men with barrows, and a wooden chute at the side might be for sliding bricks into the cutting so that bricklayers below can construct the footings.

A landslip occurred on 24 May 1861 beneath the Euston Road at Tonbridge Place (between Mabledon Place and Tonbridge Street), where the street had been opened and the cutting was being dug. The gas and water mains were damaged, telegraph poles felled, and the gardens of adjacent houses were damaged. Fortunately the houses along the Euston Road were well set-back and thus not damaged too. The slip set works back by a week, but notwithstanding this accident, by the end of the month over 30% of the line was fully complete.[28]

By mid-September 1861 the line was completed between the GWR connection at Paddington and the eastern end of the Edgware Road cutting. Much of the tunnel was nearing completion between Edgware Road and Marylebone church, beyond which the section as far as Harley Street was finished.[29] Beyond here the works were not so far advanced as the tunnel beneath the two houses on the eastern extremity of Park Crescent was still incomplete. The rest of the tunnel being constructed by Smith & Knight, as far as Euston Square, was still a huge construction site. A huge steam hoist was erected at the junction of Portland Road and Euston Road, and this lifted the soil from the workings and loaded it into waiting carts. This could lift one cartload at a time.

Looking west from the site of King's Cross station on the Metropolitan Railway. *(Illustrated London News)*

THE METROPOLITAN (UNDERGROUND) RAILWAY.—WORKS IN PROGRESS AT KING'S CROSS

The Euston Road steam hoist. *(Illustrated Times)*

Trial by water

Along the southern edge of Regent's Park the railway was constructed above the existing Regent Street Sewer. The sewer had a junction at the centre of Park Crescent, and to enable access to this a shaft 11 ft in diameter was sunk to a depth of 41 ft. A spiral staircase of York stone was placed in the shaft, wrapped around a central shaft about 5 ft wide that could be used for hoisting material from the sewer.[30]

John Jay had constructed much of his section of tunnel between Euston Square and King's Cross; just a short section between St Pancras church and Mabledon Place remained to be completed. East of King's Cross station, where the railway cut across the streets and required property demolition, some of this work was done but the houses at the King's Cross end of the cutting in the area bounded by King's Cross Road, Gray's Inn Road, and Acton Street were only acquired by the railway in September 1861. There was also heavy tunnelling work to be done beneath Clerkenwell.

The last crossing of the Fleet sewer was at the junction of Frederick Street and Bagnigge Wells Road (now King's Cross Road). The Fleet followed the line of the latter, whilst the MR cut across the street pattern. A new iron tube was constructed to carry the Fleet above the line of the railway, which was in a short tunnel at this point. Londoners were given one of their last glimpses of the river as the street was opened up and the navvies built its new tunnel whilst simultaneously taking down nearby houses along the route of the railway.

The final trial for John Jay came on 18 June 1862, when heavy rain overloaded the Fleet. This carried the sewage from 50,000 houses between Highgate and the Thames, and in times of rain its level could rise by 6 ft in as little as an hour.[31] Just north of Farringdon Street station the sewer tunnel was beneath Farringdon Road, separated from the railway cutting by new brick walls around 30 feet high. Water from the Fleet was seen forcing its way into the railway workings through the wall. The danger was soon realized, and the workmen were cleared from the site. Men were lowered in baskets to break holes in the wall to relieve the pressure, but it was too late: the foundations of the wall began to move and they were quickly hauled to the surface. The walls gave way and the railway workings, as well as the just-completed Clerkenwell Tunnel as far north as Frederick Street, were inundated with water and filth to a depth of about 8 feet. A complete works train, including the locomotive, which was in the tunnel was submerged. Fortunately the structure of the tunnel was undamaged. The web of gas mains below Farringdon Road and its immediate side streets was broken; fortunately new mains were being laid in the area, and one of the company engineers was able to immediately turn off the supply and thereby prevent a possible explosion had the leaking gas caught light.

The collapse occurred under the Farringdon Road between Ray Street and Cross Street, pulling much of the road surface down with the wall. The burial ground for St

The work to construct the Fleet crossing at Frederick Street and Bagnigge Wells Road in 1862. *(Illustrated London News)*

THE METROPOLITAN RAILWAY AND THE FLEET DITCH.

Peter's Church had previously been removed to make way for Farringdon Road, with the bodies being placed in a new mausoleum. This was broken open by the collapsing sewer, adding corpses to the unpleasant contents of the cutting.[32]

A dam was soon constructed along the line of the wall in an attempt to channel the flow of the Fleet back into the former river bed where this still existed near Vine Street. Five hundred navvies were engaged in this task, but three days after the wall fell the heavy flow of water was still resisting and washing the dam away. The entrance to Clerkenwell Tunnel was also dammed to prevent the water from flowing in, and so that it could be drained. Matters were not helped by the tidal nature of the Fleet, which soon became apparent to the workmen. One reportedly caught "a very fine eel" that had come up from the Thames.

Powerful pumps were brought to the site, and over the next week the men finally gained control over the Fleet and were able to start draining the site for the railway. Cartloads of clay and earth were brought to the site (probably from other worksites) and a combination of the flow diminishing naturally, and the addition of timber piles to the dam finally held the flow back. Only then could repairs to the sewer and the cutting walls be started. The damage was significant, setting back the completion of the MR by at least a month, and adding over £10,000 to its costs.

The temporary repairs to the sewer were completed swiftly. It was just as well; a storm in July caused it to fill, and newspapers soon reported that it was flooding the MR workings anew. This drew an angry response from the Engineer to the

The bursting of the Fleet, showing the massive sections of brickwork that were undermined and fell. *(Illustrated London News)*

Metropolitan Board of Works, Joseph Bazalgette. He noted that the flooding had occurred near the site of King's Cross station after a temporary wall built by the contractor in a small branch sewer had burst, but that the repairs at Farringdon had held up completely.[33]

Despite these two incidents, work pressed on apace. The cutting walls had been repaired by early August and the rails were extended into the site. On 31 August a detailed inspection of the route was carried out by a government inspector. Particular care was taken in examining the reinstated brickwork at the site of the Fleet sewer burst, but all was found to be in good shape. Later in the day the first trial run of a train carrying shareholders and other invited guests was made along the length of the railway.

It was expected by many that the railway would open in the autumn, but problems occurred with the signalling. Some delays also occurred in finishing the junction with the GWR at Paddington. However, by mid-December all was ready and the railway company requested that the Board of Trade (BoT) inspect the stations, signalling and other equipment so that the line could be opened to passengers. This took place on 15 December, but the Inspector, Colonel Yolland was not satisfied with some of the signalling. After alterations were made he made a further inspection on 27 December, and was satisfied with the operation of the signals. On 9 January 1863 the official, formal opening of the line took place, and passengers used the railway the following day.

The work to repair the damaged Fleet sewer involved excavating temporary channels into which the flow could be diverted whilst the damaged brickwork was rebuilt. *(Penny Illustrated Paper)*

THE BURSTING OF THE FLEET DITCH: NAVVIES CONSTRUCTING A FLEET CHANNEL.—SEE NEXT PAGE.

Extensions and rivals

It is not proposed to describe the detailed progress of every part of the Metropolitan Railway from here on, but instead focus on areas of particular interest or difficulty as the railway extended eastwards to the city of London, from its western end curving through the station at Paddington (Praed Street) round to South Kensington, and north-west from Baker Street on what became known as the 'Extension line'. These lines were constructed with a greater proportion of open cutting than the original route, as experience showed that the locomotives were not as smokeless as the railway company had hoped, and the atmosphere in the tunnels between Edgware Road and Kings Cross was prone to become rather unpleasant.

The sister company of the MR, the Metropolitan District Railway was also being built at this time. Although they became great rivals, to start with the companies were closely related: for example, the engineer for both was John Fowler. This explains many of the similarities in construction between the two lines.

The Widened Lines and City extension
A heavy traffic of passenger and freight trains joined and left the MR from its two main-line connections at King's Cross and Paddington. The extension to the city would allow railway access to the new meat market at Smithfield, and so even greater traffic was predicted for the new line. It was clear that additional tracks would be required. Powers for these were obtained in 1864, and the contractor John Kelk was appointed to build the new line; he was already starting work on the extension of the existing route via a new station at Farringdon Street, adjacent to the existing station but on a new extended route through Aldersgate Street (now Barbican) to Moorgate Street. The additional tracks would be dedicated for the main-line companies, and became known as the Widened Lines.

At King's Cross MR station the tracks were altered so that there were two serving the main-line side of the station. Where the previous single track joined with the MR tracks to the east, the new pair of tracks were continued in parallel and the connection was removed. At Frederick Street the crossing of the Fleet had to be lengthened to accommodate the new tunnel. A second Clerkenwell Tunnel was excavated; this was also parallel at first, but on a descending gradient so that its eastern portal was 15 ft below the level of the original tunnel, and on a slight curve. It took exactly the same length of time to construct as the first tunnel. A skew bridge was constructed to support the original tracks, and the new line swept below it and then ascended steeply to position itself on the southern side of the MR. This facilitated the connections with the new London, Chatham & Dover Railway line through Blackfriars, and into the basement depôt at Smithfield market.

The construction of the skew bridge, known as the Ray Street Grid-iron because of its location and metal construction, was a "tedious and difficult" piece of work because of the need to keep trains running. As the Widened Lines were at a lower level the cutting needed to be made deeper. This meant that the side walls of the

ENTRANCE TO THE CLERKENWELL TUNNEL.

A drawing of the Ray Street grid-iron in 1868, showing a locomotive on the Widened Lines passing below a train on the Metropolitan Railway (above). *(Illustrated London News)*

existing cutting needed to be underpinned to a depth of 20 ft so that they could be then extended downwards to the level of the new tracks, as demolishing them in order to deepen the cutting would have meant closing the existing railway.

The other complex alterations for the creation of the Widened Lines took place at the west end. A new tunnel was under construction from the Midland Railway's terminus at St Pancras, from the western side leading down beneath the station building to join the Widened Lines at the west end of King's Cross MR station. The tunnel signal box in the junction between the Hotel and Maiden Lane Curve junctions was swept away by the new works, and the Hotel Curve track realigned to join the Widened Lines and not the MR tracks. The Maiden Lane Curve had not been used since the tunnel was constructed, and had no track laid in it since its use by the contractors building the line.* The tunnel was partially filled in with spoil from the work to construct the Widened Lines tunnels.[34]

Open cuttings were used where possible on the extension works to Moorgate Street, so that the stations would not fill with steam from the locomotives. The route cut across the streets, and extensive property demolition was required. One source noted that almost half of the houses at St Bartholemew's, Moorfields, were demolished – some 500 properties in total.[35] These housed around 5,000 people, almost certainly living in squalid conditions, and would have been cheap for the MR to purchase.

The extension of the MR to Moorgate Street opened on 23 December 1865. The GNR was the first user of the Widened Lines, which opened for traffic on 27 January 1868. The connection to St Pancras and the Midland Railway was brought into use on 13 July of the same year.

Round to Kensington

Like the extension to Moorgate Street, the extension of the MR from Praed Street Junction, near Paddington, round to Gloucester Road and South Kensington was largely in cutting to provide better ventilation. The cuttings were similar to those in Clerkenwell, with walls sloping back slightly and consisting of a series of brick buttresses joined by shallow elliptical arches. Cast iron struts were again used above the tracks to brace the walls apart in many places; the depth of the cuttings occasionally required two rows of these, one above the other. The extension (like all that followed) was built to accommodate standard gauge tracks only, and so the cuttings were only 25 ft wide, except at the stations where they were doubled in width to 50 ft.

The high ground that forms Campden Hill crosses the route of the line between Notting Hill Gate and High Street Kensington stations, and through this a conventional railway tunnel was formed, 421 yards long. Work started in October 1865 and four shafts were sunk in order to speed up the work of boring the tunnel through having additional tunnel faces to work. The tunnel cuts through beds of clay, sand, and gravel, the latter two tending to make conditions treacherous at times. Loose sand falling into the excavations undermined properties above the tunnel, causing damage. The worst settlement was measured at 7¼ ins.

---

* Although it does not seem to have been suggested anywhere else, I propose that the principle purpose of the Maiden Lane Curve was to facilitate the construction of the MR (although I accept that this might not have been the originally intended purpose). Without a corresponding curve linking the eastbound MR line to the down GNR lines it would have been of limited utility. However, it allowed trains for the contractor direct access to the main work sites to the west of King's Cross without the need to shunt trains. John Jay, the contractor, did not open up the street to remove the earth as was done further west, and relied more heavily on trains to extract the spoil. Reports show that the track had been removed before the MR was inspected on 15 December 1862, implying that there was no intention to use this tunnel in service.

A steam crane in use at Craven Hill Gardens, showing the trench in which the tunnel side wall was to be constructed. *(LTM)*

Unlike the Clerkenwell tunnel, a smaller heading tunnel with a face 9 ft square was excavated first to help drain water from the gravel in the top section. This was then expanded out subsequently, with light sheeting being pushed into the sands and gravels at the level of the arch ahead of the main tunnelling face to support the soil above the line of the tunnel. Scaffolding was used to provide temporary support whilst the brickwork was erected. Work progressed in lengths of 12 ft or 12 ft 6 ins, although the engineers disagreed with this approach and felt that 6 ft lengths would be safer, particularly if the brickwork was erected as quickly as possible after excavation. The pressure above the tunnel crushed some of the wooden scaffolding in the heading tunnel after about five months, and the scaffolding needed to be doubled to provide sufficient support. However, this prevented wagons from passing along the tunnel, thus complicating the work and relying more on manual labour. The tunnel was completed in January 1867.

The contractors, Kelk, Waring and Lucas, also underpinned a number of buildings along the route. This extension passed through a more expensive area of London, and it was cheaper to purchase an easement and underpin buildings than it was to purchase them (or, if this was not possible, at least the underpinned building could be re-sold, if purchase was required). This underpinning required delicate work in

The gap between the houses at Leinster Gardens, with the tunnel brickwork being constructed, and before the erection of the fake façade. *(LTM)*

Bayswater station under construction, with rudimentary wooden scaffolding supporting the overall roof and a contractor's cart on the platform. *(LTM)*

inserting girders beneath the load-bearing walls and transferring the weight of the buildings onto these and thus onto the side walls of the railway.

One location that has always interested and amused people is at 23 and 24 Leinster Gardens, where the railway passes beneath the road at right angles. This road is bordered on both sides by white-painted five-storey houses. The residents were not keen on losing a pair of the houses to accommodate a railway cutting and so the company erected a fake façade across the gap, decorated to appear like the adjacent houses. The doors have no letterboxes or knockers, and the windows are painted grey, and occasionally practical jokes have been played on deliverymen not aware of this unusual address.

The stations on the extension were built to a similar design, with arched and glazed overall roofs above the platforms. These were supported on decorative iron brackets set into the yellow brick retaining walls. The semi-elliptical wrought iron ribs spanned the station at 22 ft intervals, and were connected longitudinally by lattice girders and purlins. This framework held the glazing panels. The ribs were assembled on site from sections, and wooden scaffolding was used to support the roof during the construction. There were two widths of roof installed, depending on the number of platforms to be spanned. High Street Kensington and Gloucester Road received spans of 83 ft 11 ins, as they both had four tracks and platforms. The other

Work at No. 1 Brickfield on the MDR. *(LTM)*

stations, from Paddington (Praed Street) to South Kensington, and then on the MDR to St James's Park, as well as at Charing Cross (now Embankment) all had spans of 50 ft 5½ ins. The ends of the canopies had attractive wind screens with a pattern of radiating struts placed across them. These were merely decorative though, as the plans to glaze them were never carried out.

The Metropolitan District Railway

The MDR was constructed from West Brompton to Mansion House, although the section between Westminster Bridge and Mansion House opened later because of the complication caused by the Victoria Embankment. A branch also led from Earl's Court to the MR station at High Street Kensington.

The contractors for the MDR established two large brick kilns at their worksite at Earl's Court. Clay from the Campden Hill Tunnel and cuttings on the MR extension from Paddington was transported to these for baking into bricks. Temporary railway tracks were laid and three locomotives and 120 wagons were used to move the clay. Around 140 million bricks were made here for the railway.

Since the construction of the first section of the MR the use of machinery had increased. Whereas the steam-powered hoist used by Smith & Knight in the Euston Road was a novelty, the Kensington extension made far greater use of steam. Fifty-two steam engines were employed along the line, either for cranes and hoists, or powering pumps to keep the workings dry. The work of excavating the soil was still highly manual though, and over 2,000 men were employed along the line between West Brompton and Westminster Bridge. Two hundred horses helped move the wagons of spoil and bricks along the line of the railway.

The spoil removed from the cuttings which was not used for brickmaking was loaded into wagons and transported via a connection onto the West London Railway. It was taken to Shepherd's Bush and other places along the line for disposal.[36]

The cut and cover tunnels were built in a different way to those of the original MR tunnels in the early 1860s, to help reduce the cost and disruption. Instead of digging up the full width of the road beneath which the tunnel was to pass, instead two trenches each 6 ft wide were made along the line of the retaining walls. Within these the walls were built to a height of 4 ft above where the tunnel arch would start. Only then would the ground be excavated to this same depth, and the scaffolding and centrings for the arch be erected. This saved having to construct scaffolding down to rail level. The MDR made use of iron centrings, unlike the wood used by the MR initially. The arch would be built from brick, and once the mortar was set the scaffold and centrings would be dismantled and the road reinstated above. Workers would then enter the tunnel and remove the remaining earth* down to rail level. The retaining walls for sections of open cutting were built in the same way, but once complete the earth in between would all be removed. This reduced the risk of the side of a cutting collapsing, and the cost of scaffolding.

A triangle of land was enclosed by the railway to the west of Gloucester Road and south of High Street Kensington station. A bridge was built over the line near Gloucester Road to give access to the triangle. As an experiment part of the bridge

---

* This piece of earth is called the 'dumpling'.

The scene at the junction of Victoria Street and Vauxhall Bridge Road, with a trench cut into the ground ready for the tunnel side wall to be constructed. *(LTM)*

was made of concrete, a material that Fowler was enthusiastic to try. The section, which was a flying arch, comprised 200 tons of concrete poured into shuttering made of planks. It was left for three weeks to set before the planks were removed.[37]

Unfortunately the concrete used for the arch was not a strong mix, and the bridge collapsed when the shuttering was taken away. The bridge was reconstructed on the same site, entirely in concrete, using a stronger Portland cement. The central arch was 75 ft wide and 7 ft 6 ins high, and at the centre the concrete was 3 ft 6 ins thick. When the shuttering was removed the bridge remained standing, and tests were then made of its strength. A short length of railway track was laid across it, and seven wagons weighing 49 tons fully laden were rolled back and forth whilst the deflection of the arch was measured. Fully ballasted track was then laid, to increase the dead weight on the bridge, and once this had settled the truck were rolled across again in increasing numbers. The movement that was measured was so small as to convince the engineers that, if a good cement was used, a concrete bridge was stronger than a similar structure made from masonry.[38]

Between Gloucester Road and South Kensington two parallel tunnels were constructed, the tracks of the MR being in the northern tunnel and those of the MDR in the southern tunnel. For most of the distance the tunnels shared a common pier

The second concrete arch spanning the cutting between Earl's Court and Gloucester Road. The arched roof of the latter station can just be seen in the background, above the two tunnel mouths. *(LTM)*

wall (the centre wall between them), but as they approached South Kensington they diverged to allow for the wide central platform with its bay road. These tunnels were built without inverts, as it was thought by the engineers that the sand and ballast in which the foundations were built would form a solid base. They were wrong, and shortly after the MDR opened movement of the walls was detected near Gloucester Road. An invert was constructed along the tunnels as a result.

Water continued to be a problem, as it had been for the builders of the MR, particularly once the cuttings were excavated below the level of the sewers. Near Victoria two steam pumps ran continuously to remove around 4,000 gallons of water every minute. The line had eleven temporary pumping stations established during construction, although once open this reduced to five. Wells were dug at each site (Earl's Court, South Kensington, Sloane Square, Victoria, and Temple) into which the water could drain, and permanent steam pumps then lifted the water into nearby sewers. Duplicate equipment was provided at each location to reduce the risk of flooding.

The MDR was more affected than the MR, as it ran closer to the Thames and was also crossed by many of the streams and sewers that ran into the Thames. A variety of techniques was used by the MDR's engineers to cross these watercourses. At Earl's Court, the Counters Creek Sewer was in a brick tunnel underneath Warwick Road. The railway was threaded over the sewer and under the road, with the top portion of the sewer pipe being broken out and replaced by iron plates bolted down to keep the pipe secure beneath the rails. The bridge above the railway was made of iron girders for strength and to ensure sufficient headroom for trains.

Another famous quirk on the Underground is at Sloane Square station, where the River Westbourne passes above the platforms in a large iron pipe. It was not possible to divert it beneath the railway, so instead the 9-ft-wide brick pipe was carefully demolished between the points where the cutting walls for the station would be, and a wooden trough constructed to temporarily carry the sewage. This was supported on wooden trestles as the cutting for the station was excavated beneath. Between the side walls of the station, running at a skew across the station, the pipe was constructed from rings of cast iron, each 5 ft 11 ins long (except at each end of the pipe, where special segments with angled ends accommodated the skewed angle of the pipe against the brickwork). Each ring is made of six segments which appear identical, but are thicker at the bottom of the pipe than at the top. The segments are held together by bolts through flanges on the outside. The pipe is set into the brick of the original sewer tunnel where this passes through the walls, and is supported by wrought iron girders on either side, to which it is bolted. It crosses the station at an angle of 48°, and the length between the side walls of the station is just 66 ft. The pipe was constructed around the temporary wooden trough, and once complete the trough was broken up and removed. The pipe incorporated an expansion joint to allow for any change in the length of the pipe caused by temperature alterations, although it is doubtful that this was really needed.[39]

A similar pipe was constructed just east of Victoria station for the Tyburn, which flows here through the King's Scholars' Pond Sewer. The crossing is less obvious than that at Sloane Square as the railway is in a tunnel. The Fleet is crossed at Blackfriars, where it disgorges into the Thames. Work here was complex as the Victoria Embankment was being completed as the railway was constructed, Blackfriars Bridge was being built, and the railway bridge for the LC&DR was overhead. The Fleet was in a very large brick pipe 12 feet wide by 17 feet high and was in the way of the railway. The solution was to rebuild the southernmost portion of the Fleet tunnels between the end of New Bridge Street and the Thames and provide additional brick-built chambers either side of the sewer tunnel. These were at a lower level, with weirs where they joined the original tunnel; the lower level gave the clearance necessary for the MDR to pass over them. The additional chambers ensured that the capacity of the sewer was maintained, else it might have backed up during times of heavy rainfall.

The construction at Blackfriars was further complicated by the need to thread it beneath two subways that provided a connection between the City Gas Works and their wharf on the Thames,* as well as an existing pedestrian subway, and

---

* The City of London Gas Works occupied the block of land between Tudor Street and the Thames, west of where Unilever House stands today. When the Victoria Embankment was constructed the tunnel linking to their wharf was made to allow them to bring coal onto their site without having to cross the Embankment at street level. After the gas works closed around 1880, the floors of the two subways above the railway tunnel were removed allowing gases from the railway tunnels to escape to the river opening, giving improved ventilation.

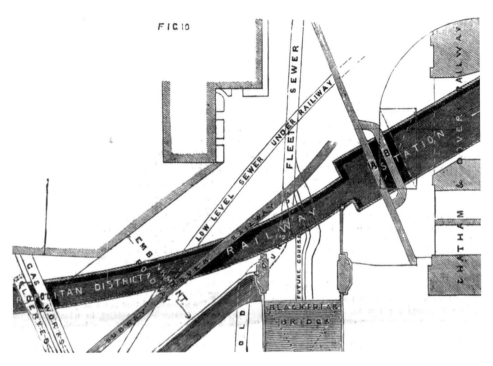

A plan of the tunnels immediately west of Blackfriars station, showing the tangle through which the MDR tunnel had to be threaded. *(Engineering)*

above a low-level sewer. The low-level sewer was routed into an elliptical cast iron tunnel directly beneath the railway, and the roof of the railway tunnel was made from closely spaced girders supporting brick jack-arches to maximize the headroom without needing the space that a brick arch would have occupied. The space above and between the jack arches was filled with concrete, and then coated with a water-proofing layer of asphalt, as was usual for the MDR.[40]

One of the more sensitive areas through which the line was constructed was at Westminster, where it had to pass by the Westminster Abbey, dating back to the fourteenth century, and beneath Parliament Square. The tunnel at Broad Sanctuary, at the east end of Tothill Street, does not have the usual recessed arches between buttresses, but instead the walls are of solid brickwork 5 ft 6 ins thick, connected by a concrete invert. A layer of peat, 7 ft thick, was placed between this and the soil on the south side of the line to help insulate the Abbey against vibration from the railway, which it was thought might endanger its foundations.[41] The peat almost certainly came from a large deposit found immediately to the west, beneath Tothill Street. The Abbey authorities had obtained specific legal protection when the Act for the MDR was passed by Parliament, and their engineer had powers to oversee the construction of this section of tunnel.

Eastwards from Westminster the line was built into the new Victoria Embankment. Had the railway been able to raise its finance sooner, then it would have saved money by being constructed as part of the Embankment; instead, the delays meant that it had to be re-excavated once the Embankment was nearly completed. The proximity of the Thames meant that this section was not on particularly solid ground. The workmen building the line had to dig deep to ensure that the retaining walls either side of the line would be secure, and at Charing Cross station they descended 25 ft below the level of the rails in order to find a secure footing.

From Thames Tunnel to East London Railway

The story of the Thames Tunnel, constructed by the Brunels, has been briefly told in the Introduction. After opening there were no funds to build the planned ramps to allow vehicular traffic through, and it remained in use as a foot tunnel until its closure in 1869 for conversion into a railway. Four years earlier, it had been purchased by the East London Railway Co., who had started work constructing a line from Rotherhithe southwards to New Cross. The northern part of this line was in cut and cover tunnel, constructed by a consortium of contractors made up of Thomas Brassey, George Wythes, and Lucas Bros. There were three stations: one at Rotherhithe, in a cutting south of the Thames Tunnel shaft; one at Deptford Road (now called Surrey Quays), just south of the tunnel portal; and a temporary terminus at New Cross, next to the LB&SCR station. This section of railway opened in 1869.

The MDR being constructed along the Victoria Embankment in front of Somerset House. *(LTM)*

On the north side of the Thames the work was rather harder. Thomas Andrew Walker was the contractor, and he had to contend with passing the tunnel beneath the eastern section of the London Docks and a large warehouse. Neither could be closed during the construction work. Walker formed the tunnel beneath the dock basin by building a cofferdam half-way across the dock and draining the dock within. The area in the cofferdam was then excavated down and the twin-track tunnel constructed beneath, before the dock bed was reinstated above. The cofferdam was then dismantled and replaced across the other half of the dock. The remainder of the tunnel was made within this dam, great care being taken to ensure that a waterproof connection was made where the two tunnels joined beneath the dock.

On the north side of the dock stood a large brick warehouse used for storing sugar. This required underpinning, a task made more difficult by the basements beneath it. Small vertical shafts were excavated beneath the brick piers supporting the building, and filled with concrete down to the level of the railway tunnel foundations. In this way a solid and deep foundation was provided. Once this work was completed the tunnel was then formed through the concrete pillars. Where these intersected the tunnel they were carefully cut away after the tunnel brickwork was in place, and the brickwork reinstated in the holes that were left.[42] The works at the docks were not completed on time, and the railway company had to pay £45,000 in compensation to the London Dock Company.

By comparison the rest of the works up to the Great Eastern Railway near Shoreditch were straightforward. The tunnel was made as cut and cover, resulting in the loss of some terraced housing where the company judged that it was cheaper to purchase and demolish the houses than alter the route or perform underpinning. This section of the railway opened for traffic in 1876.

Into the country

In 1864 a company called the Metropolitan & St John's Wood Railway (M&SJWR) was incorporated, and obtained an Act of Parliament for the construction of a railway from Baker Street to Swiss Cottage. After some delays in raising the necessary finance, work started in 1865. It was constructed beneath the roads in a single-track tunnel, this being both for economy and also to save having to obstruct the streets completely during construction work.[43] Although it had a double-track connection with the MR at Baker Street, this was to the east of the MR platforms and so the M&SJWR constructed its own platforms just beyond the junction. There were three further stations, at St John's Wood Road, Marlborough Road, and Swiss Cottage. The first two of these were in open cuttings, but Swiss Cottage had its platforms partly underground.

The tunnels were constructed of brick with arched crowns. At each of the stations the line had two tracks, allowing trains travelling in opposite directions to pass, but shortly beyond each end of the platforms the tunnels narrowed to take a single track. Spoil removed from the excavations was dumped into the lake in Regent's Park to reduce the depth, following the death of 40 people in January 1867 when they fell through ice.[44]

Passenger services on the M&SJWR began in April 1868, with trains running through to Moorgate. The trains were operated and the stations staffed by the MR,

The Iverson Road bridge under construction, showing the large amount of timbering used to support the arch. This is shaped to allow road users access through the works. Blue Staffordshire bricks were used for the main arch barrel. *(The Engineer)*

under a commercial arrangement. The through services were discontinued after two accidents at Baker Street Junction, and the line was then run as a shuttle. Unsurprisingly, the passenger numbers and financial return for this small company were very poor.

This situation might have continued had the M&SJWR remained with its terminus at Swiss Cottage, but the ambitions of the MR Chairman, Sir Edward Watkin, were to drive it out into the countryside surrounding London.* After some false starts in the early 1870s, work finally began on the extension in 1878. The tunnel was extended from Swiss Cottage to a station on the Finchley Road, whereupon the tracks continued in the open. After passing under West End Lane at the next station, West Hampstead, the line began to rise on an embankment. This climbed at a gradient of

---

* Although nominally independent, the fact that the MR worked and staffed the M&SJWR meant that it was controlled to an extent by the MR. During the 1870s the two companies jointly promoted some of the extensions referred to in this section; meanwhile, the MR looked to take over the smaller company at the best price, and finally succeeded in 1882.

Iverson Road bridge has eight separate brick arches each offset from its neighbour, as can be seen in this modern photograph. The band of dog-tooth brickwork can also be seen on the front face of the bridge. *(Author)*

around 1 in 95 in order to elevate the line sufficiently to pass over the North London Railway (NLR), which was itself on an embankment 25 ft high. The foundations for the bridge over the NLR had to cut through this latter embankment in order to reach suitably solid ground. Two spans were formed: one crossing the NLR, and a second to allow the NLR to be widened to four tracks at a future date without the need to disturb the MR. This widening has never taken place.

West of the NLR bridges the MR continued on a brick viaduct. Most of the arches were semi-circular and of about 30 ft in span, but larger skewed arches of 104 ft and 84 ft spans were constructed where Iverson Road and Loveridge Road were crossed respectively. Metal arched bridges were used to cross Edgware Road and Christchurch Road, as the headroom under brick arches would have been too restrictive.[45]

Constructing brick arched bridges

Arched bridges and viaducts were, until the middle of the twentieth century, almost always built of brick or stone. In London brick was the favoured material because of the readily available clay.

The arches are usually semi-circular or formed from the segment of a circle; the latter type are known as segmental arches. Work starts by constructing the foundations and building the piers. At the point from which the arch will start (called the 'springing'), a course of bricks is sometimes made to support the wooden framework on which the arch is built (the 'centring'), although this can just be supported from beneath by scaffolding. Bricklayers then lay several courses of bricks over the centring to form the arch barrel, bonding them to the piers. The spandrels (side walls) can then be constructed using horizontal courses of brickwork, starting above the piers and extending across the ends of the arch barrel as the courses progress upwards. The space between the spandrels and above the arch is then infilled with loose material, which acts as the foundation for the road or railway across the bridge.

Skewed arches, as at Iverson Road, are usually built with the courses of bricks parallel to the axis of the arch, which means that they will meet the springing at an angle. The bricks at this junction will be cut. Likewise, the bricks on the outer face of the arch will either form a dog-tooth effect, or will need to be cut or made to give a smooth surface.

Viaducts, which are a series of adjacent bridges, need to be constructed carefully to manage the sideways forces exerted by the arches. Either the piers need to be thick enough to resist these forces, or the arches need to be formed at the same time so that the forces on one pier are balanced from both sides.

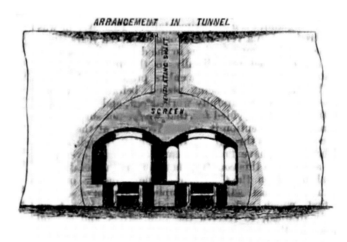

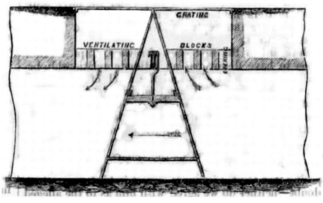

Cross-sections across the tunnel (above) and along the tunnel (below) showing the arrangement of the ventilation screens. *(The Engineer)*

A short section of viaduct west of Edgware Road led the line onto an embankment which gradually reduced in height as the land was rising in this direction. The remainder of the extension, which continued to Harrow, involved only minor earthworks. Services began running to Willesden Green in 1879, and to Harrow the following year. Perhaps surprisingly, the line between Swiss Cottage and Baker Street remained single track between the stations until July 1882, when new tunnels to the east of the original tunnels were opened to carry a new 'up' line (i.e., trains towards London).

Clearing the air

The noxious air in the original long tunnel of the MR has already been mentioned. The problem only worsened as the company operated a more intensive train service in order to meet passenger demand. Some passengers were taken from the stations suffering badly from the effects of the smoke and fumes, and a handful actually died. However, a scientific study in 1867 showed that the air contained less carbon dioxide than within some London theatres and law courts, and only small amounts of sulphurous acid gas. The study looked also at the health of the MR drivers and firemen, who spent considerable amounts of time in the tunnels, and determined that they had a lower sickness rate than their equivalents on the open-air GWR. They concluded

> ...confidently to state that the atmosphere of the Metropolitan Railway is not unwholesome or injurious to health.[46]

In order to provide better ventilation the glazing at the top of the light shafts at Baker Street and Gower Street were removed. In between the stations small ventilation shafts were made up to the road level, with cast iron grating blocks installed in the roof of the tunnel. It was hoped that the 'piston effect' of trains moving along the tunnels would push air through and thus bring clean air in from the portals, but with a double-track tunnel this tends not to happen so much.

In the mid-1870s some new ideas were tried. Firstly, screens were constructed across the tunnels where some of the ventilation shafts were located. The screens were made of thin planks, and were arranged in pairs with their tops touching but bases farther apart. The screens had apertures cut in them that would allow trains to pass through; these had sufficient tolerance in their shape to cope with the swaying of trains, and even the accidental opening of one of the carriage doors. The slope on the screens directed the air pushed in front of the train upwards and through the shaft into the street, and in doing so pulled fresher air into the tunnel behind the trains.[47]

Secondly, in 1879 a long wooden partition was built between the tracks from Gower Street to Portland Road, effectively separating the double-track tunnel into two separate single-track tunnels. The aim was to improve the piston effect along this section of line. It was not a great success and lasted for just seven years.

Another experiment at Portland Road involved blowing 60,000 ft^3 of air per minute through a canvas tube into the space under the platform. The intention was that the air would blow up from the front edge of the platform to give the passengers some fresh air. It was not a success, and only lasted seven months.[48]

In 1897, the BoT appointed the Metropolitan Railway Ventilation of Tunnels Committee, who were to investigate the problems of ventilation on the MR and report back. They noted that despite using "best Welsh smokeless coal", the atmosphere between Baker Street and Gower Street was "commonly thick with smoke and steam, and very unpleasant".[49] The oldest section of the railway, between Edgware Road and King's Cross, had the worst atmosphere, although the uphill line in single track tunnels between Marlborough Road and Swiss Cottage was a close second (with gradients as steep as 1 in 44). The Committee examined three possible remedies:

- fans to extract air from the tunnels – these were considered to be practical, but would have difficulties with the currents of air from passing trains, and discharging the tunnel air in a way that would not cause a nuisance
- additional ventilation holes – unified opposition from local authorities, who objected to "foul gases" being discharged at street level
- electric working of the line – felt to be the most satisfactory solution by far.

A cross-section of the tunnel beneath the Minories, showing how the brick arch was supported by the concrete side walls. *(The Engineer)*

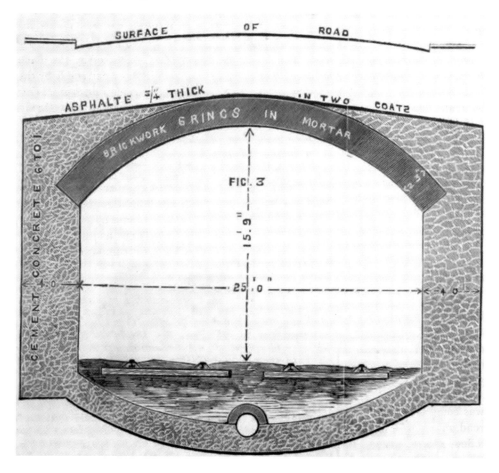

The Committee concluded that electrification was the best way of dealing with the ventilation problem, and that given it was likely to be adopted shortly, the expense of fans was not justified (and might even cause electrification to be delayed). They did recommend the opening of additional ventilation holes as a temporary measure, stating that they would have to be closed if required to do so after three years of use.

Joining the Circle
In 1875 the MR continued further into the City of London with a short extension from Moorgate Street to Liverpool Street. Initially trains ran into the Great Eastern Railway main-line terminus through a short tunnel, as their own station had been delayed. A few months later the MR opened their station, located just to the south of the main-line station. The following year another short extension brought the line to a new terminus at Aldgate. The costs of the extensions were high: there was no undeveloped land or slums to be cleared in the City of London, and so property was either purchased and demolished, or expensively underpinned. A small amount of money was made when the MR sold several hundred cartloads of bullocks' horns, which were discovered in a thick layer 20 ft below the surface in 1876.[50]

Parliament kept making demands for the completion of the Inner Circle, by building a railway between the MR and the MDR's terminus at Mansion House. The MR and MDR resisted, as they were struggling financially (particularly the MDR) and the costs would be even higher with poor returns. However, they were eventually forced into building the line, at which point the MR rapidly constructed an extension from Aldgate to Tower Hill. By doing this, the extension would be owned solely by the MR and hence it could claim all the passenger revenue for trains passing over it. This was calculated to annoy the MDR, who were expecting joint ownership of the line at least as far as a junction just south of Aldgate station. The contractor was Thomas A. Walker, who had built part of the East London Railway, and between 1879 and 1886 was responsible for the building of the Severn Tunnel.

The first part of the extension was the bridge carrying Aldgate High Street over the line. A number of large gas mains were beneath the road surface, and so heavy wrought iron plate girders were used to ensure that these would not be disturbed. After a short section of open cutting the railway entered a tunnel below the street called Minories. Construction differed from previous tunnels, in that the retaining walls for both the cutting and tunnel were cast from Portland cement concrete, as was the tunnel invert. Only the arch was of stock brick, laid up to 3 ft in thickness because of the heavy buildings overhead. Where the line passed beneath the viaduct of the London & Blackwall Railway from Fenchurch Street it was carefully threaded beneath a viaduct arch, with the piers either side being underpinned. The tunnel continued beneath The Crescent, where a gap was formed in the houses to make the railway. This was left open as the line continued to a temporary wooden station called The Tower of London in a cutting. This station was built in just 60 hours in what one author describes as "an attempt to establish squatter's rights".[51]

The final section of railway between Mansion House and The Tower of London was complex and costly because of the large, heavy buildings on both sides of the road, many of which also had cellars. For this reason the new tunnel was placed at a deeper level than had been the case previously. The work started by removing the

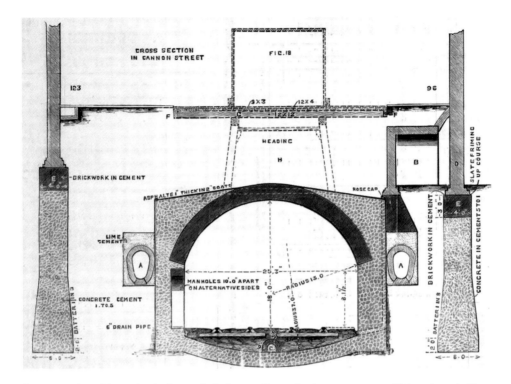

A cross-section of the underpinning works in Cannon Street. Replacement sewers (A) have been built on both sides of the railway tunnel and a cellar (B) is supported on both the tunnel and sewer. The building foundations (D) are shown supported on the brickwork (E) below which lie the concrete columns. *(The Engineer)*

kerbs and replacing the road surface with two layers of planks above large wooden baulks. A section of this was removed to create a shaft, sunk to a depth of about 10 ft, from which a heading was excavated along and beneath the road. From this, smaller side headings were excavated until they reached the foundations of the buildings. The soil was then excavated from beneath a short length (up to 5 ft) of the foundations to the depth of the rail tunnel invert. This was filled with concrete to within 3ft of the foundation base, and then completed with brickwork so that the foundations were supported by a new column. Once a series of these columns were finished the earth was dug out from between them and the support beneath the foundations made continuous.

New sewers were then built under the roadway and either side of where the railway tunnel would be built. Once these were in use the main heading beneath the roadway was dug down and widened so that the space for the tunnel was clear, and the tunnel invert and side walls constructed from concrete. The brick arch was then formed. The cellars of buildings were supported on temporary needle balks* that in

---

* These were wooden struts threaded into position through holes in the tunnel headings beneath the cellars, providing support until the permanent support beneath was constructed.

turn were supported by the building underpinning and the tunnel walls, and often by walls placed on top of the new sewer formations. Finally the space above the tunnel was backfilled with soil and the roadway was reinstated. Unfortunately the opportunity to create a pipe subway in the space above the railway tunnel was not taken, even though this was suggested in the press at the time.[52]

Fortunately for the MDR, the houses on the north side of Eastcheap and Great Tower Street were demolished, as the City Corporation wanted to widen both streets. The Corporation therefore met half the cost of the property and the demolition work, which was about £500,000. On the south side of Cannon Street between Mansion House and Cannon Street stations all the properties were demolished, although as this was just because of the alignment of the railway the cost was paid entirely by the MDR.

Construction costs

The costs of cut and cover tunnelling during the period between 1860 and 1884 varied depending on the type of tunnel or cutting, the soil through which the tunnel was made, and the type of adjacent buildings.

One linear yard of railway cost the following amounts:

MR original 28 ft 6 in wide cut and cover tunnel	£47.5s.0d
MR 28 ft 6 ins wide Clerkenwell tunnel	£69.7s.6d
MR 25 ft wide Campden Hill tunnel	£63.0s.0d
MDR 25 ft wide cut and cover tunnel	£39.17s.0d
MDR 25 ft girder covered way	£52.2s.0d
MDR 25 ft cutting, 25 ft deep	£66.14s.6d
MDR 25 ft cutting, 42 ft deep	£107.15s.6d

These figures include excavation, cartage, brickwork, concrete, drainage, and (for the deep cutting) cast iron struts to span the cutting.

Birth of the tube

The circular shield

It was during the construction of Lambeth Bridge in 1861 that the key idea necessary for the construction of tube railways occurred. The engineer for the bridge was Peter Barlow, and he had designed a suspension bridge that would link each bank of the Thames a short way upstream of the existing bridge at Westminster. The bridge rested on four cylindrical piles sunk through the river bed and into the London clay.[*] These were made of circular iron rings, 12 feet in diameter, pressed down into the soil and filled with concrete and then brickwork once in position. The bridge was then constructed on top.

Peter William Barlow (1809–1885)

Barlow was the son of an eminent mathematician, Peter Barlow, who taught at the Woolwich Military Academy. His early engineering career was on the Liverpool & Birmingham Canal. He then moved to railway work, with the London to Dover railway line, where he became their principal engineer under Sir William Cubitt. He remained involved with railways, bridges, and tunnelling work throughout his career, producing many papers for the Institution of Civil Engineers. His son, also called Peter, followed him into engineering and worked on the Tower Subway, and his brother was the engineer for St Pancras station in London.

At some point during the construction, Barlow considered what would happen if such rings were pressed horizontally through the clay, rather than vertically, to create a tunnel that might pass below a river. In 1864 he took out a patent for what we would now term a tunnelling shield. The patent, number 2207, described the shield thus:

> In constructing tunnels for railways, particularly where the tunnels are to pass under rivers or under towns and places where the upper surface cannot without serious injury be broken up or interfered with, a cylinder of somewhat larger internal diameter than the external diameter of the intended tunnel is employed, such a cylinder being by preference of wrought iron or steel. The forward edge of this cylinder is made comparatively thin. Within this cylinder

---

[*]   The cylinders were supposed to have been sunk to a depth of 18 feet, but when the bridge was demolished in 1929 the depth was found to be only about 8 feet.

and near the forward end thereof, are upright plates parallel to each other, also formed with cutting forward edges in order to cut freely through the soil in front when the cylinder is forced forward. The earth is continuously removed from within this cylinder, and the cylinder is from time to time forced forward a short distance to admit of a ring of iron being put together within the inner end of the cylinder, such iron rings being of a strength suitable for forming a permanent lining to the tunnel.

The main aspects of the shield are encompassed in the detail of the patent. The shield was circular, to give the greatest strength against the load placed on it by the soil above. It had a cutting edge at the front to loosen the soil. The shield protected the workers within, and was long enough to allow the permanent structure of the tunnels to be constructed at its rear, meaning that the only exposed soil would be the vertical face of the tunnel. Later in the patent Barlow went on to describe how cement would be injected behind the permanent tunnel structure via holes in the tunnel segments to fill the void left by the shield and ensure that the soil above does not settle, with unfortunate consequences for buildings above.

Another advantage of the circular shield, which was possibly not appreciated at the time, was that it meant that all of the segments making up a ring of the tunnel lining were the same (with the exception of the key piece). This would have achieved economies of scale in casting them, and it would also have eased the construction process. The amount of light available to the tunnellers would have been unimaginably low by comparison to today's brightly lit world. Not having to sort through a selection of differently shaped castings would have made their task simpler.

The year before he took out his patent Barlow put forward plans for a tunnel beneath the Thames downstream of London Bridge and near to the site where Tower Bridge was later built. According to *The Daily News*, the scheme would link Irongate Stairs near the Tower of London with Horselydown on the south bank.[53] It must be recalled that Tower Bridge was not opened until 1894, and London Bridge was very congested with port traffic passing between the north and south sides of the river. A tunnel would not interfere with river traffic, but there was local opposition to the scheme from wharf owners and it fell through.

In 1866 Barlow returned with a new plan for a tunnel, but this time to link the banks of the Thames just upstream of the Tower of London. The Act was rejected after opposition from the Tower authorities because the shaft was to have been in the road leading to the Tower stairs.

The Tower Subway
The following year, having discussed the matter with the Tower authorities and come to an agreement with them, Barlow submitted a tunnel Bill for the third time. He described the scheme in a short book that he wrote. *On the Relief of London Street Traffic* as a "subway omnibus system", fitting in a transport niche somewhere between the buses and trains, and operated below the surface. Single carriages would operate without locomotives through a single tunnel made of cast iron. The tunnel would descend from the shafts on each bank to a low point beneath the river, allowing the carriages to be accelerated by gravity, and leaving only "friction and

the resistance of the air" to be overcome. He calculated that to operate a carriage with twelve passengers having a combined mass of 2 tons would require one man-power of continuous effort if a service was operated every 2½ minutes. To get up and down the shafts Barlow proposed the use of hydraulic lifts.

The construction of a mile of single cast iron tunnel around eight feet in diameter was estimated to cost £28,000 for the iron segments, plus £6,000 for the excavation. With the need for shafts and the purchase of land for these, Barlow generously esti-mated a cost of £60,000 per mile. Based on these estimates, The Tower Subway at 1,340 yards (a little over one-quarter of a mile) was reckoned to cost £16,000.

This small sum gave rise to queries in the House of Lords when the Bill was being considered, and witnesses were cross-examined to see if the amount was unduly low. Barlow was supported by their evidence, and Royal Assent for the Tower Subway Act was granted on 29 May 1868. In August it was reported that the Tower Subway Company had sold 500 of its 1,200 shares of £10 each (the remaining £4,000 of non-share capital was to be borrowed). The dividend, estimated at 20% in Barlow's book, was now suggested to be in the order of 32% once the railway was operational – "exclusive of revenue from parcels". The directors guaranteed a minimum dividend of 4% for 15 years on the remainder of the shares to be issued. Naturally, Barlow was one of the Directors; the others were Francis Hewson and Robert Richardson. Barlow's son, also called Peter, was the company engineer.

The following month it was reported that negotiations for the purchase of the land* were proceeding well, and that the amounts to be paid were less than had been budgeted. Sadly, this was not the case on the north side, and the Crown Estates charged the company the high price of £1,300 for the 100 square feet of land required. On the other side the land ended up being rented for £10 per year.[54] The lift manufac-turers Eastons, Amos and Anderson had agreed that they could provide the hydraulic lifts for the budgeted amount, and the tunnel contractor had likewise agreed to the £9,400 set aside for building the tunnels.

At some point around late 1868 a decision was made to move the carriage through the Tower Subway using a stationary engine, instead of through human muscle-power. This was placed on the south side of the Thames, operating the carriage through means of a steel cable.

Constructing the subway

The contractor was a 24-year-old South African called James Greathead. He had been a pupil of Barlow's in the mid-1860s, and that his bid was accepted shows that Barlow had faith in his abilities. Barlow had patented another tunnelling shield in 1868, and Greathead used a modified version of this for the Tower Subway. It was a cylinder, around 4 ft 9 ins long and 7 ft 3 ins in diameter, weighing about 2⊠ tons. Its front cutting edge was made of cast iron, and inside a wrought iron partition filled the circle, giving it strength. The centre of the partition included a rectangular opening about 2 ft 6 ins wide by 4 ft high through which the soil was excavated; this

---

*   On the north side of the Thames the shaft was to be on Crown property; on the south side the land was owned by St Olave's Board of Works.

could be closed to seal off the working face in the event of water entering.* It was particularly important that this opening did not reach the top of the shield, as in the event of a flood of water entering from the tunnel face the section of partition above the opening would maintain an air pocket allowing the workmen to breathe. On the rear edge of the shield were sockets, into which screw jacks were fitted. These were used to press the shield forward into the clay. The shield was manufactured by Bells, Goodman and Co, of the Walker Engine Works and Foundry in Newcastle-upon-Tyne.

James Henry Greathead (1844–1896)

Greathead was born and educated in Grahamstown, South Africa, and came to the UK in 1859 to complete his education. In 1864 he began a three-year pupillage under Barlow, after which he worked with Barlow's brother on the Midland Railway.

In 1869 he began his work with Peter Barlow on the Tower Subway. In the 1870s he became resident engineer of the extensions of the MDR to Hammersmith and Richmond. In 1884 he started work as engineer on the City & South London Railway (see p 65), with John Fowler as one of the consulting engineers. He was joint engineer to the Waterloo & City Railway (see p 84) and then the Central London Railway (see p 95).

In January 1994, a 10 foot high statue of Greathead was erected in Cornhill, outside Bank station, atop a ventilation shaft for the station. The crest of the C&SLR is on the plinth.

(Photo: *The Engineer*)

The work started on 16 February 1869 with the sinking of the shaft adjacent to the Tower of London. This work was performed by Thomas Tilley, "the well-known artesian well engineer".[55] With a diameter of 10 ft, and a depth of 58 ft it was constructed of iron rings to a depth of 30 ft and then brickwork. This took just under two months to complete. During the work a bag was found which contained 300 silver coins. The mix of twopenny, fourpenny, and sixpenny coins were from the reigns of Henry III and Alexander VII of Scotland, and had to be handed to the Government under the treasure trove laws.[56]

---

* There is a discrepancy in the records about the shape of the shield partition which needs clarification. Drawings in *The Engineer* (26 March 1869) show an hexagonal arrangement of plates, with an hexagonal opening in the middle through which the excavation would be carried out. This was also described in *Les Galeries Souterrain*, published in 1878 (in French). However, Greathead states in his work on the C&SLR that the opening was rectangular, and this is supported by drawings from journalists who visited – for example, the *Illustrated London News* in October 1869. The hexagonal shield was Barlow's original design; however, the subway was constructed using a shield designed by Greathead after he was appointed as contractor, and thus featured the rectangular opening.

At the bottom of the shaft a large horizontal tunnel (10 ft in diameter) would be driven northwards for 35 feet to house a small waiting room for passengers. In the opposite direction the tunnel dipped down at a gradient of 1 in 29 to the centre of the river, and then ascended at the same gradient to the foot of the shaft on the south bank. Beneath the river a minimum cover of 18 ft of soil was maintained, although the average was 30 ft. Barlow was very keen to avoid the inundations that had delayed the construction of Brunel's Thames Tunnel, and made extensive borings of the river bed from a boat to understand what he would be tunnelling through. Despite this, visitors to the subway once it opened could hear the beat of the paddles from steamers passing along the Thames overhead.[57]

The tunnelling commenced on 26 April, and was entirely manual. Clay was excavated through the doorway in the shield until there was space for a man to climb through. He would then dig more clay until a second man could join him. Together they would remove clay until the entire face of the tunnel had been excavated to a depth of 18 inches. As the clay was excavated it was taken back to the base of the shaft, from where a hoist powered by a steam engine lifted it out for disposal. Tunnel segments were taken back into the shaft in the same way. Within the clay were found shark's teeth and various shells from marine species, as well as large 'clay stones' which caused the miners some trouble to break up and remove.

The six screw jacks would then be tightened using ratchet braces against the last tunnel ring and the shield would be forced forwards by another 18 inches. This slid the shield forward into the space excavated at the front, and also removed it from behind the last tunnel ring. Holes in the segments of the new ring allowed the space behind, typically about 1 inch deep, to be filled with blue lias cement, injected by hand using syringes. This set fast and helped prevent settlement of the ground above, as well as forming a protective coating around the iron exterior. Insufficient force was obtained with the syringes to fill the void completely, and the grout had to be rather more fluid than was best for getting it to set well.[58] Tests had been carried out before construction started to ensure that the cement would not react with the iron of the segments.[59]

The screw jacks on the rear of the shield were then wound back in and a new tunnel ring of cast iron erected. Each ring comprised three large segments about 7 ft long, weighing around 4 cwt (200 kg), and a smaller 'key' segment just 10 ins across. This latter piece had parallel sides so that it could be hammered into place to secure the ring, which was held together with ¾-in bolts through the flanges on the sides of the segments. These flanges were about 2 in deep. The external diameter of the tunnel was 7 ft 1¾ ins. The segments were ⅞ in thick, reducing the internal diameter to 7 ft ¼ in, but with the flanges there was a clear space of just 6 ft 7¾ ins across. Oakum was used between the segments to seal the joints, which were then pointed using medina cement. The tunnel was so dry that all of the water required to mix the cement had to be transported down to the workmen in buckets from the surface.

Work proceeded like this night and day, with the activities overlapping. The excavation work could take place at the same time as the grouting, and would continue whilst the tunnel ring was assembled. Average progress for the tunnel was 5 ft per day, although the maximum was 9 ft in a single day, making a total of six iron rings. At this rate, the tunnel passed beneath the high water mark on the north bank of the Thames on 26 May, after one month of work, and the corresponding point on the south bank on 8 September. There was no shaft to connect with as yet; delays had occurred in purchasing the land, and this was only completed on 5 October. The shaft came up on the west side of Vine Street.*

Work on sinking the shaft started just two days later, and it was completed on 27 November (in a similar time to the north shaft). This shaft was only 52 feet deep, but tapered slightly; it had a diameter of 10 ft for the first 20 ft below the surface, 9 ft for the next 20 ft (all lined with iron) and then 8 ft diameter in brickwork for the remaining 12 ft to the bottom of the shaft. The sinking of the iron parts of the shaft was troublesome, and some 80 tons of kentledge (weighting) had to be applied to force the cylinder to descend into the ground.[60]

Once this shaft was finished there was little construction work remaining. Completing the tunnelling work took exactly one more week, and the southern waiting room was finished on 20 December.

Rails and lifts

Work then began on the mechanical engineering for the Subway. A 4 h.p. stationary engine with a single horizontal piston, located in a chamber at the foot of the each shaft below the level of the tunnel, drove a drum over which the steel cable ran for pulling the carriage. This was operated back-and-forth depending on the direction that the carriage was to run, with the engine at the receiving end of the tunnel pulling the cable and the other engine running free. A separate 5 h.p. vertical two-cylinder steam engine worked the lift. Both engines in each shaft received their steam from a single boiler.** Nothing appears to have come from the interest from the aforementioned hydraulic lift company.

The lifts themselves were wrought iron cages 6 ft 6 ins high, with a rectangular floor of 5 ft by 6 ft, accommodating about seven passengers. To reduce the load on the engines, counterweights were used, and these could be adjusted so that they balanced the typical load at any time.*** Safety catches would arrest the lift if the chain broke, and a fan governor was fitted to the main shaft to limit the maximum speed. Spring buffers were placed at the base of both shafts to absorb any impact from the cages. The engines and lifts were manufactured by T. Shaw, Head & Co. of Stockton-on-Tees. The top of each shaft was protected by a small metal cabin, described in *The Times* as being "like a slightly exaggerated sentry box", through which admission was gained to the lift cage via sliding doors. The lift cages were padded or upholstered for the comfort of the passengers.

Bells, Goodman & Co., who had made the shield, also supplied the carriage (as

---

* Subsequently renamed Vine Lane. The site of the southern shaft has now disappeared beneath the More London development, although access is still maintained.

** According to the article in *The Times*, 31 March 1870, each shaft contained a single engine which was used to power both the lift and carriage cable. The confusion probably lay from their being one boiler and two engines in each shaft, which were probably seen as being a single 'engine'.

*** Various reports suggest that the counterweights were left set at the weight of the lift cage plus three people, thus ensuring that the lift engine never had to move more than the weight of about three or four people.

Drawings showing (left) the workmen tightening the screw jacks to drive the shield forwards, and (right) the workmen erecting a tunnel ring. They are both looking along the tunnel towards the tunnel face, with the rectangular opening in the shield partition just visible behind the men. Note the candles on the tunnel wall, which would have provided the only illumination for the men, and the temporary wooden track for removing the spoil. *(Illustrated London News)*

well as the iron tunnel and shaft segments). This was of steel construction with eight wheels beneath running on two rails 2ft 6 ins apart. Its length was about 10 ft 6 ins, with a width of 5 ft 3 ins and a height of 5 ft 11 ins. The twelve passengers sat on upholstered and padded longitudinal seats. There were no side windows as there was nothing to see in the dark tunnel outside. Brakes working against the wheels could be operated from either end of the carriage by the guard, who rode on the step. Movement was achieved by a gripper below the carriage permanently clamped onto the moving steel cable. It was important that the men managing the engines slowed them down correctly for the carriage to stop at its appointed position at the end of the tunnel. Buffers with vulcanized india-rubber springs prevented the carriage from overshooting, and catches held it in position whilst passengers boarded and alighted. The guard carried a lamp which he would wave on the approach to the station. This would be seen by a signal-man, who would instruct the engine operators to slow the engines by means of an electrically operated bell. The signal-men probably had the draughtiest job on the subway, being stationed at the ends of the tunnel. A contemporary report described them as

> ...seen with hair blowing wildly about – for there is a very strong wind ejected from the tube by the progress of the carriage.

The carriage ran upon steel rails spiked to wooden sleepers. These were placed every 3 ft and were set into the concrete that filled the lowest portion of the tunnel. Lightweight rails weighing just 30 lb/yd could be used because of the relative lightness of the carriage (when compared to conventional railway equipment).

When the Tower Subway was completed it was found to have cost more than expected, somewhere around £18,000, but part of this can be explained by the additional tunnelling to provide bigger waiting rooms than originally planned, and the use of more powerful steam engines.

The equipping of the subway was completed in February 1870, and passengers began to be conveyed on a trial basis. This was somewhat unusual, as the formal inspection and approval of the subway by an Inspector from the Board of Trade was not completed until April. Nevertheless, passengers were carried and fares were collected. A single trip cost 1d for a second class ticket, and 2d for first class. There was no difference between the seating or carriage for the two classes; purchasers of first class tickets merely gained priority over the other passengers for access to the lifts and the carriage. Tickets were purchased from an official standing at the door of each of the metal cabins over the shaft. The novelty of the new service was such that the fare was temporarily increased to 3d in April to help reduce queuing and congestion. The announcements in some newspapers that the subway was open to the public[61] probably did not help, but these had only been caused by the company's over-optimistic announcements of an opening in mid-February.

The public reaction

A journey on the subway would start with the purchase of a ticket from the blue-coated official outside the cabin at the top of the shaft. The passenger would enter the lift and descend to the level of the tunnel in 25 seconds. At the bottom of the shaft the passenger would take a seat in the plain, whitewashed waiting room until the carriage arrived. Contemporary reports remarked on the coolness of the air, and also the lack of damp. Light came from paraffin lanterns which sometimes blew out in the draught from the approaching carriage; the company claimed them to be temporary, and that gas lighting would be installed.[62] The tunnel itself was closed off from the waiting room by a circular partition. Upon arrival of the carriage a door in this partition would open and the passengers would alight. After boarding the guard would set the carriage in motion by signalling to the engine operators, and the under-river trip would take about 70 seconds. Descent from the carriage would be followed by a short wait for the lift before another 25-second ascent to the surface. The *Illustrated London News* cheerfully stated that it would be possible to make the journey between street level in a minimum time of one minute 45 seconds (although given the timings of the lift and carriage journeys this should surely have been two minutes at its most optimistic), and that even if a passenger just missed the lifts *and* the carriage then the journey could take no longer than five minutes.[63]

Although the service was still experimental, the paying passengers did not hesitate to complain when problems occurred. A letter to *The Times* on 18 April notes that the author received

...rather a rude shock by a demand of 3d being made on me for a ticket upon which a fare of 2d only was printed. I paid my money, however, and took my place in the iron cage, being curiously scanned by a crowd of unwashed idlers who surrounded the entrance, and whom the courteous and long-suffering official endeavoured in vain to disperse. There I sat and fidgeted for 20 minutes or half an hour, when, finding that the officer in charge was unable to assign any cause for the delay and could not give me any hope of a speedy commencement of my journey, I asked to be allowed to return him my ticket and to receive back my fare, to which he at once assented.

The letter was signed "Disappointed". Barlow responded via a letter in the same newspaper,[64] pointing out that the service was only open to the public "at the urgent request of persons in the locality". It is likely that the income from the fares helped the company too. Delays were caused by the cable catching on the pulleys and breaking, but these were initially reported by the media as teething troubles. It seems likely that if the gripper was not released properly at the end of each journey the strain on the cable could cause it to snap.[65] Services would then have to be halted until the two ends of the cable could be found and rejoined.

A fatal accident occurred on Thursday 23 June. The subway was not open to passengers due to some work being done, and one of the workmen, Thomas Janning ascended in the lift on the south side of the river to collect some tools. The ticket collector in the lift, Robert Nicolson, told the inquest into the death that he warned Janning to stay in the lift whilst Nicolson signalled to the engine operator to stop the lift at the top. For some unexplained reason the lift did not stop immediately and bounced off the buffer at the top as Janning jumped out, trapping his head between the lift ceiling and the edge of the shaft as it descended. The inquest, held two days later, decided that it was a case of accidental death.

The experimental period of operation led to some changes. The communication between the engine operators and with the guard caused problems, and the single cable being wound back and forth was replaced by an endless cable. The carriage was equipped with a gripper that now only clasped the cable when the carriage was to be in motion. As the carriage approached its terminus the gripper would be released and the brakes applied to bring it to a stand at the right point. This allowed the service to be operated "with perfect regularity".[66] Alternative safety equipment was also fitted to the lifts, possibly as a result of the accident, and had been inspected and approved by the authorities.

The official opening of the Tower Subway was on 2 August. At the half-yearly company meeting, held on 30 August, it was reported that an income of £30 per week was being made, sufficient to pay the working expenses as well as the capital and interest charges. The Board also noted that the subway could handle three times as much traffic. Alas, this was true but the traffic that had been so optimistically predicted when the shares were being sold never materialized.

A tarnished dream

The subway's creditors were unhappy with their returns and filed with the Court of Chancery on 16 September 1870. An Extraordinary General Meeting (EGM) of the company was held on 3 November at which it was proposed to raise an additional £8,000 through sale of shares and debentures which would pay 6% interest. Of the new capital, £6,000 would repay existing debts and the remainder would be used to improve the subway. In case the Court of Chancery refused to sanction this scheme, it was advised that a new parliamentary Bill should be prepared for this purpose.

Barlow noted that the traffic was "rapidly improving", with the ticket sales on the south bank from the previous day being the best ever. The meeting concluded by creating a committee of five shareholders to examine the company's accounts, at which point it was adjourned.

One week later the meeting reconvened. The recommendation of the shareholders was that the company should appoint a receiver, and should continue with its plan to raise further capital. Barlow disagreed, and voted against the plan. However, on 17 November the Master of the Rolls appointed the company engineer, Peter Barlow junior, as receiver to the company. This was an unpaid role, to help with the company finances. Around the same time, a Bill was deposited with Parliament to raise the additional capital, as agreed at the EGM.

The subway was closed to passengers when the receiver was appointed; the exact date seems to have gone unrecorded. The lifts and carriage were all removed (the engines were allegedly left *in situ* and just bricked up)[67], and a wooden floor was laid through the tunnel. Wooden spiral staircases comprising 96 steps were constructed within the shafts and gas lamps were installed along the tunnel about every 40 ft, connected to a gas pipe run through the tunnel. The subway reopened to the public on 24 December as a foot tunnel, costing ½d to cross the river. Turnstiles were installed at the foot of the stairs that counted the number of people passing through as the fares were collected. Not surprisingly the tunnel became known as the "Ha'penny Subway".

With the lack of waiting for lifts and a carriage, it was claimed by some that there was no appreciable difference in the time to cross the river on foot.[68] By early January around 2,500 people per day were using the tunnel, bringing an income of £6.25; slightly more than was collected when the carriage was in operation, and with rather lower working expenses. *The Standard* reported on 16 January 1871 that the working expenses prior to closure were around £35 per week, or £5 more than the company was making from fares. If true this would certainly explain the rapid failure of the company to satisfy its creditors. The same article claimed the subway to have been a failure, and that this was proven by its conversion into a foot tunnel. Barlow wrote back refuting this view,[69] and claiming that one of his original plans had been for the subway to be used for pedestrians, but that the company wanted to try out the idea of a small railway first. He was probably correct in stating that the foot traffic would bring in more revenue than could possibly be achievable by such a short railway.

Despite the earlier claims of the tunnel's watertightness, it appears that inevitably some water made its way in, giving the subway a cold, damp, and probably rather sinister atmosphere. One visitor described using the subway:

The inside of this tube presents the appearance of a subterranean corridor, of which the end is invisible. It is lighted by a row of lights as far as you can see, which shed a veiled light, like sepulchral lamps; the atmosphere is foggy; you go along considerable stretches without meeting a soul; the walls sweat like those of an aqueduct; the floor moves under your feet like the deck of a vessel; the steps and voices of the people coming the other way give forth a cavernous sound, and are heard before you see the people, and they at a distance seem like great shadows; there is, in short, a sort of something mysterious, which without alarming causes in your heart a vague sense of disquiet.[70]

Foot traffic through the tunnel continued to rise. The week ending 20 January 1871 saw 20,325 people pass through, and the following weeks this increased to 24,212 and then 25,205. The half-yearly company meeting on 8 February reported that the income was such that a return to mechanical operation was out of the question, and was very pleased to report that after paying the working expenses the company would be able to pay the 6% interest on the proposed new debentures as well as a 10% dividend on the original shares. The meeting concluded by agreeing to proceed with the new Bill.

The pedestrian traffic stabilized at about 24,000 people per week from early February. The opening hours increased from 13 March, being from 04.30 – 00.30 then on.

The new Bill progressed through the various stages of the Parliamentary process, finally gaining Royal Assent as the Tower Subway (Capital) Act on 25 May 1871. The summer months saw the traffic decline, probably as a result of the stuffy conditions in the tunnel, and in November 1871 the Directors reported that a new larger entrance was being constructed at the Tower of London which would give improved ventilation. Details of the structure are vague, but it might have been made of brick with a conical wooden roof.[71] With the cooler weather passenger numbers recovered back to around 20,000 per week. The drop in numbers was probably behind the dividend declared in September being only 4%. This level of traffic continued through the winter months, and the divided in February 1872 increased slightly to 4½%.

The subway then settled down to a largely uneventful existence for the next 25 years. Like Brunel's tunnel, the numbers using it and its reputation gradually declined. A report of May 1872 refers to a "riot" in the subway during which lights were extinguished; the crime of putting out lights occurs with tedious repetition over the succeeding years. Those caught extinguishing the lights were fined between 10s and 40s, or alternatively imprisoned for 7–14 days. The courts repeatedly warned about the dangers of explosion that were caused when the gas continued to flow without flame, and the company had to occasionally pay compensation to those who injured themselves in the darkness.

Through the 1870s a dividend of 4% was typically declared at each six-monthly company meeting, but this was not always paid owing to lack of funds. In 1877 it was discovered that some of the Subway's employees were altering the counters on the turnstiles for the purposes of fraud – it would appear that the count from the turnstiles was used to audit the amount of money collected by the staff from those using the tunnel. By manipulating the counters the staff could steal from the fare revenue. This presumably also led to under-reporting of the use of the tunnel. The subway company took the supplier of the turnstiles to court in 1879, alleging that the supplier was contracted to maintain the turnstiles in working order. The court rejected the claim, as the "judge and jury [...] were of the opinion that the defendants did not guarantee that their mechanism would insure the honesty of the Company's servants".[72] The counter-claim of the turnstile company for payment for work done but not paid was upheld, and they were awarded £25.

On 20 May 1878 a man shot himself in the subway; the inquest returned a verdict of "suicide whilst of unsound mind". Various assaults were reported in the 1880s, including a vicious attack on a 70-year-old man who was pushed back down one of the staircases by a gang of youths who snatched his gold watch and chain.[73] In 1894, a fraudster stood at the top of the stairs collecting money from unsuspecting tunnel users, who then discovered the turnstiles when they reached the bottom. Two of those he defrauded were so annoyed that they reclimbed the stairs, found a nearby policeman, and had him arrested. His sentence was three months hard labour.

By the early 1880s the dividend dwindled and then ceased. The sinister atmosphere of the tunnel did not attract people, who would only use it because they had no choice. The alternative was to walk up to London Bridge, or to use one of the private ferries; however, the latter would operate once sufficient passengers were present, and so delays of over an hour were not uncommon. One man recalled a visit in 1884, describing it as "a dismal, frightening tunnel". The poor lighting and noise of water trickling, combined with the loneliness of the walk through, did not endear the walk to him.[74]

Tower Bridge was opened near to the subway on 30 June 1894. The directors of the subway company had been concerned about loss of traffic to the bridge for some years; after all, the only advantage that the subway could claim was that its users would not get wet during inclement weather. The bridge was free to use, and only required stairs to be used when the bascules were raised, and if the user was not inclined to wait.* Just two months after the bridge opened the number of subway users had fallen drastically, and the company was pursuing a claim for their losses against the Bridge House Estates, who owned Tower Bridge. The subway company had objected during the Parliamentary approval for the bridge and the Act for the bridge's approval included a clause to protect the subway company against loss.

In December 1895 the company lodged a claim for £30,000 against the Corporation of the City of London (who created and oversee the Bridge House Estates). This immediately went to arbitration, with the City of London claiming that the Tower Subway Company had been practically insolvent for all its existence, and that they had "looked upon the building of the Tower-bridge as a 'godsend'",[75] in that they could now claim a large sum of money to repay their shareholders who had lost out on the poor returns from the subway. Witnesses on behalf of the City of London claimed that the wooden flooring and staircases in the subway were mostly rotten, that the tunnel was leaking, and that 417 bolts holding the segments together were missing. In their opinion it would not last more than another ten years. However, the arbitrator found in favour of the subway, but awarded them just £11,500. With this completed the subway closed on 7 March 1896.

The subway was put up for sale by the directors in November 1896. An Act was deposited with Parliament to enable the sale to occur, with the profits to be split amongst the shareholders and the company dissolved. This came to the notice of the General Hydraulic Power Company, who in late 1896 proposed purchasing the subway so that they could run hydraulic power pipes through it and connect the

---

*   The high-level footbridges were closed in 1910. Like the subway and Thames Tunnel before it, they gained a reputation for criminal activity.

networks that they operated on each side of the Thames. An agreement was signed on 31 December 1896 for the sale of the subway for £3,000. The final Tower Subway Act, dissolving the company, received Royal Assent on 15 July 1897. The company was no more. The final company meeting occurred on 23 September, at which the company funds were distributed. Ordinary and preference shareholders received 5s 3d for each pound they had invested, and the Directors each received a lump sum of £100 to compensate them for their trouble in bringing the legal action against the City of London.

The legacy of the Subway
Although commercially it was a failure, the Tower Subway was a pioneer and left a huge legacy. It was the first use of a circular tunnelling shield to create horizontal tunnels beneath a city. The shield was the first to extend backwards far enough protect the tunnel whilst the lining was constructed. The lining was the first for a tunnel to be made of bolted and flanged cast iron segments. The use of lifts to access a tunnel was pioneered. All of these were essential for the next idea: a proper underground tube railway.

The first tube railway

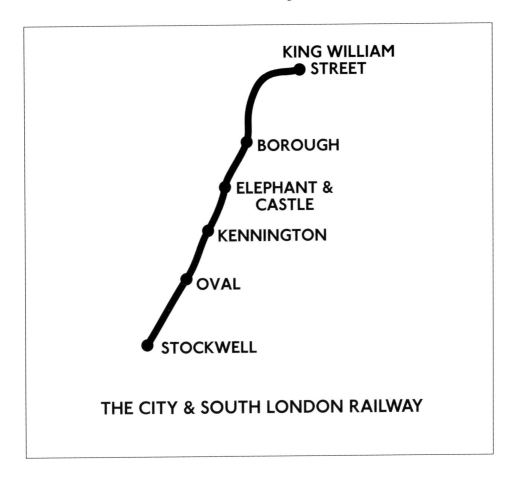

KING WILLIAM
STREET

BOROUGH

ELEPHANT &
CASTLE

KENNINGTON

OVAL

STOCKWELL

THE CITY & SOUTH LONDON RAILWAY

Before the Tower Subway had even opened, Barlow and Greathead were planning a more ambitious scheme. This would link Borough High Street with the City of London, and would have two 8-ft diameter tube tunnels, operating some form of railed transport between the end points. The timing initially seemed good: the Tower Subway had just opened fully in 1870 when the Bill for the scheme was being considered, but the rapid fall in fortunes of the subway made it impossible to raise the necessary finance.

In 1884, Greathead put forward a new scheme, called the London (City) and Southwark Subway. This was along the same route as the previous plan, but in the south it continued to the road junction at Elephant & Castle. The line was to have one intermediate station, at Great Dover Street in Borough, and a continuously driven cable in each tunnel would propel the trains.

The gestation and planning of this line are not of concern here; suffice to say that by the time the railway opened on 18 December 1890 it had been extended to Stockwell at its southern end, changed its method of propulsion to electricity, and changed its name to the City & South London Railway (C&SLR).* Greathead had also called upon the expertise of Sir John Fowler and Sir Benjamin Baker to assist with the engineering and provide credibility, especially for the Parliamentary cross-examination as the Bill progressed through to Royal Assent.

A Liverpool contractor, Edmund Gabbutt was awarded the first contract for the work between the City and Elephant & Castle. When the extension to Stockwell was authorized, the contract was given to Walter Scott & Co. The latter company took over Gabbutt's contract after he fell ill and was unable to continue. The construction of this new railway had much in common with the Tower Subway, which is unsurprising given their shared connection of James Greathead. The tunnels were somewhat larger, being 10 ft 2 ins diameter north of Elephant & Castle and 10 ft 6 ins to the south. The difference in sizes was a result of the plans to use cable haulage. The northern section would have operated at 10 mph because of the sharp curves, whilst the southern section would have run at 12 mph. The higher speed was felt to warrant a larger tunnel size.[76]

There were a number of key differences between the construction of the Tower Subway and the C&SLR, and it is these that are focused upon here.

Constructing the tunnels
Construction on the C&SLR started in June 1886 in the middle of the Thames. This might seem an odd place from which to build a tube railway, but the problem was finding land on which to sink the shaft. The problem was solved by building a 35 ft by 100 ft staging in the river at Old Swan Pier and sinking a 13 ft diameter shaft into the river bed until the clay was reached to a sufficient depth for the running tunnels to be protected. Brickwork was then used to continue the shaft deeper into the clay, and this included forming four openings so that both running tunnels could be accessed from it, one above the other. This unusual decision allowed four tunnel faces to be worked at once, and also superimposed the tunnels to the north of the river beneath Swan Lane. A further advantage of a shaft in the river was the ease of removing spoil by barge, rather than carting it through the narrow streets of the City.

A hoist on the staging was used initially to sink the shaft, by removing the spoil from within the metal tube so that it slowly sank to the right level. As the bottom edge of the shaft was undermined through the removal of the spoil it descended through the river bed. The hoist continued in use by lifting a large metal bucket that was filled with the spoil from the tunnelling faces as the work progressed. The bucket was also the mechanism by which the workers accessed the tunnels – as well as the journalists who were occasionally invited to see and report on the workings. One of these described the process:

The adventurous stranger who wishes to see the curious nether world that has been scooped out through the London clay must go and wait until a

---

*   For ease of reference this chapter refers to the line as the C&SLR throughout.

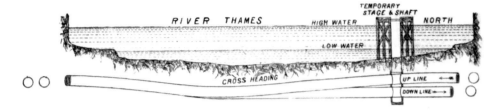

A cross-section of the C&SLR beneath the Thames, showing the shaft from Old Swan Pier and the change in alignment of the tunnels between the south and north banks. *(The Engineer)*

Brobdingnagian bucket of earth has been hauled up from below and discharged into a truck and then must get into the bucket himself, or, if he has any regard for his broadcloth, stand upon its edge and hold on to the wire rope while he is lowered down through the hole in the Thames to the tunnel below.[77]

Tunnelling started on 28 October 1886, when the first shield began to cut the upper running tunnel southwards. The twelve tunnelling shields were made by William Sewell (who represented Walter Scott & Co.),[78] and were similar to that of the Tower Subway, but 5 ft 11 ins long and 11 ft 4½ ins diameter, and with a larger aperture in the partition for the removal of the clay from the tunnel face, covered by a sliding iron door.* A double skin of steel plate was used for the cylindrical shell, as this allowed all of the rivet heads to be concealed between the two layers, making it smooth both inside and out. An advance heading was excavated in the clay further ahead into the tunnel face for a few feet. This was found to increase the rate of tunnelling considerably, in part because the shield could help break away the remaining clay more easily. The cutting edges were made of steel, and could be adjusted to cut a slightly wider tunnel if a curve was being made, although in practice the tunnellers just tended to excavate a slightly larger tunnel rather than adjust the cutters. Hydraulic rams made of cast steel now replaced the screw jacks to make the job of pushing the shield forward rather easier. These were powered by hand pumps within the shield, it taking around ten minutes for the shield to advance by the length of one tunnel ring. Six to eight men would operate the pumps at once, as they were fitted with sufficiently long handles, generating around 1,800 p.s.i.[79]

The segments were 1 inch thick, and slightly longer than the Tower Subway segments, forming rings 1 ft 7 ins long north of Elephant & Castle, and 1 ft 8 ins long to the south; no explanation has been found for the difference in length. Six main segments and one key piece formed each ring, and between each segment thin strips of pine, with pre-drilled holes, were placed to form a tight seal as the rings were bolted together. A line of tarred rope performed the same function between adjacent rings, and once the bolts were tightened the joints were grouted with cement. After some experience had been gained with the process the pine and tarred rope were omitted and the joints were sealed purely with Medina cement. The two pieces forming the tunnel invert were assembled first, followed by the two tunnel sides.

---

*   The iron doors were not successful and were soon removed. In their place were fittings for 3-inch planks designed to be quickly dropped into position.

Finally the two pieces that made up the crown were lifted into position and held in place with props from the invert until the key piece was inserted and all the bolt holes aligned. Only then would the final bolts be inserted and tightened. This process was carried out within the tail-skin of the shield, so that there was no exposed clay.

Protecting the cast iron

No one knew for sure how or even whether the cast iron tunnel rings would react when left in the clay for many decades. In order to protect the segments of the C&SLR, they were dipped into a mixture of pitch and tar whilst they were still hot from being cast. This formed a waterproof coating over their entire surface. Later railways used Angus Smith's Composition, which was coal dust in anthracene oil. Red lead was sometimes used on the faces that were bolted together. Later on, bituminous paint was found to be effective.

On the occasions when tunnels were dismantled, due to the construction of junctions or other works, the segments removed were found to have negligible corrosion. Even the unprotected segments removed from the Tower Subway that were removed in late 1940 during bomb damage repair were found to show no signs of corrosion.

The hydraulic rams drove the shield forward by pushing against the new tunnel ring. The tail-skin of the shield was pulled from behind the ring, leaving a small annular space between the outside of the tunnel and the clay. Grout was then injected through holes to fill this void. The grout was first injected via a hole in one of the lower tunnel segments, and was pumped in until it started to ooze from one of the higher holes. The lower hole was then plugged and the grout injected via the upper hole until the whole of the space behind the ring had been filled.[80] Again, some mechanization had occurred since the Tower Subway, and Greathead had designed a machine which used compressed air at 50 p.s.i to force the cement into the voids. This allowed the grout to be thicker, and enabled the void to be filled to a greater extent than had been possible with the hand syringes used on the Tower Subway. The container of grout had a central horizontal axle on which paddles were mounted. A handle on the outside was turned by one of the workmen to keep the grout mixed and prevent it from setting.

The compressed air used for the grouting machines was also allowed to leak out in the shield when the grouting had stopped. This helped to clear the atmosphere in the tunnel and provide fresher air to the tunnellers.[81]

A problem encountered when grouting was that the grout had a tendency to leak out from the front edge of the tunnel, where the hydraulic rams pressed. Initially this gap was sealed by pressing clay and sacking in, but this was found to be slow and ineffective. Instead an arrangement of six wooden boards was made which was fitted to the front edge of the tunnel lining and held in place by the rams.

One mechanical contrivance that Greathead invented previously for an abandoned tunnel scheme at Woolwich was not used. This was an hydraulic segment-lifter, which aided the installation of the heavy cast iron tunnel segments at the rear of the shield. He decided that this would merely get in the way in the C&SLR tunnels, and with the segments weighing a mere 4½ cwt (229 kg) that the six men operating the shield could easily install these with just some pulley blocks.

Navvy descending Shaft

A contemporary illustration of one of the navvies standing on the hoist bucket to descend into the tunnels. *(Penny Illustrated Paper)*

Progress was initially slow, with barely 23 ft excavated in the first fortnight. The work progressed night and day through two shifts, with only Sundays off. As the men learnt how to use the shield and its equipment the pace picked up, and by February 1887 it was reported that 9 ft 6 ins of tunnel could be excavated per day, at each of the tunnel faces.[82]

Beneath the river all was well, with the second (lower) tunnel started in February 1887 once the first tunnel had reached the southern side of the river. This tunnel rose at a steeper gradient than the upper tunnel, and was brought gradually round so that the tunnels were at the same level, side-by-side, beneath the southern bank of the river.

The overall rate of progress increased further once the sites for the stations at Great Dover Street (today called Borough) and Elephant & Castle were acquired in mid-1887.[*] At each site a 25-ft diameter shaft was sunk (in July 1887 at Great Dover Street; in December 1887 at Elephant & Castle) to the level of the tunnels. They were sunk by assembling a ring or iron with a sharpened lower edge on the ground where the shaft was to be made. Iron segments similar to those for the tunnel were then bolted together on top of the ring, and the ground was excavated out of the centre. As more and more iron rings were assembled on top the cylinder started to force itself into the ground from its own weight, aided by the removal of spoil. Once the shaft reached the level of the clay no more iron rings were added to the top. Instead, the lowest edge was underpinned and brickwork used to take the shaft down to the correct level.

At the base of the shafts, tunnel headings were dug across from to beneath the road where they would intersect the railway tunnels. Shields were lowered down the shafts, rolled along the headings, and with that four new tunnelling faces were started from each station although the shields in each direction were purposefully kept about 100 yards apart. In general the tunnel at the upper level was in advance of the lower.

After the contract for the section between Elephant & Castle and Stockwell was let to Walter Scott & Co. in August 1887 the company lost no time in acquiring the

---

*   It would seem that the company waited until the under-river tunnels were proven before spending money on the station sites and additional tunnelling equipment.

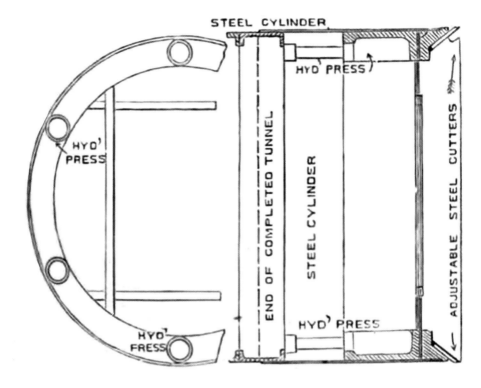

STEEL CYLINDER

HYD' PRESS

HYD' PRESS

HYD' PRESS

HYD' PRESS

END OF COMPLETED TUNNEL

STEEL CYLINDER

ADJUSTABLE STEEL CUTTERS

Cross-sections of the tunnelling shield used on the C&SLR. The drawing on the right is along the length of the tunnel, showing the cutters at the far right and the completed section of tunnel at the left. The hydraulic rams are resting against the last completed tunnel ring. *(The Engineer)*

station sites at Kennington, Oval, and Stockwell, with the contractor starting work on the shafts as soon as he was able. By early 1889 the tunnels were progressing at an average rate of 80 ft per day, and around 80% of the tunnelling was complete.

Different techniques were tried for the excavation of the tunnel faces. Wooden wedges fixed to the front edge of the shield extended 2 ft into the clay in front, helping to break it up and make it easier to excavate. This innovation alone doubled the speed of tunnelling. Another experiment was with a shield that used water jets to cut into the clay. A pump within the shield drove water from a large tank through nozzles at the cutting face. The mix of water and clay was then pumped back from the base of the shield, and into a settling tank, where the lumps of clay could be removed. The water was then pumped back round to the nozzles.[83] It was found that this method was more effective in loose ground.

Within the tunnel, behind the shield, sleepers were laid across the width of the tunnel with their ends resting on each side, and timber was laid upon these to form a floor. Small wagons, full of the spoil from the tunnelling work, were pushed along temporary tracks to the shaft, where they were tipped into the waiting bucket. Later on in the work the wooden floor was removed and clay was placed in the tunnel

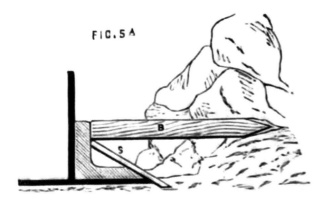

FIG.5A

The lower edge of the shield showing how wooden wedges were fitted to break up the clay. *(The Engineer)*

invert. Amazingly ponies were used to haul the wagons from the shields back to the shafts.[84] Lowering ponies into the tunnels down the various shafts must have been a tricky operation.

Once the shaft beneath the river was no longer required – because the tunnels were completed between King William Street and the shaft at Great Dover Street, and the materials for King William Street had been brought in – it was closed over. Brickwork sealed it off just above the level of the upper tunnel, and this was made watertight with concrete, asphalt, and puddle (a type of clay used for waterproofing). The metal shaft above this was removed and no trace remained in the river. Below the level of the tunnels the shaft had been sunk an additional 9 ft. This remained as a sump to collect any water entering the tunnels, and from which it could be pumped out.

Immediately north of Elephant & Castle, a tunnel was made linking the running tunnels and forming a crossover line. It was long enough to hold a train, and could therefore act as a siding as well. At the north end of the siding, where the connection was made with the running line, the siding tunnel was brought to a point adjacent to the running tunnel. A larger diameter tunnel was then formed into which both connected, and the points on the track were located within. At the southern end the points were placed in a continuation of the platform tunnel, which would have had two tunnels through its headwall, the left-hand one being the siding and the right being the 'main' line.

The tunnel construction did not proceed without incident. The tunnellers cut through a bed of soft sandy ground near an old sewer as they bored beneath Newington Causeway. The result was the collapse of the road surface for a length of about 60 ft, just beneath the bridge carrying the London, Chatham & Dover Railway, on 18 April 1888. Both the railway service and the horse trams running along the street had to be suspended. The tram tracks were subsequently propped up on stout timbers, and crossovers installed to allow services to resume. It took two months for the hole to be filled in, during which time the road was closed to all traffic except for the trams.[85]

Working in compressed air

Unlike the Tower Subway, the C&SLR was not constructed entirely through clay. Work on the upper tunnel leading northwards from the shaft commenced in mid-1887. All was well as it passed under the river's edge and headed beneath Swan Lane. As the tunnel approached Upper Thames Street the clay suddenly finished and a bed of water-bearing gravel was encountered. Quickly the door in the face of the shield was closed, and the men installed a bulkhead across the shield. Greathead had anticipated this, and so the necessary equipment was quick to arrange. The bulkhead was soon replaced by an airlock constructed in the tunnel behind the shield.

The airlocks were built of brickwork with iron doors at each end.' The brickwork was made airtight through grouting being forced into the spaces around the doors using the tunnel grouting machinery. Pipes were incorporated into the structure to allow compressed air through to the tunnel face, and water out. The airlock itself was a rather cramped 3 ft 9 inches wide and high, and 12 ft long. Its structure meant that it was fixed into the tunnel and the work continued beyond it until better ground was reached, at which point it could be dismantled.

Compressed air was let into the space between the airlock and the cutting face, as this would hold back the water. The airlock was then used by the miners to enter the cutting face without losing the compressed air. At the end of each shift they would leave via the airlock, being decompressed to avoid getting the 'bends'. Fortunately the gravel pocket only extended for about 50 yards, after which the airlock was removed and normal tunnelling resumed. Beneath Arthur Street, and back in better ground, the tunnels curved sharply to the right to reach the terminus. No special segments were used to form the curves, but the packing between adjacent rings was altered to enable the curve to form whilst maintaining a watertight tunnel.[86] The lower tunnel climbed on a steeper gradient so that at the entrance to the platform tunnel it was alongside the other tunnel. This became the southbound tunnel because of the heavy gradient of 1 in 15, which would have been impossible for an electric locomotive and train to climb.

The worst encounter with water-bearing gravel was at Stockwell. On the approach to the site of the station a bed of water-bearing gravel was detected. The airlocks were erected in the two shields whilst they were still completely in the clay, and they advanced upon the gravel. This was difficult in a horizontal tunnel because the water pressure was lower at the top than at the bottom, and therefore the pressure of the air needed to be controlled very carefully. In the C&SLR workings 15 p.s.i was normal. The technique for making the tunnel was by pushing a poling board (a long wooden plank) into the gravel at the tunnel crown, supported at one end on the shield. The gravel started to be mined out from under the board, and further boards were inserted either side. The face was supported by flat boards held in position by

The experimental apparatus for breaking up the clay using jets of water. (*The Engineer*)

wooden props wedged against the segments of the completed tunnel to the rear of the shield. These prevented the aperture in the shield partition from being closed in the event of a rush of water, and so an airtight screen was fitted to the tunnel crown a little way behind the shield to preserve an air pocket in the case of a disaster.

By proceeding in this manner a circular wooden framework was created at the tunnel face. Holes in every other one of the boards allowed lime grout to be injected into the gravel around the tunnel, helping to consolidate it and preventing the compressed air from escaping into the gravel bed. This also reduced the load on the air compressor. Naturally the progress slowed through gravel, to a maximum of 5 ft per day.

Stations and passageways
One of the many unusual features of the C&SLR was the construction of the platform tunnels on the original section of the railway. Greathead had no experience of building the large tunnels that these required, and wanted to reduce the amount of excavation required by making these tunnels with a flattened lower half. He therefore made the 200 ft long platform tunnels with a lining of brickwork 3ft thick. "Good stock bricks" were used for all of the tunnels except King William Street, where Staffordshire brindles were used.

The platform tunnels were made by enlarging the tunnels already bored using the tunnelling shields. The cast iron segments were unbolted and the rings dismantled, for a section of tunnel between 5 ft and 9 ft in length. The clay outside the tunnel was excavated to enlarge the tunnel to the appropriate size, and heavy wooden scaffolding erected to support the brickwork, which was placed as close to the clay as possible to provide support. Greathead claimed afterwards that

> Notwithstanding all the precautions taken, however, some slight disturbance of the material overhead generally took place, but in the later work of Messrs. Walter Scott and Co. this was reduced to a comparatively small amount.[87]

This is rather glossing over the actual situation. The brick platform tunnels were a poor decision, as the ground invariably settled during the enlargement process and behind the brickwork. The road and nearby houses were damaged at Borough station, with ground settlement in the order of 3–8 inches. At Stockwell it was not surprising that a length of the road sank, given the problems with the water-bearing gravel that had been encountered.

The two termini had single tunnels 26 ft wide and 20 ft high to accommodate one track and two platforms.* At all other stations there were separate platform tunnels in each direction. These were 20 ft wide by 16 ft high. Elephant & Castle had its

---

*   This was the original plan, when cable haulage was intended. A single track would have had the cables in both directions running between the rails. This would allow the gripper to be moved from the incoming cable to the other cable when the train departed. With electric traction there was no need for this, and Stockwell was built with a single island platform between two tracks. King William Street had been completed by the time that the electric traction decision was made, hence it retained the originally planned layout which proved troublesome. It was rearranged to have the same layout as Stockwell in 1895.

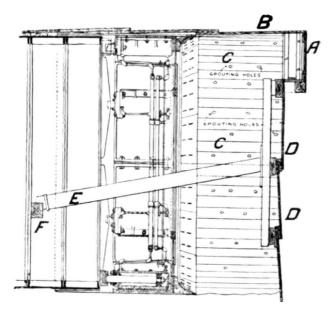

A cross-section along the shield showing how the tunnel face was timbered to prevent it collapsing in water-bearing ground. *(Copperthwaite)*

platforms at the same level, as there was to be a crossover and siding between the running tunnels. The other stations had the platform tunnels at different levels, with the lower of the pair being built first and then one wall of the upper tunnel built on top of one wall of the lower. The lower lift landing was placed at an intermediate height, with sloping passageways up and down to the platforms.*

The station at the northern end of the line, in the City of London, was at King William Street. Unlike other sites, where the property was purchased and demolished so that a shaft could be sunk, here the building was too expensive and so just the shop unit on the ground floor was purchased and the building was retained. Work started in March 1888, when the interior was cleared out, and the windows were removed and boarded up. A 4 ft square heading for the shaft was then sunk from within the building to a depth of 75 ft, and supported by timbers. The spoil from this had to be removed by horse-drawn carts at the station site, but this was the only material that used this route. The heading linked into the tunnels being excavated below, and so when the heading was enlarged to become a circular shaft 25 ft in diameter, all the spoil was taken down into the tunnels and removed via the river shaft at Old Swan pier. Likewise, all of the materials necessary for constructing the station were brought in via the river shaft.

The buildings around King William Street suffered severely during the construction of the station and tunnels, with supports having to be provided for some buildings

---

* There was one slight exception, at Borough station, where the lift landing was at the height of the northbound tunnel and stairs were used to access the southbound tunnel. Printz Holman has suggested that this was to allow the transfer of the rolling stock onto the line when cable-haulage was intended. It was used to transfer a locomotive and carriage into the tunnels at Borough for testing, before the main surface connection at Stockwell was completed.

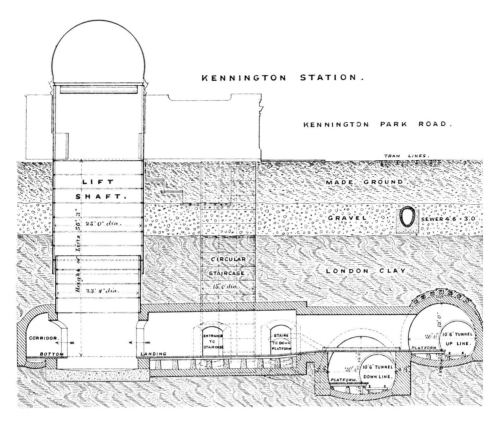

A cross-section of the station at Oval, showing the offset platforms at different levels, inclined passageways between the platforms and lifts, and almost empty dome above the station building.

and damage to the road in Arthur Street West so bad that the gas mains below the surface were broken. At this location it seems likely that the pocket of water-bearing gravel that had required the tunnel to be made in compressed air was also partially to blame. A scare was caused when pieces of masonry fell from the nearby Monument in early October 1888, which was again blamed on the railway construction. The Monument was immediately closed to the public and shrouded with scaffolding so that a detailed inspection could be performed. Although it was rumoured that the structure had been condemned,[88] the City Architect soon announced that it was safe. The foundations were perfectly sound, but some of the decorative paterae had been fixed to the column using iron bolts instead of copper. Rusting of the iron had caused some of them to fail and send the chunks of masonry street-ward. The remaining paterae were removed as a safety precaution and the Monument was then reopened.[89] That the bolts failed at the same time as nearby buildings were being propped because of ground movement caused by the railway construction suggests that the construction work might have caused the problems with the Monument, although these were underlying and probably would have happened some time later regardless.

A curse and a blessing

In retrospect there were many failings in the C&SLR. The tunnels were too small, requiring expensive modification in the 1920s (see later chapter). The brick platform tunnels allowed large amounts of subsidence to occur to buildings above, which was costly for the company to remedy. Having been designed for cable haulage, the final system was not particularly well-suited for an electrically operated railway, with its sharp curves and steep gradients. It was not unknown for trains approaching King William Street station to stall part-way up the slope and have to roll backwards to take a better run up.

And yet, despite all this, it was a great success. The company pioneered the concept of a tube railway. Greathead faced up to, and overcame, the challenges of tunnelling using compressed air in water-bearing ground. The diminutive electric locomotives and hissing hydraulic lifts proved that a public transport system bored at depth below a city could work. The year after it opened only one tube railway was approved by Parliament – the Central London Railway. The following year, with the experience of the C&SLR in mind, four new schemes were proposed and all were successful.

One of the innovations that is often overlooked today was the placing of the tracks into separate tunnels. Prior to the C&SLR, double track railways almost always had both tracks placed in the same tunnel. Although Greathead might have originally done this to reduce the amount of excavation, and keep the headroom down for safety, he soon realized other advantages and set them out:

1. They could be constructed where a single double line tunnel could not be, as for instance under Swan Lane.
2. The lines could be placed at different levels at the stations for convenience of access.
3. Where junctions are intended, or may be required at a future time, the placing of the lines at different levels enables a junction without a level crossing, to be made without the cost of extended "fly-over lines."
4. A dip could be given to the lines for obtaining a higher speed or lower cost of working or both, approaching the stations, at such a moderate inclination that trains could always surmount them [and] on leaving the stations, such a steepness as to secure rapid acceleration.
5. Where headway is important, as, for example, at crossings of sewers, or railways, or under a river-bed, the two tunnels give an advantage as compared with one.
6. Greater safety in construction is secured where the tunnel is of little more than one-fourth the cross-sectional area of a double-line tunnel.
7. The two tunnels are cheaper than one, and involve less carting and disposal of excavated material.[90]

These considerations still hold true today.

The techniques by which the first tube railway was constructed have now been explained. What has not been described is how the tunnellers, deep beneath the surface, know how to steer the tunnelling shield to follow the correct course.

Setting out a tube railway

Much of this chapter is based on a very informative booklet published by the London Passenger Transport Board in 1934, entitled *How a Tube Railway is Constructed*. It is of great historical value as it shows the techniques and tools used eighty years ago to drive tunnels for miles through London's subsoil to an accuracy of a fraction of an inch. Modern technology (described in many of the later chapters) has superseded many of the techniques in this chapter, but the principles remain the same.

Making the plans

This chapter assumes that a particular route had already been chosen, but that the detailed course of the tunnels was still to be determined. The construction of a tube railway started with a map, working out how best to join the points that the railway was to serve. In the late 1890s, when many tube railways were being planned, the overriding factor was to keep the tunnels beneath the alignment of the streets, so that payments to property owners could be avoided. This was a result of Parliament appointing a Joint Select Committee on the Electric and Cable Railway (Metropolis). One of its recommendations was that free easements should be given to underground railways where they passed beneath public streets. This decision both reduced the cost, but increased the curvature, of much of the tube railway construction in the first half of the twentieth century.

A rough route would first be plotted on a large-scale map, keeping to the streets but also minimizing curves. Given a sufficiently large scale of map the boundaries of the tunnels could be drawn on accurately. This was necessary to keep them a small distance (typically around 5 ft) apart. Curved tunnels were made with a larger diameter to accommodate any overhang at the end of carriages, and this had also to be taken into account. Platform tunnels were larger still. This work enabled the horizontal alignment to be determined. A survey in the streets along the course of

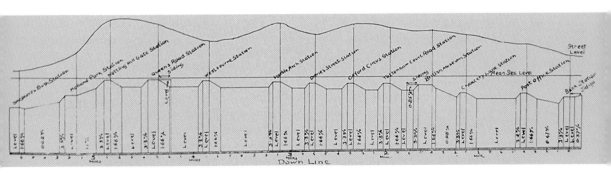

A diagram showing the gradients for the CLR 'down' tunnel, i.e., from Bank to Shepherd's Bush. Sidings were made on the level. The vertical scale is exaggerated (otherwise it would be difficult to perceive the gradients). The curvy line along the top shows the ground level. *(The Tramway & Railway World)*

the proposed railway was then made, to ensure that the tunnels really would avoid encroaching unexpectedly on any private property. In his work on tube railways, Halden recommended that this work took place between midnight and 05.00, to avoid traffic.[91] Reference points at closely spaced intervals along the route were also added. These were marked on the maps, and on the pavements and street surfaces too by means of metal plugs. A theodolite was used to carefully record the angles between each of the line segments, to an accuracy of 1 second (i.e., one 3,600th of a degree). All measurements were taken using steel chains or bands which had been carefully checked and for which the thermal expansion was known. Plans were then made showing the centre lines of the tunnels.

To an extent, the early railway builders had an easier job with the vertical alignment (i.e., the depth of the tunnels). Except where they needed to disturb the surface for shafts and stations, everything else was usually at a depth where there was nothing apart from the geology to worry about. Nowadays there are so many underground tunnels and structures that the vertical alignment is very difficult to plan. One important consideration was (and still is) the avoidance of level tunnels. This might seem odd, but level tunnels tend to pool water from leaks, whereas in tunnels built on a gradient the water will drain to sumps, which are built at the low points.[92]

Boreholes would be taken along the line of the route to assess what the subsurface is like, particularly the depth of the clay layer. Greathead did this for the C&SLR, but apparently not during the planning phase. Instead the borings were made in advance of the shields so that the tunnellers knew what conditions to expect – very important when water-bearing sands and gravels are known to be in the area. His boreholes were 3 inches in diameter.

The engineers can now decide where to place the shafts along the route. Some of these will be at station sites, but other temporary shafts might be provided just to facilitate the construction. Others might be reused for tunnel ventilation when the railway is complete. The location will depend on a number of factors, not least the geology and the availability and prices of property.

Tunnel gradients

Railway engineers aim to keep their lines as level as possible, as the effort required to move a train on an uphill gradient is significantly greater than on the level. Gradients of 1 in 25 are generally the steepest to be found on railways, and these are exceptional; on main-line railways the aim is usually to keep gradients to 1 in 100 or less.

Railways on the surface are constrained by topography and the cost of engineering work. Beneath the surface, these factors are reduced, and other concerns need to be taken into account. By making the running tunnels dip down between stations the engineer can facilitate the operation of the railway. The gradients will help accelerate trains away from the station and decelerate arriving trains. Lift shafts can also be shorter, reducing tunnelling costs and lift operation costs, as well as journey times for passengers. Of course, not all stations and lines can follow this principle everywhere; where a tube railway is on a reasonable gradient because of the surface gradient (for example, heading on the Northern line up from Camden Town to Golders Green) it is not possible. The CLR was the first tube railway to use this principle at almost every station. Gradients of 1 in 30 accelerated trains away from the stations, whilst easier gradients of 1 in 60 slowed them on the approach, making the tunnels at the stations about 8–10 ft above the level of those between the stations. It was subsequently calculated that these gradients on the CLR reduced the power consumption of the trains by around 15%.[93]

A drawback of placing these gradients at each side of the platform tunnels was found when the platforms needed lengthening in the 1930s; see p 219 for more details of this work.

Aligning the tunnels

The first part of actually building a tube railway is to sink one or more of the shafts. The early lines of the London Underground sank large-diameter shafts as they would subsequently be used for lifts. Shafts were sunk at a rate of about 4 ft every 24 hours, including the installation of the lining.[94] After the introduction of escalators the shafts were made smaller for reasons of economy.

From the base of the shaft a heading was tunnelled out at right angles to the line of the running tunnels. Headings were cut by hand (and still are), as it was not cost-effective to construct a small tunnelling shield for a short length of tunnel.

Theodolites were used in the street to locate the centre line for each running tunnel. This was done by reference to the metal plugs inserted in the surface during the survey. A point was defined on the far side of the shaft that joins to the theodolite via the centre of the shaft by a straight line, such that the line met the tunnel centre line at right angles. A steel wire plumb-line was lowered into the shaft on the side furthest to the running tunnel, and on the straight line. A second plumb-line, with a finer steel wire was lowered on the closest side of the shaft, again on the straight line. The plumb-bobs (weights) of both plumb-lines were immersed in tanks of water to keep them still and prevent swaying. Heavy plumb-bobs, typically 50 lbs, were recommended for getting the lines taut and stable.

The plumb-lines had different thicknesses so that both could be seen when they were aligned through the theodolite; the finer wire had to be the closest. This was done when the theodolite was on the centre line for the first running tunnel. Then the theodolite could be transferred to the heading below ground. It was set up the same distance from the closest plumb-line as before, and then gently adjusted from side to side until the wires were aligned. It was now directly on the centre line for the tunnel below ground, and the tunnel will run at right angles to the theodolite. If the heading extends to cut the line of both running tunnels, as was usually the case, then this process was repeated on the surface and below ground to obtain the exact centre line for the other tunnel.

Boring the running tunnels

The tunnellers excavated short lengths of tunnel by hand in the direction indicated, and in these the tunnel lining segments were bolted together. After a short distance a larger tunnel was created, called the shield chamber. These can still be seen at the

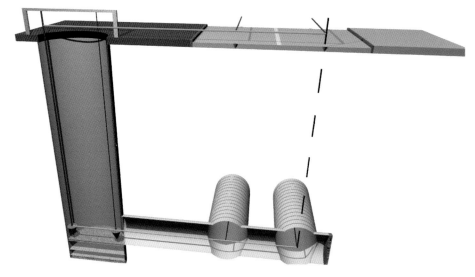

A cut-away diagram showing how tunnel alignments were transferred from the surface to the tunnels. The magenta lines along the road indicate the centre lines of the tunnels, as plotted from the plans of the railway, and regularly marked by metal plugs (foreground). The green line is at right angles to the tunnel centre lines, and passes through the two blue plumb-lines in the shaft. At the base of the shaft a heading is driven on an alignment that also connects the two plumb-lines (in cyan). At the surface the distance between the centre line of each tunnel (magenta) to the plumb-lines is measured. This distance is measured along the heading below ground; thus the centre lines of the tunnels (in red) are now known within the heading and tunnelling can begin. The black dashed line show the effective transfer of the point from the street to one of the tunnels that is achieved by this method. *(Author)*

end of several platform tunnels on the Underground.* They are large enough for the shield to be erected on a cradle made of wood or concrete. Once in place, the shield had the tunnel segments which had already been installed to press back against with its hydraulic rams. On some occasions the manually constructed section of tunnel was dismantled once the shield had progressed some distance away, it being provided just to start the shield on its journey by giving it something to push against.

Before work started, the alignment was checked again. Plumb-lines fitted to the crown of the tunnel next to the heading were used to ensure that the shield was heading on the correct path. For a pair of parallel tunnels one shield started off first, with the second following some distance behind. Greathead kept all of his shield pairs on the C&SLR about 100 yards apart. This avoided the ground from being too disturbed at any single point. Any plumb-lines or markers in the tunnel were installed at least twenty tunnel rings back from the shield, as the rings closer in were still likely to be moved slightly when the shield was driven forward with its hydraulic rams.

The shield was 'steered' through the ground by adjusting the pressure in the hydraulic rams. Greater force had to be exerted on the outside of any curve, so to

---

*   For example, the north end of the northbound platform at Hampstead, and the north end of the southbound platform at Marylebone.

make a level tunnel start descending, the rams at the top require greater pressure, and to make a right-hand curve the left-hand rams must press harder.

In good solid ground such as clay an advance heading would often be excavated in front of the shield for several feet. This made the work of breaking up the soil at the tunnel face easier. Of course, it would be dangerous if the heading were to break into water-bearing ground, and so further trial borings were made as the shield advanced. A carpenter's long-handled auger, several feet long, was pressed into the earth at the tunnel face to perform this task.

Regular checks were made on the location of the shield once it was away from the initial heading. For the early railways, iron staples were secured in the wooden packing between rings about every 50 rings, and nicks were filed in them for sighting from a theodolite. A decade or two later iron hangers (sometimes called 'dogs') were fitted to the tunnel crown at regular intervals (about every 35 ft). These were very carefully positioned, and plumb-lines were hung from them to check on the tunnel alignment, performing the same function as the nicks in the staples, but being easier to sight. A bar was placed across the horizontal diameter of the shield with a notch at its centre point. A vertical slit of light was then aligned with the plumb-lines and the offset between this and the notch on the bar noted. This was then used to correct the direction of the shield when tunnelling straight sections. A similar process, but lining up on horizontal bars hung from the dogs and using a horizontal slit of light was used to ensure that the tunnel maintained the correct level. By adjusting the height of the horizontal bars the correct gradient was maintained. Curves were tunnelled by calculating the amount of horizontal offset required for a set distance, and the using the plumb-lines to again check the accuracy. Measuring the distance along the tunnel was performed with metal tapes as these do not stretch or shrink in the constant temperature of the tunnel. Unless special segments were used, which only occurred for the sharpest curves, the curvature was provided by fitting thicker packing between the segments on the outside edge of the curve.

One problem soon discovered was that the repeated action of the hydraulic rams on the completed tunnel tended to slacken the bolts holding adjacent rings together. This would be caused by the compression of any packing between the rings, and was remedied by keeping a workman in the tunnel about 10 – 15 rings behind the shield to re-tighten the bolts. None of the sighting marks (staples with nicks or dogs) were used close to the shield for the same reason. On curved sections of tunnel extra care had to be taken as the compression tended to flatten out the curves.

Another issue that occurred in the shield, especially during or after curves were constructed, was that the shield tended to roll, i.e., rotate about its central axis. This was due to the axis of the hydraulic rams not being completely parallel to the axis of the shield. Although the tunnel is circular, this made it difficult for the team working in the shield when the floor was not level. It also made the measurement process described above more difficult. When roll was detected, a 'plough' would be fitted to the cutting edge of the shield. This was an angled piece of metal that caused the shield to rotate as it was pushed forward into the clay, and would be fitted to counter the roll. Once the shield was level the plough would be removed.*

---

*   A photograph illustrating the roll is on p166.

It was thought at the time that by making the shield circular the effect of it rolling would be minimized, as a circle looks the same after any degree of rotation. However, it seems likely that circular shields rolled *because* of their shape, and had they been made with a less symmetric shape then roll would not have occurred. This was borne out by the lack of rolling when constructing tunnels with a horse-shoe cross-section.[95]

Cost and effort

Copperthwaite, writing in 1906, documented the costs of creating a single tube tunnel with an external diameter of 12 ft 6 ins (around the standard size for London). Each Greathead shield cost around £450 to manufacture. Two teams of men would be required to work each shield, each formed as follows:

Role	Cost per 10-hour shift
1 ganger	10s
4 miners	9s each
4 miners' labourers	7½s each
4 general labourers	7s each
1 boy	4s

This totalled 216s per day, or £10.16s.0d. Once the cost of maintaining the shield and the cast iron segments and packing were included, a single ring of tunnel (20 inches long) cost between £17 and £19 to construct. Each shield would create about 45 rings, or 75 ft of tunnel in a week, assuming the ground through which it passed was good clay.

A table was also provided by Copperthwaite comparing the amount of spoil to be excavated and materials required for different tunnel diameters for each yard of tunnel made through clay:

Internal diameter		Excavation		Cast iron		Wrought iron		Grouting	
ft	m	yds³	m³	tons	tonnes	cwt	kg	yds	m
10·50	3·20	11·30	8·64	2·50	2·54	1·75	88·90	12·00	10·98
11·50	3·51	13·63	10·43	2·83	2·88	2·00	101·60	12·90	11·80
11·68	3·56	14·00	10·71	2·85	2·90	1·95	99·06	13·09	11·98
12·00	3·66	14·25	10·90	3·48	3·54	2·04	103·64	13·40	12·26
12·42	3·79	15·70	12·01	3·01	3·06	1·95	99·06	13·90	12·72
12·58	3.84	16.01	12.25	3.05	3.10	1·95	99.06	14.05	12.86
15·00	4·58	24·00	18·36	5·70	5·79	3·50	177·81	17·00	15·56
21·20	6·47	45·16	34·55	8·25	8·38	6·45	327·68	23·56	21·56
25·00	7·63	62·44	47·77	11·55	11·73	10·25	520·72	27·75	25·39
30·00	9·15	91·50	70·00	20·00	20·32	12·00	609·63	34·00	31·11

Note: The 12 ft tunnel was of a heavier construction than the others, as it was for use in water-bearing gravel.

The cast iron was that used for the tunnel lining. The wrought iron comprised the nuts and bolts used to connect it together. The grouting is the length of joints to be grouted inside the tunnel.

The tunnel diameters in the first column of the table above are all standard sizes used by tube railways in London by 1906, as follows:

10·50	10 ft 6 ins	C&SLR running tunnels
11·50	11 ft 6 ins	CLR running tunnels
11·68	11 ft 8¼ ins	BS&WR, GNP&BR, and CCE&HR running tunnels
12·00	12 ft	BS&WR under-river section running tunnels
12·42	12 ft 5 ins	CLR running tunnels on curves
12·58	12 ft 7 ins	CLR running tunnels on curves
15·00	15 ft	Shield chambers
21·20	21 ft 2½ ins	Station platform tunnels
25·00	25 ft	CLR cross-over tunnels
30·00	30 ft	C&SLR island platform tunnels

In order to advance a Greathead shield by the length of a typical tunnel ring, 20 inches, around 7·77 cubic yards of clay was excavated. The work would take just under two hours for an experienced tunnelling team. The following tasks had to be performed:[96]

	Minutes
Preparing for cutting, getting skips and conveyor up to face	12
Excavating	30
Preparing to build in lining, erecting stage for top rings and key	8
Erecting iron lining segments	18
Preparing for grouting, mixing lime, etc.	15
Grouting	28
Total	111

The Waterloo & City Railway

The first of the four tube railway schemes submitted to Parliament in 1891 to be opened was the Waterloo & City Railway (W&CR). This was a short line built to carry passengers from the main-line terminus of the London & South Western Railway (L&SWR) into the City of London (hence the name). Waterloo was too far from the City to be a convenient walk for many, and the W&CR was to Waterloo what the MR had been to Paddington. For this reason it received financial backing from the L&SWR, which enabled it to start construction far sooner than the other railways promoted at the same time. In June 1894 the firm of John Mowlem & Co. was appointed as contractor for the construction of the railway.

Tunnel construction

The W&CR started just below Waterloo station in the arches that supported the main-line platforms. From here the line descended into 1½ miles of twin tube tunnel that passed beneath the Thames just upstream of Blackfriars Bridge, and then followed the line of Queen Victoria Street to its terminus station, which was initially called City and is now part of the complex Bank underground station. The tunnels were larger than those of the C&SLR, with an internal diameter of 12 ft 1¾ in on most sections, and 12 ft 9 ins on the sharper curves. The corresponding external diameters were 13 ft and 13 ft 7¼ in. Each ring was 20 inches long and comprised seven segments plus a short key piece. No packing was used between each segment, but a strip of creosoted wood up to ½ inch thick was placed between adjacent rings. For the very sharpest curves special radial segments were made which when assembled formed rings which were ⅜-inch longer on the outside of the curve, and ⅜-inch shorter

A cross-section through the station, showing the large arch at the southern end which supported the two original arches above. *(The Engineer)*

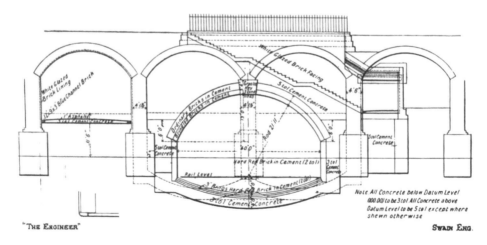

on the inside curve. All of the segments were manufactured by Head, Wrightson & Co., of Teesside, who had contracted to supply up to 400 tons of segments each week.

At Waterloo, much of the work was done using the cut and cover technique, beneath the station arches. The platforms and their tracks were placed beneath two adjacent arches, where there was sufficient width, although the piers of the arches required substantial underpinning because of the depth of the station. To the south of the station a small depot with the power station for the railway was built. It was found that there was not enough room to fit the crossover necessary to let trains switch from the arrival to the departure platform. The solution was to demolish the central pier between the two arches at their southern end beyond the platforms (and which separated the two tracks) and build a new single arch of 40 ft span and 3 ft thickness of brickwork with massive central granite keystones on which the original two arches would rest. The tunnel inverts were also removed and replaced by a single invert of brickwork, also 3 ft thick.[97]

To the north of the platform area at Waterloo the ground was dug down to a depth of about 32 ft on a curve, at which point the line entered the tube tunnels; this was just beneath the southern side of the station approach road. Where this work passed under the piers supporting the main-line station, cross-girders were placed between the side walls to support the piers, effectively underpinning them. The tunnels were placed just 2 ft apart at this point so that they could both pass beneath the arch of the viaduct carrying the main-line railway from Charing Cross, and not beneath its piers; the chosen arch was just east of the York Road bridge. Thereafter the tunnels moved apart to keep a fairly constant distance of 4 ft between them. The risk when placing tunnels close together is that the potential for ground settlement is greatly increased, but beneath this viaduct there was no real alternative.

Plan of the W&CR under Waterloo main-line station, and showing the sharp curve beneath the Station Approach. The start of the tube tunnels can be seen underneath the latter, then passing close together beneath the viaduct. *(The Engineer)*

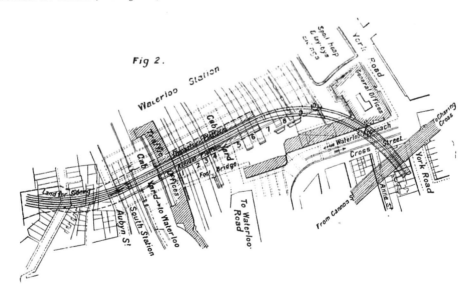

Like the C&SLR, the first shaft for the W&CR was sunk from staging in the Thames, directly over where the tunnels would cross the river. The staging was on the southern side of the river, and work started on 18 June 1894. The tunnels were to be side-by side throughout the line, and so two 16 ft diameter cast iron shafts were sunk in the river. Brickwork was used once the shafts were deep into the clay, and ladders fitted inside both for access. These were to be the only shafts used for building the running tunnels for the railway. All of the materials were delivered to the staging so that they could descend the shafts, and all spoil was removed from the shafts and taken away by barge to the marshes near Barking. Steam cranes on the staging lifted the spoil from the workings, and lowered machinery and tunnel segments back down. Timber rails were installed in the shafts after the shields had been lowered, to act as guide rails for the spoil tubs, and prevent them damaging the air pipes and wires that were also in the shafts.[98]

The first shield was in place in the up (i.e., northbound) tunnel by 1 November 1895, and tunnelling started 25 days later. The second shield was used to bore the up tunnel southwards to Waterloo, and started work in December. The following month the final two shields started work in each direction in the down tunnel. With the tunnels being larger the shields were more spacious than those of the C&SLR, which made the working conditions easier. The aperture through the partition in the shield was 5 ft 6 ins wide by 6 ft 6 ins high. The front of the shield held eighteen

Two cross-sections of the tunnelling shield. On the left, the rectangular aperture in the partition can be seen, around which is the pipework for the hydraulic rams with a pump on either side. On the right, the cross-section shows the cutting face (to the right) with the rams immediately behind. The tail-skin in which the tunnel rings were erected can be seen at the left, just overlapping with the last tunnel ring. *(The Engineer)*

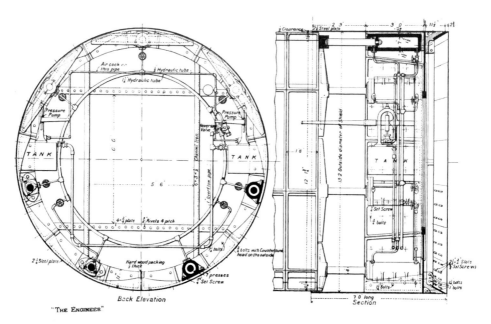

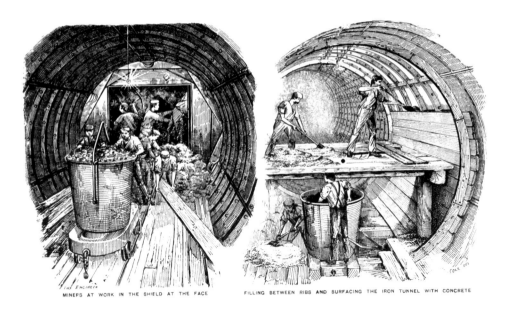

MINERS AT WORK IN THE SHIELD AT THE FACE   FILLING BETWEEN RIBS AND SURFACING THE IRON TUNNEL WITH CONCRETE

On the left, a drawing of the workmen excavating clay from the tunnel face, with electric lamps to light them. Rails set in the wooden floor allow a flat wagon to be used to remove a large bucket of spoil. On the right, another group of workmen are shovelling concrete behind wooden shuttering boards to fill the space between the tunnel segment flanges. *(The Engineer)*

steel cutters, each 1 inch thick, forming a continuous conical ring. These would break up the clay around the advance heading that was usually driven in advance of the shield.

At the rear of the shield the tunnel segments were erected and the key piece inserted at the tunnel crown. Once a ring was completed the blue lias grout would be forced into the space between it and the clay using the same type of compressed air grouting apparatus as Greathead had used previously. Then seven hydraulic rams (one against each of the main segments) would push the shield forward. These took their pressure from a circular main connecting them all to the pumps in the shield. Valves allowed the pressure in each ram to be varied so that the shield could be directed along the correct path. Each shield was manned by two gangs of 15 men on alternate shifts of 10 hours each; two such shifts could complete 10 ft of tunnel.

The W&CR company decided to fill the tunnel segments with concrete to the depth of the iron flanges, as it was thought that this might reduce the noise in the tunnels. A mix of six parts 'ballast' (presumably gravel) and one of cement was used, being held into the segments by wooden shuttering placed along the sides of the tunnels. The key piece was filled with a different mix, containing rather more cement together with fine sand. To fill this small segment an ingenious box was deployed, with wooden sides and a metal base on rollers. The box was filled with the cement, and it was hung below the key piece on straps from the bolts joining the segments. The rollers were then used to raise the base of the box and thereby force the cement into the segment. Metal pins passing through the straps held the base in place under the segment for 24 hours, and the wooden box frame was removed immediately.

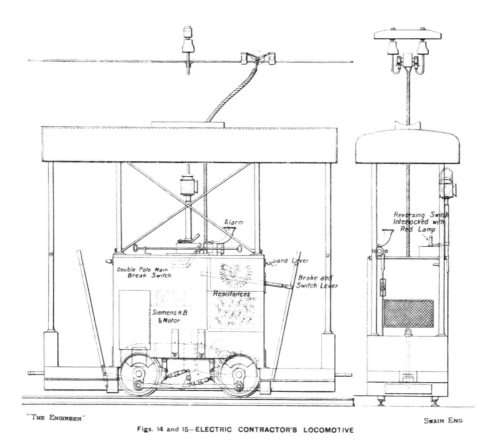

Figs. 14 and 15—ELECTRIC CONTRACTOR'S LOCOMOTIVE

Side and end views of the Siemens electric locomotive. *(The Engineer)*

Electric locomotives

A wooden footbridge connected the river staging to the shore. The staging held offices for the engineers, space for stockpiling tunnel segments and coal, and air compressors (made by Markhams), with tanks for the compressed air beneath the staging so that they could be cooled by the river water. There were five cranes of different lifting strengths, as well as boilers and dynamos for generating electricity; each dynamo supplied 120 amps at 100 V. These were used to illuminate the staging and offices, as well as the tunnels (at 200 V, presumably by placing pairs of dynamos in series) as they were excavated. Space was left for additional dynamos to be installed as the amount of electricity required increased. Electricity was used for another innovation in this railway: electric works locomotives.[99]

Once the tunnelling shields were some way distant from the shafts the effort expended in moving skips of earth became significant. Mowlem ordered two small electric locomotives from the electrical firm of Siemens Brothers,[*] and the first of these started work in March 1895. They worked on 18-inch gauge track and drew

---

*   Siemens Brothers had supplied electric locomotives to the C&SLR in 1891.

their power from a pair of overhead wires at around 200 V. These were supported on insulators held on wooden blocks that fitted onto the bolts holding adjacent tunnel rings together. There was insufficient room for a solid conductor pole (as used on trolleybuses) to be turned around when the locomotives were reversed, so instead a flexible lead linked the locomotives to a trolley which ran along the tops of the overhead wires.

The locomotives themselves were built on a heavy wrought iron frame. A single Siemens electric motor drove the wheels via a small oil-filled gearbox. Just three main controls were required: an emergency switch which cut off power immediately; a reversing switch which reversed the polarity of the motor, and also mechanically rotated a red lamp so that it always faced forwards; and the control lever. This passed power to the motor via a set of resistances to control the speed, as well as operating the brakes by being mechanically coupled to the brake blocks. This arrangement prevented the motors from receiving power whilst the brakes were being applied.

Five tons of wagons and their load could be pulled at 7 mph on the level, and at 3 mph on a gradient of 1 in 60. Sand could be dispensed onto the rails to give extra grip, which was found to be useful on the gradients. Workers in the tunnel were warned of the presence of a locomotive by the driver sounding a pneumatic signal horn. The horn was also used at the foot of the main shaft to signal to the crane above that it was needed to lift the spoil trucks up and out of the tunnels.

Working in compressed air
Tunnelling in compressed air was required for the tunnels on the north side of the Thames at Blackfriars where the tunnels passed beneath the Metropolitan District Railway. The MDR had had protective clauses inserted into the Bill for the W&CR as it passed through Parliament and these mandated the use of compressed air because the layer of clay thinned out beneath the MDR.[100] The contractor designed their own airlock, which was a wrought iron cylinder 13 ft long and 5 ft 9 ins diameter. This was placed in the tunnel within an airtight brick bulkhead, which incorporated seven other pipes for various services (one of these was a 30 ft long metal tube with valves at each end which allowed rails to be passed through the bulkhead). It was rather more commodious than the C&SLR airlocks; the workers could sit and keep their hats on whilst inside! They had to remain inside for at least 1¼ minutes whilst it was being pressurized or depressurized, but if materials were the only traffic in the airlock then the pressure could be changed more rapidly. One account described it

> screaming out through the open valve, sending a draught through the tunnel that could be felt many yards away. Gradually the rush of air diminishes, and the massive iron door is swung back easily on its hinges. Nothing but dense cloud is visible at first, for the operation of diminishing the density of the atmosphere has formed clouds in the lock. By degrees the vapours pass away, and the laden trucks come into view.[101]

An electric bell was used to signal between the men managing the controls for the airlock from each side.

Since there was no other need for tunnelling in compressed air towards the City,

UNDER PRESSURE IN THE AIR LOCK

the expense of two airlocks was removed by placing a single airlock in the up tunnel, opening a temporary connection between the two tunnels on the City side of the airlock, and building a solid bulkhead in the down tunnel to the south. A rail connection was made through the opening between the two tunnels so that the wagons could pass between them; this was done by hand as neither locomotive was operated in the compressed air sections of tunnelling. In this way just over 200 ft of both tunnels was constructed under compressed air. Once the shields were clear of the MDR the bulkheads and airlock were all removed and conventional tunnelling proceeded.

Both tunnels were constructed using compressed air at the Waterloo end of the railway. This was no surprise given the marshy nature of the area, which was described for its readers by *The Times*:

> The macadam of Stamford-street lies on a thin layer of made ground, a short distance beneath which is still the black mud and peat of primeval days. This, again, rests on a stratum of loose, water-soaked gravel, which, indeed, is in direct communication with the river. Unfortunately for the engineers, the friendly clay dips and thins off, its place being taken by gravel...[102]

The down tunnel was first to approach the gravels that lay in a slight depression above the clay layer. This tunnel started to rise first, to provide a long, shallow incline into Waterloo that would not overly tax the trains. The up tunnel was able to descend away from Waterloo more steeply, as this would help to accelerate the

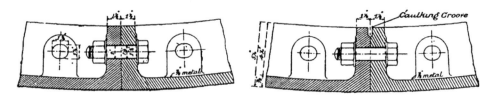

Horizontal Joints.

The joints between adjacent
tunnel segments in the same
ring (above, both drawings)
and adjacent rings (right).
(Copperthwaite)

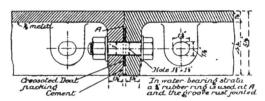

Circumferential Joint

trains toward the City, and also kept it just below the level of the gravel, which lay beneath Stamford Street. However, this tunnel was also build using compressed air as it neared the gravels to prevent a sudden collapse of the thin layer of clay above. The pace of excavation slowed dramatically in compressed air. By way of example, at the shareholders' meeting in February 1896 it was explained that the city end of the tunnels being made in clay were advancing at 73 ft per week, whereas at the Waterloo end progress was only 23 ft per week. The segments used in water-bearing ground were slightly different to those used in clay, in that they had a small space ¾ inch deep on the inside of the flanges between adjacent segments within the same ring (i.e., the longitudinal joints). This was filled with a special caulk to form a rust joint.* The circumferential joints, between adjacent rings, had rubber packing placed towards the outside of the joint, and was packed with the rust jointing caulk in front. The rubber kept the water out until the rust joint had hardened.

The technique of using wooden poling boards was used again, but with rather more elaborate construction. This became a little tedious to use, having to be dismantled and re-erected for each 3 ft 4 ins of tunnel (this distance came about from how the tunnel was being made in the gravel). Harley Dalrymple-Hay, the resident engineer, then devised a modification to the shield that removed the need for the timber. He fitted a hood to the front of the shield at the top, consisting of a pair of metal plates that extended forwards by 2 ft, and followed the curve of the cylinder round for one-third of its circumference. This replaced the function of the poling boards, just leaving the tunnel face to be supported by a series of vertical planks.

The hooded shield, as it become known, could not just be driven forward into the tunnel face. Instead, the miners excavated small pockets of gravel in front of the

---

* A rust joint is made by inserting a paste of iron filings, ammonium chloride (sal ammoniac), and sulphur. These react together to form a hard, water-tight bond.

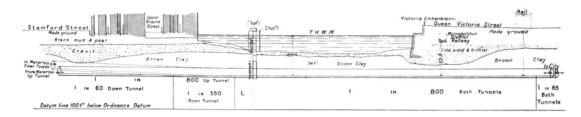

A cross-section beneath the Thames showing the down tunnel just cutting into the gravels beneath Stamford Street, and on the north bank, the layer of sand and ballast that caused the MDR to demand working in compressed air beneath their tunnel. *(The Engineer)*

hood to a depth of 23 inches and filled them with "well-pugged clay", i.e., clay that had been kneaded to remove air and give it a plastic consistency. By making these pockets extend about 22 inches further into the gravel than the shield, when the shield was advanced both it and then the tunnel behind it were given some water-proofing by a thin skim of remaining clay over the top. The clay also prevented the compressed air from escaping into the gravel, and thus saved costs with the air compressor. This technique became standard for boring tunnels in water-bearing ground on subsequent tube railways.

Dalrymple-Hay continued to experiment with the hooded shield after the first version began to buckle and was rapidly converted back to its original form. He found that by extending the hood further round the shield, making the hood part of the outer skin, and reinforcing it with a substantial box girder and several angle plates that he had a viable machine for tunnelling through water-bearing subsoil.

Tunnelling ground to a halt in the Waterloo end of the down tunnel on 29 January 1896 when air started to escape from the tunnel into the gravels and the air compressor could not cope with the increased workload. It was decided to work on just one tunnel at a time in the waterlogged ground, and so work was then concentrated on completing the up tunnel, which happened in October 1896. According to the records some work on the down tunnel had restarted by this time, and there was just 155 yards remaining.

Harley Hugh Dalrymple-Hay (1861–1940)

Dalrymple-Hay was associated with the underground railways of London for most of his working life. His career started with the Midland Railway, working to the Chief Engineer, before moving to the L&SWR. In 1894 he was appointed as resident engineer to the W&CR, thus beginning his work on underground lines. He was appointed as consulting engineer to the UERL in 1902, where he was closely involved with the Baker Street & Waterloo, Great Northern, Piccadilly & Brompton, and Charing Cross, Euston & Hampstead Railways.

Photo: *(The Engineer)*

He founded his own civil engineering practice in 1907, and was involved in many of the major civil engineering works on the London Underground right into the 1930s. Another tube railway on which he consulted was the Post Office Railway, in London. In the 1920s he also planned a major tunnel beneath the Hooghly River in India. He received a knighthood in 1933.

An enormous shield

At the City end of the railway the largest tunnelling shield ever made was being erected in a chamber to the south of the station site. This would be a great improvement over the crude tunnel enlargement performed on the C&SLR. Instead, a 23 ft diameter shield would first create the crossover tunnel south of the platforms, and would then be used to bore out the two parallel platform tunnels. The external diameter of the shield was 24 ft 10 ins, and it was 10ft long. Such a tunnel could not be dug without a way for the men to reach the crown, and hence there were two horizontal and two vertical partitions to form nine compartments in which men could work. The front end of the shield did not feature cutters, presumably as the greater force of the rams at the back would ensure that the any remaining clay adjacent to the leading edge would be trimmed off. Three times the number of men were needed, performing the following roles across two shifts:

- 12 miners;
- 11 labourers;
- 10 fillers;
- 2 grouters;
- 2 boys;
- 4 men to bolt the segments;
- 2 hydraulic operators; and
- 2 gangers.

Twelve-hour shifts were worked in this shield, and it advanced 6 ft every 24 hours. The two gangs of men swapped between day working and night working each week.

The hydraulic power for the shield was not created manually, as this shield had 22 rams placed around its rear. Instead a shaft was sunk from the surface and the London Hydraulic Power Company connected a mains into their system, supplying water at 750 psi. Even this was not sufficient, and an 'intensifier' was towed behind the shield on rails in the completed tunnel; this increased the pressure to around 2,000 psi.

The crossover tunnel was excavated during December 1896; January saw the giant shield dismantled and re-erected on the site of the up platform, and in February the excavation started. The 330-ft-long platform tunnel was completed in April, and the shield was then moved to create the down platform tunnel. Meanwhile the shield for the conventional running tunnel was brought to the north end of the newly-finished up platform and started work cutting a siding tunnel for a short distance to the north of the station. For unexplained reasons the work to bore the down platform tunnel remained paused until August; this tunnel was finally completed around mid-September.

One final tunnel required by the W&CR was the connection to the surface at the City. The company had decided not to provide lifts, but instead constructed a long, sloping tunnel that connected with a new set of subways beneath the street that

Beyond Bank station both running tunnels continued so that sidings could be provided. The northbound siding was closed and the trav-o-lator tunnel built through it, opening in 1960. The southbound siding tunnel was reused to form a passageway between the Waterloo & City line and the Northern line, opening in 1993. At the far end of the siding part of the original Greathead shield used by the W&CR tunnellers was found. This has been preserved *in situ*, painted red, and provided with an adjacent plaque describing it for the passengers who walk through it every day. The steel cutters can be seen on the outer edge of the shield, at the right-hand side of the photograph. *(Author)*

were being constructed by the Central London Railway. The contract for the tunnel (again with Mowlem & Co.) specifically forbade them from connecting the tunnel to the platform area until it had at least 5 ft of clay above the tunnel crown. This tunnel was therefore bored from the surface down to the platform level, as water could be pumped out as it proceeded. If the work had started from below there was a risk of flooding the railway workings if water-bearing ground was struck. It had the same diameter as the standard running tunnels; this probably saved paying for a new size of segment to be cast just for this tunnel.

The W&CR opened for passengers on 8 August 1898, having been formally opened the month before by the Duke of Cambridge.

The Central London Railway

The Central London Railway (CLR) was first promoted in 1889, with its first Bill going before Parliament for scrutiny in 1890. Its timing was poor; with the C&SLR still unopened despite this having been predicted for over a year the confidence in tube railway schemes was low. The Bill was rejected after much opposition from property owners and the MR and MDR which saw the potential that the CLR had for stealing passengers from them.

Benjamin Baker (1840–1907)

Baker was born in Somerset, and was educated at Cheltenham Grammar School. His first job was as an apprentice at the Neath Abbey Ironworks, where he gained an appreciation of the materials that would dominate his work. His engineering career began in London on the designs for Victoria station and the Pimlico railway bridge, during which time he demonstrated his great ability and also great ambition. After this he became an assistant to John Fowler in the latter's engineering practice, and worked on the engineering for the MDR and the extensions of the MR from the late 1860s, supporting the more senior engineers.

(Photo: *The Engineer*)

Baker published a series of articles about the optimum layout and management of railways in urban areas in the 1870s, and continued to work on the sub-surface lines in London as they inched their way towards completing the Inner Circle. The following decade he and Fowler were consulting engineers to the C&SLR. He worked in the USA on the Hudson River Tunnel in 1890-91, and in the 1890s he worked on the CLR.

The works for which he is most famous are the Forth Railway Bridge, designed with Fowler, and the Aswan Dam in Egypt. Upon completion of the former, in 1890, he was given a knighthood, together with Fowler.

The scheme returned the following year, and with the C&SLR being seen as a success the Bill was quickly approved. The engineers for the railway were Sir John Fowler, James Greathead, and Sir Benjamin Baker, who were able to use their considerable experience of the C&SLR to demonstrate the improvements offered by the CLR. Although financial support for the railway was provided by a mining finance company called the Exploration Company Ltd, it was not until 1895 that shares were offered. The response was lukewarm, and the Exploration Company ended up funding rather more of the line than it had planned. The CLR appointed the Electric

Traction Company as main contractor for the construction works, and they in turn appointed three different companies to construct the tunnels and stations:

- Bank station to Post Office station (inclusive): George Talbot
- West end of Post Office station to Marble Arch station: Walter Scott & Co.
- West end of Marble Arch station to Shepherd's Bush station: John Price

The company began to acquire the sites for the stations and depot in late 1895, and demolition was underway in the first half of 1896. Shafts were sunk at all of the station sites so that as many tunnel headings could be worked as was practical, to speed up construction of the 6½ miles of twin tube tunnels. The shafts were created in a slightly different way to the C&SLR. The iron rings were allowed to sink under their own weight from the surface as the soil was excavated out from within. The difference was that once the clay was reached the metalwork was underpinned, and then excavation continued downwards to the correct depth. As this proceeded additional iron rings were constructed on the bottom of those already in place.[103] Each ring was 4 ft deep, and as they were horizontal no key pieces were required. The depth of soil for one ring could be dug out, and the ring completely installed, in one 10½-hour shift at most sites.

The pipe subway at Bank

Work started outside the Mansion House, in the City of London, with the construction of the sub-surface ticket hall and an oval of passageways that surrounded it. Agreement was reached with the W&CR, whose tunnels were rapidly approaching their City terminus, that they would connect their stations via underground

The construction of the shaft at Bond Street station. *(Cassell's Magazine)*

passageways and share the costs for the work. A site was taken in front of the Royal Exchange to perform the work, and from this location a narrow shaft was sunk. A horizontal heading was driven westwards to the eastern edge of the oval subway, and then two headings were driven. These were all held up with timber props, and the maze of gas and water pipes, electrical cables, and sewers carefully supported.

Beneath the oval passageway, the excavations continued down to create another level as a pipe subway. Around the outside of this new sewers were created and the existing sewers that were under the centre of the roads diverted. Similar work was carried out near the junction with Poultry, where the sewers diverted around the stairways and upper concourse of the W&CR. New pipes for gas, water, and hydraulic pressure, and new cables for electricity were placed into the pipe subway and connected up.* Shafts were dug on the outside of the pipe subway underneath each road junction to intercept the existing services, and here they were diverted into the pipe subway. The services were duplicated as ring mains around the subway so that any section might be shut off for repair and an alternative route would be available. The pipe subway had drainage connections into the adjacent sewers, a wooden walkway for engineers to use, and electric lighting. Because of the difficulties encountered here it was not until early 1898 that the utilities began to be diverted. This delayed completion of the entire railway, and the company had to apply to Parliament for an extension of time in their Bill for 1899.

Once the pipe subway was in use, the old pipes and cables were disconnected and removed from across the centre of the site. The central area within the oval passageway was dug out to form the CLR ticket hall. Headings were driven on a north/south alignment across the site, with temporary walls erected to support them. The road junction above was initially supported on timbers between these walls, but as the space was enlarged iron columns were inserted as supports with girders placed across them. Small sections of the road were closed in turn, the surface removed until the timber framework was on show, and then a permanent roof was constructed of steel troughing on the girders. This had been manufactured in advance, and assembled in a field to ensure that all the components would fit together correctly.[104] The permanent road surface was placed immediately on the steelwork and the CLR ticket hall gradually filled the entire space within the wall that defined the inner side of the oval passageway. Meanwhile the public passageway above the pipe subway was completed. It was 15 ft wide and 9 ft high to cope with the high volume of traffic expected, for as well as providing access to both the CLR and W&CR stations it would allow pedestrians to cross safely beneath the busy Bank road junction. One of the conditions placed on the railway company by the City Corporation for constructing the station beneath the junction was that the CLR would provide free passage to pedestrians, and stairwells were provided to all the pavements around the junction.

---

*   The pipes consisted of a 30 inch gas main belonging to the Gas Light and Coke Co., a 24 inch high-pressure gas main for distributing gas between depots, two 24 inch water mains belonging to the New River Co., and a 6 inch main belonging to the London Hydraulic Power Co., transmitting water at 800 psi. A number of pneumatic tubes belonging to the Post Office were also present.

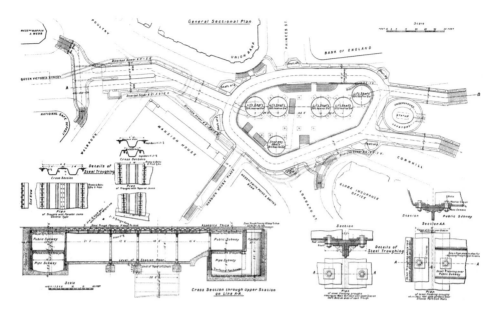

Plan and cross-section of Bank station, showing the subways leading to stairwells in the pavements, and the pipe subway beneath. *(The Engineer)*

Plan of pipe subway, with cross-sections of two of the interceptor shafts outside the Mansion House and at Princes Street. *(The Engineer)*

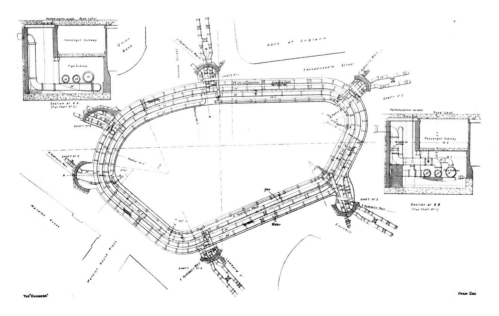

The steel troughing being installed over the ticket hall and subway in 1899. *(The Engineer)*

Boring the tunnels

The first tunnel construction started from the shaft at Chancery Lane station, which had been completed in September 1896. A month later an unpleasant accident occurred here when, on 14 October, a wire cable on a hoist snapped, dropping an iron skip weighing 7 cwt (356 kg) onto a group of workers. The site foreman was killed instantly, and two other workers hospitalized with serious injuries.[105]

At each station site one shaft was sunk for a spiral staircase to the platforms, 18 ft in diameter. At least one 23 ft diameter shaft was sunk to accommodate lifts.* Mains supplying hydraulic pressure from the London Hydraulic Power Company were connected to power work lifts placed into many of the shafts for the removal of material (at some stations steam power was used). As shafts were completed headings were driven from them to the line of the running tunnels. These headings were for the most part temporary, because the final station layout required the passages from the lower lift landings to be above the platforms. A small shield chamber was constructed at the end of the heading and the shield was assembled. The work then began on the construction of a running tunnel through the platform site. The chamber and first section of tunnel would be later dismantled when the larger diameter platform tunnel was constructed by enlarging the running tunnel.

---

*   A single lift shaft 30 ft (9.15 m) in diameter was initially provided at all the stations west of Marble Arch as well as Bond Street. The remaining stations had two lift shafts of 23 ft diameter, except for Post Office (3 shafts, two of 23-ft and one of 18 ft diameter) and Bank (5 shafts, each 20 ft in diameter).

Inside the pipe subway. *(Cassell's Magazine)*

The shields were then set to work creating the running and platform tunnels in the clay. In October 1897 over 3,000 men were at work on the railway, and thirty shields were boring their way through the subsoil.[106] Two sizes of shield were used: 12 ft 8 ins for the running tunnels, and 22 ft 10 ins for the platform tunnels. The running tunnels thus had an internal diameter of 11 ft 8 ins, reduced to 11 ft 6 ins by the filling of segments with concrete. This only tended to be done on the sections of tunnel adjacent to stations, as the opening of the W&CR proved that the concrete lining showed little effect in reducing noise. Another experiment was carried out to see if the tunnels themselves could be lined with concrete.

A concrete lining experiment

An experiment was carried out by the CLR to see if the tunnel could be lined with concrete. Some cast iron rings were used to support the concrete from one side, and the hydraulic rams supported the other. The concrete was 'green', i.e., partially set, and because it was not possible to provide reinforcing it had to be thicker than the cast iron rings. Problems were encountered in casting it over the crown of the tunnel and so the experiment was concluded and cast iron continued to be used.[107]

The larger shield for the platform tunnels was similar to that used for the large tunnels of the W&CR. However, it featured a new innovation to make the job of the tunnellers easier. A hydraulic segment lifter was included at the rear of the shield. This was a large hydraulic ram for moving the segment, which itself could be moved

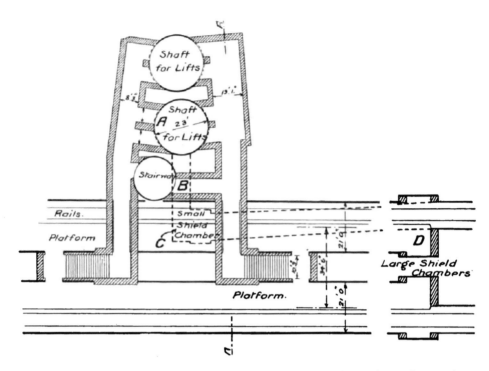

Plan of Marble Arch station showing the temporary heading used to start boring the running tunnels (B) from a small shield chamber (C). This chamber was destroyed when the platform tunnel was excavated, which would have started from the large shield chamber (D) at the east end of the platform. *(Copperthwaite)*

by smaller rams and a chain drive. This apparatus would hold the heavy segments in place whilst the men bolted them together.[108] The smaller shield was also similar in design to that used on the W&CR, with a slightly smaller diameter.

The running tunnels were assembled in the same way as for the previous tube railways, although a line of tarred rope was inserted into the joints between rings, as had been done initially for the C&SLR. This was found to prevent the grout from leaking back into the tunnels when it was injected. In the larger station platform tunnels alternate rings were built with the longitudinal joints staggered, probably to give the tunnels additional strength. No special segments were used to make the curves, even on the tightly curved westbound platform at Bank. Here hardwood packing up to 1.31 inches thick was used to form the 300-ft radius curve. In running tunnels curves were formed by inserting thin iron plates into the joints between rings. The accuracy of the tunnel construction was variable; at best, when the tunnels between Bank and Post Office met, the last segments from each shield were bolted together almost perfectly (with "a little humouring of the rings and a little stretching"[109]). However, extensive realignment work had to take place in the 1930s to allow new rolling stock to be used on the railway (see p 219).

Beneath Stratford Place, near to the site of Bond Street station, the tunnellers cut through an old well. Closer inspection showed that it had been used as a plague

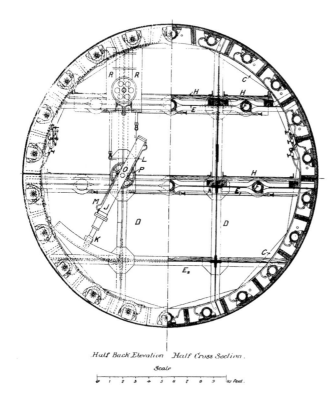

A cross-section of the shield used to construct the large platform tunnels of the CLR. The left-hand half of the diagram shows the view from the rear, with the hydraulic segment erector. The right-hand half shows a section through the middle of the shield. *(Copperthwaite)*

Half Back Elevation   Half Cross Section.

Scale

Workmen on the large tunnelling shield in an unidentified CLR platform tunnel. *(Cassell's Magazine)*

Workmen excavating clay from a tunnel face near Tottenham Court Road station. *(LTM)*

pit several hundred years before. Investigation was hampered by the nature of the ground, and to keep the work on track the shaft was hermetically sealed with concrete.[110]

Intermediate reversing sidings were provided to the east of Queen's Road (now Queensway) station, west of Marble Arch, and west of British Museum station (between Tottenham Court Road and Holborn; the station was closed in 1933). These were located between the running tunnels and were constructed in the same way. Each included a short locomotive siding, in addition to the longer siding for reversing a complete train. This would allow a new locomotive to pull the train out of the main siding after the original locomotive had uncoupled, avoiding the need for locomotives to push trains. The junctions at these sidings were formed in large cylindrical tunnels. Each siding required two, one for each running line, as a single tunnel large enough to accommodate all three tracks would have been very costly, and would have increased the risk of subsidence. The siding tunnels were level, unlike the adjacent running tunnels which were sloping downwards away from the station. At the end of the sidings a doorway led to a flight of stairs which descended to a cross-passage between the running tunnels, ensuring that no one could get trapped in one of the reversing siding tunnels.

Both of the shields just described worked in the same manner as the Greathead shields used on previous railways, in that the excavation was largely manual. A new piece of technology was introduced by Walter Scott on his section of CLR though, which mechanized the cutting of the tunnel face. This was the Thompson electric excavator.

The Thompson electric excavator
Between Berners Street (west of Tottenham Court Road) and Red Lion Street (east of Holborn) the bottom of the tunnels cut through the lower edge of the London clay and into the Reading beds. These were found to consist of hard red clay and

A crossover tunnel (probably at Marble Arch) under construction in 1898. *(The Engineer)*

even harder limestone, with some sandy layers. A conventional shield was impeded by a hard rock layer, and this was where the electric excavator designed by Mr T. Thompson (one of Scott's engineers) showed its potential. The machine consisted of a metal chain with 37 buckets attached, similar to a dredger, and driven by a 200 V electric motor drawing up to 100 amps. The support for the chain could be moved around as directed by the operator, and would remain in position, or could be set to slowly move horizontally, vertically, or both. The far end of the chain was placed against the tunnel face and the buckets excavate the soil and rock using wrought iron chisel-pointed teeth . The motor and other equipment was mounted on a wheeled framework, termed a 'goliath', which ran on rails placed either side of the tracks used by the muck wagons. This framework allowed the wagons to pass underneath the excavator so that they could be directly loaded by the buckets as they brought the soil back from the tunnel face.

The excavator was used by wheeling it forward into the shield so that the end of the excavator arm was adjacent to the tunnel face. It would then be set to move slowly forward, or horizontally, or vertically, or some combination of the three. The operator stood on a platform at the left-hand side of the machine with controls for the movement and the motor, and drove the arm to clear the next 1½–2 ft from the tunnel face. If the machine jammed he could switch it off, and even reverse the chain if that was required to extricate a bucket. The usual operation was to position the end of the

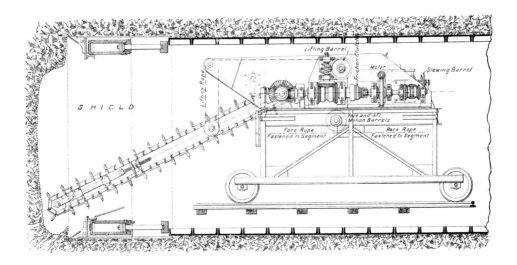

Cross-section of Thompson electric excavator showing the controls on its framework and the cutting arm (above), and photograph of it in action (below). *(The Engineer)*

excavator at the tunnel floor and set the machine to slowly cut a slice upwards to the tunnel roof. This was then repeated with the arm moved slightly to the side, and in this way almost the entire face would be cleared mechanically. Only a small section at the top of the face could not be reached, and this was easily broken away when the shield advanced; this took place after the excavator was wheeled back out of the shield.[111] The shield itself was manufactured by Markham & Co. of Chesterfield, to a slightly different design to that used with hand excavation, in that almost all of the central partition was omitted to allow the excavator the maximum reach.

Markham & Co. Ltd
The company origins go back to the formation of the Broad Oaks Foundry near Chesterfield in 1872. The foundry called in the receivers in 1886 after a slump in the coal and iron businesses, and three years later was bought by Charles Paxton Markham (the grandson of Sir Joseph Paxton, who designed the Crystal Palace) from whom the new company took its name. Over the following years the foundry produced a wide variety of engineering products, especially winding gear for mines, water turbines, and tunnelling machinery.

The company changed owners a number of times in the twentieth century following the death of Charles Markham in 1926. In 1996 it was bought (together with another engineering company called Davy International) by the Norwegian engineering firm Kværner ASA, who merged their two acquisitions a year later. The Broad Oaks site was closed in 1998, and the business located at the former Davy site in Sheffield. The name DavyMarkham was adopted in 2006.

Markham & Co. manufactured 516 tunnelling shields, rotary excavators, and tunnel boring machines (TBMs) before it withdrew from this market in 1998. The table below shows the number that were supplied for the construction of the tube railways in London.

Period	No. manufactured
1889 – 1901	100
1901 – 1914	113
1918 – 1924	64
1924 – 1937	30
1972	3

The two TBMs used for boring the UK underwater section of the Channel Tunnel were also made by Markham, in a joint venture with the Robbins Company of Seattle.[112]

The company also manufactured a large metal bridge deck used over the ticket hall excavation at Bond Street station for the construction of the Jubilee line ticket hall in the early 1970s (see p 282).

The excavator gave a considerable increase in speed, and a decrease in the number of men required to do the work. Once the men were used to the machine their greatest speed of advance was around 7 ft per 10 hour shift, with six men on the shift. Without the excavator this would have been around 5 ft using 15 men. However, much of the benefit was lost because of poor reliability. Much time was wasted through motor and connection failures, and overall progress in the tunnel with the excavator was similar to those being excavated by hand.[113] It was only ever used at one tunnel face and the lack of overall improvement meant that its use was not extended elsewhere.

John Price, the contractor for the western section of CLR tunnels, introduced his own mechanized tunnelling shield with rotating teeth to cut through the clay. A compressed air motor rotated a central driveshaft on which the cutting head was fitted. Bearings supported the driveshaft within the shield, and on girders bolted to the completed tunnel behind the shield. This did not prove to be as successful as the Thompson electric excavator as it could not be steered accurately, and the central driveshaft, gearing, and motor obstructed the tunnelers.[114] It was used on later tube railways in London though, with greater success following modifications.[115]

Completing the CLR

All three contractors had a need to tunnel in compressed air during their contracts. For John Price, this was where the tunnels surfaced, to the west of Shepherd's Bush station (probably due to the waterlogged nature of the ground). On the section being driven by Walter Scott there were concerns about the stability of the Holborn Viaduct if the ground shifted whilst a tunnel was bored beneath it without compressed air to

The entrance to an airlock, built into a temporary tunnel wall, near Notting Hill Gate station. *(LTM)*

help support the ground, as well as the presence of the Fleet River. George Talbot used compressed air on his contract when constructing reversing sidings beneath Threadneedle street, to the east of Bank station. Here it was concern about the stability of the Mansion House, the Bank of England, and the Royal Exchange that led to the platform tunnels and beyond being driven in compressed air at around 20 p.s.i. Despite this caution, a fissure opened in the foundations of the Mansion House, but this was attributed to the much shallower work of forming the pipe and pedestrian subways and ticket hall.[116]

The construction work for the CLR was completed at the end of July 1899.[117] Work then continued in installing the track, and signalling necessary for the railway to operate. The locomotives and carriages were delivered to the depot site at Wood Lane, where a power station had been constructed. By the end of the year all was ready except for the electrical equipment, which was in progress. Two sets of generating plant had been installed at Wood Lane, and the substation at Notting Hill Gate was nearly ready. The locomotives had all arrived and were waiting to be used.[118]

The first experimental train operated on 1 March 1900 between Shepherd's Bush and Queen's Road (now Queensway). Although the test proceeded satisfactorily, various alterations to the electrical equipment were suggested as a result, and so the planned opening date for the line was put back one month. Trains continued to operate on the line, both for testing purposes and for training the new drivers and guards. On 27 June 1900, the line was formally opened by the Prince of Wales, and the public service started just over a month later, on 30 July.

The Great Northern & City Railway

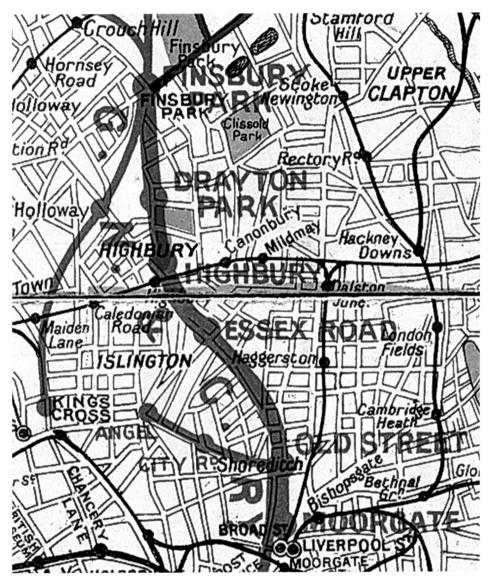

Map showing the Great Northern & City Railway (in thick red) together with its connections with the Piccadilly Tube and the City & South London Railway, both in thinner red.

Workmen excavating the tunnel face from within the tunnelling shield. *(The Engineer)*

Although, as its name might suggest, the main-line Great Northern Railway (GNR) provided support for the GN&CR, by the time that Parliament had approved its first Act in 1892 the support was beginning to wane. The only reason that it was ever built was because Messrs S. Pearson & Son Ltd, the contractors, accepted payment in the railway company's own shares, and ended up running the railway for a number of years after its completion. It was a short line, just 3·42 miles long, following a very direct course from Finsbury Park station to Moorgate in the City of London.

Work started on building the tunnels in mid-1899 from a shaft sunk adjacent to the Regent's Canal, where the power station would later be built. Further shafts were then sunk at the sites for stations at Essex Road and Old Street. By early 1900 the tunnels were being excavated from the canal shaft, and another shield was being installed in its launch chamber at Essex Road. Most of the sections of the tunnels were driven southwards from each shaft, except at the canal from which shields proceeded in both directions. More shafts were sunk and shields started as the sites were purchased, and by mid-1902 the tunnels had been completed between the surface station at Drayton Park and Moorgate. The northern section of tunnels, from Drayton Park to Finsbury Park, were completed in August 1903, having been delayed by problems negotiating with the GNR.[119]

The most notable feature of the GN&CR was that its tunnels were designed to accommodate main-line trains, as it was originally intended to have a link with the GNR at Finsbury Park and use electric locomotives to pull carriages from its trains to the southern terminus at Moorgate. The running tunnels were therefore made with an

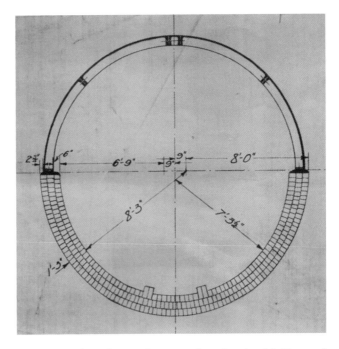

A cross-section of a completed running tunnel on the GN&CR, showing the upper half in iron segments and the lower half in brickwork. *(Author's collection)*

internal diameter of 16 ft. The greater size of tunnel meant that the six shields used (manufactured by Markham & Co.) bore more resemblance to those used to make platform tunnels on the previous railways. A double skin, with brackets connecting the two cylinders together, gave great rigidity to the shield. Partitions divided the shields into six compartments, in three rows of two, so that six men could excavate simultaneously. Behind them, a segment erector was driven by two hydraulic rams and could position any of the segments where they were needed. Sixteen hydraulic rams, able to exert a force of two tons per square inch, pushed the shield forward.[120] Each ring was the usual 20 inches long, but composed of eight main segments and two key segments, one each at the centre of the roof and the invert.

Uniquely amongst tube railway tunnels in London, the lower half of the running tunnels for the GN&CR was reconstructed from brick. The iron segments were unbolted and the lower key piece removed; the four lower segments were then dismantled, and an additional 4 – 5 inch thickness of clay was removed. Three rings of blue bricks were then constructed in place of the missing segments. A metal shoe plate was fitted to the top edge of the brickwork to form the connection with the remaining 180° of iron segments that formed the tunnel crown. The lower half of the tunnel ended up with a slightly smaller diameter of 15 ft 4 inches as a result of this work, which was claimed to reduce the cost of the ironwork as well as reducing noise in the tunnels. Many commentators were sceptical about the claimed savings of £30,000, noting that the cost of the work probably nullified the reduced cost of iron segments; the company insisted that the high cost of iron at the time of construction resulted in "a considerable saving in cost".[121] Although it was not stated at the time, photos of the platform tunnels indicate that they were not reconstructed with brick for their lower halves, but retained full rings of cast iron.

One of the 16 ft diameter running tunnel shields being dismantled within a crossover tunnel. *(The Engineer)*

The platform tunnels were constructed to two different sizes. At the termini, Moorgate and Finsbury Park, they were 23 ft in diameter and 450 ft long, and at all intermediate tunnel stations they were 21 ft in diameter and 420 ft long. These platform tunnel shields were larger versions of those used for the running tunnels, and also used hydraulic segment erectors to help construct the cast iron lining.

The crossover tunnels were made differently to the others. To maximize the width they were made with a circular crown of 15 ft radius, but an elliptical invert of the same width but only 12 ft depth. No shields were used for these tunnels; they were mined by hand.

Unusually, an additional station was constructed on the line after the running tunnels were made, and prior to opening. This was at Highbury Corner, known today as Highbury & Islington station. Parliamentary approval for the station was granted in August 1902, and work started on the opening out of the running tunnels at the site in early 1903. A straight, level section in both tunnels had been made at this point in anticipation of a station, which was in part requested by the local authority.

The GN&CR opened on 14 February 1904, although it was not until 28 June that Highbury station opened (and even then its lifts were not ready).* Work had already started on an short extension southwards from Moorgate Street to a new station

---

*   Ironically, Highbury was the most lucrative station on the line, which makes it seem odd that it was omitted from the original plans.

The remains of the shield in the southbound tunnel, a few metres south of the platform at Moorgate. The hydraulic equipment has been removed, but the brackets that would have held the hydraulic rams are easily visible around the circumference of the shield. This section of tunnel was not reconstructed with the lower half in brick, and so the cast iron segments are clearly visible all round, with the upper key piece in the tunnel crown. *(Nick Catford)*

at Lothbury. Progress was slow, and ground to a halt soon after starting when it was found that the GN&CR was not going to be profitable. Although the powers to construct the extension were kept alive for some years, work never resumed. The Greathead shield used to construct the southbound running tunnel is still in place at the end of the tunnel to the south of Moorgate.

The three Yerkes tube railways

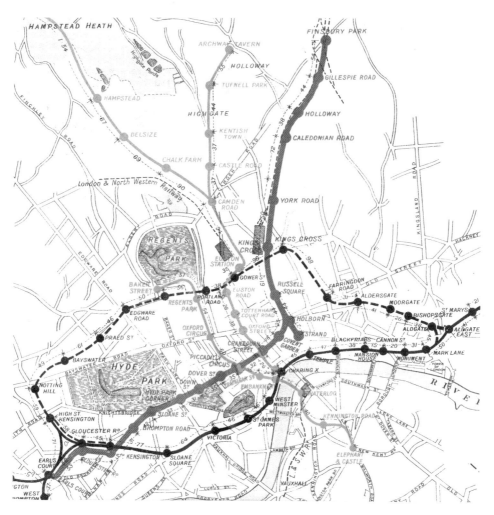

This map, included in a prospectus for the Great Northern & Piccadilly Railway, also shows the two other Yerkes tubes and, in black, the Metropolitan and District Railways.

Although many tube railways had been proposed and successfully gained Royal Assent for their Acts of Parliament, finding the finance for their construction was a different matter. The C&SLR had not been a financial success, and investors in the 1890s were reluctant to pour more money into holes in the ground. The CLR, with its larger tunnels and better traffic along a major London axis started to persuade people that perhaps tube railways had a future. However, the major investment came not from the UK, but from the USA.

The history and involvement of the American financier Charles Tyson Yerkes has been documented elsewhere. Suffice to say here that his involvement in London public transport started in 1900 when he took over the moribund Charing Cross, Euston & Hampstead Railway which had languished since its approval seven years earlier. He then bought shares in the Metropolitan District Railway and took effective control in 1901. Later that year he fused the MDR's interest in the Brompton & Piccadilly Railway with another unbuilt tube railway, the Great Northern & Strand, and formed a line from Finsbury Park to Hammersmith with the lengthy name of the Great Northern, Piccadilly & Brompton Railway. Finally, in 1902 he purchased the Baker Street & Waterloo Railway, on which construction work had started under the supervision of its engineer, Robert Galbraith, with Benjamin Baker as consulting engineer. The financial collapse of the company that had backed the BS&WR had led to work being largely suspended in May 1901. In 1902 the Underground Electric Railway Company of London (UERL) was formed to manage the construction and operation of all three tube railways and the MDR.

James R. Chapman (1852–1934)

Chapman was born in Boston, and worked for various railroad companies in the American west. He developed an excellent reputation for his construction and electrification work. He started out in Kansas City in 1888, and three years later was responsible for the electrification of the forty-mile streetcar network in Grand Rapids, Michigan.

In May 1894 he was hired by Yerkes to work for the Union Traction Company in Chicago, to electrify the horse-drawn commuter lines operated around the city. This work involved the construction and equipment of many of the surface and elevated railroad lines, including their power stations. Within five years he had delivered over 400 miles of new electric commuter lines. He remained with this company, as well as the Lake Street, Union, and Northwestern Elevated Railroads until his resignation on 1 March 1901, so that he could come to London.

(Photo: *Western Electrician*)

Chapman came across to London with his wife and daughter in the same month, as part of Yerkes's team of experts for building the underground railways. One of their colleagues later noted that "all of these men had contempt for office work, and forms of any kind were an anathema ... they carried their offices in their hats".[122] He was appointed as General Manager and Chief Engineer. In London Chapman was responsible for the design and equipment of the new Lots Road power station, the electrification of the MDR, and the design of the track and equipment for the three tube railways owned by the UERL. He remained with the company through the opening of the lines and helped with the specification and design for the first escalator installations. He retired from the UERL, and from active business around March 1910. He died in Buffalo, New York, at the age of 82.[123]

The Baker Street & Waterloo Railway

Since work had been started at the end of 1898, it was no surprise that the BS&WR was the first of the Yerkes tubes to be completed. There was little in the way of innovation in most of its construction: tunnelling started from staging erected in the River Thames just upstream of Charing Cross railway bridge, 150 ft from the left bank,* and was performed using standard Greathead shields for the most part, made by Markham & Co. One of the staff of the contractors, Perry & Co., had designed a shield with a rotary cutting face for use in the water-bearing ground, but the company management thought that this would be too risky.[124]

Two shafts, 16 ft in diameter and 50 ft deep were sunk into the river bed from the staging, and brick chambers formed at the bottom of both, from which the shields were launched. Like the staging constructed by previous tube railways, offices, cranes, and facilities for generating electricity and compressed air were all installed on the wooden platform, which was 370 ft long by 50 ft. Standard gauge railway tracks ran along each side of the staging for the use of travelling steam cranes, used for loading and unloading the barges that served the staging. Access to the staging was provided by a wooden stairway leading up from its northern end to a walkway installed beneath the railway bridge. The barges that received the spoil from the tunnel made their way downstream to a point east of The Nore, a sandbank at the mouth of the Thames estuary, where the spoil was dumped. Roughly 500,000 cubic yards of material was disposed of here.[125]

The shafts were each made of six very large cast iron rings, 8 ft deep and comprising six identical segments, together with a 2 ft deep cutting edge at the bottom. As with the C&SLR and the W&CR, the iron shafts acted as their own kentledge to force the shaft into the river bed as the material inside was excavated. Manœuvring such a large and heavy structure on a wooden stage above the river was a challenge. The staging had holes for the shafts to open though. Wooden platforms were built below the staging and the cutting edge and two rings above this bolted together on them, forming cylinders 18 ft in height. Timber baulks were then placed across the

---

*   It had been intended that the staging be near to the right bank, but the geological conditions of the river bed (discussed later) forced the company to seek permission from the Thames Conservators to move to the left bank.

The staging erected in the Thames south of Charing Cross railway bridge, which is visible in the background along with the white footbridge used for access to the staging.

openings in the staging and chains attached to the sections of shaft to hold them in place whilst the platforms were dismantled. The cylinders were then lowered into the river, and further rings constructed on top.

Once the shafts were 10 ft into the clay, they were continued downwards in brick for another 22 ft, with chambers at the base for the launching of the shields. Tunnel eyes were left on opposite sides of each shaft through which the shields would pass; these were circled by five rings of brickwork, and propped until the shields could be placed into position.[126]

The first tunnels were constructed north-westwards, towards Charing Cross, and work on these started in February 1899. Conventional Greathead shields were used for this work, as it was in solid London clay; these weighed 29½ tons.[127] They were 9 ft 8½ in (2·96 m) long, and the hydraulic rams at the rear could advance the shield with a force of 160 tons. The running tunnels in the clay had an internal diameter of 11 ft 8¼ ins; the intention had been to match the 11 ft 6 ins of the CLR, but it was found that by completely omitting the concrete infill of the segments and making the flanges slightly shallower that a couple of inches more room could be made in the tunnels. As the shield advanced the tunnellers dug a short heading roughly 6 ft across in front of the shield, as this made it easier to drive it forward.

The external diameter of the tunnel was 12 ft 6 ins. On curves down to a radius of 10 chains the tunnels were slightly larger, 12 ft internal diameter, and for sharper curves they were of 12 ft 6 ins internal diameter. The curved tunnels had to be larger to avoid the overhanging ends of cars striking the tunnel segments. Junction were placed into large cylindrical tunnels.

At the stations the conventional running tunnels were made through the site of the platforms. A short section of the tunnel would be dismantled at one end of the site for the platform and eight lining rings of larger size would be quickly erected whilst the tunnel was propped. The larger shield for boring the platform tunnel would be erected in this space, and would then be driven for the length of the platform as the running tunnel segments were removed. The face of the shield was divided into nine compartments, each with a workman excavating the ground in front. The platform tunnels had an internal diameter of 21 ft 2½ ins.

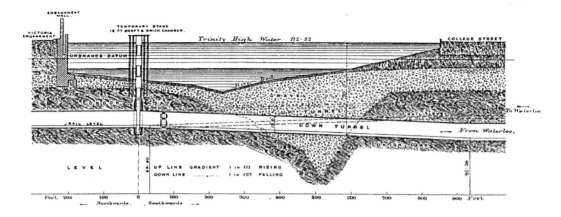

A cross-section of the under-river section of the BS&WR, showing the shaft descending from the staging and on the south bank (right) the tunnels at different levels. *(Copperthwaite)*

Due to a dip in the London clay on the south side of the Thames, tunnelling in compressed air was necessary almost from the outset. The shields heading southwards under the Thames were made by the Widnes Foundry Company. They had diameters of 13 ft, and the tunnels had an external diameter of 12 ft 9¾ ins and an internal diameter of 12 ft. Both shields were made with hoods projecting forwards by 4 ft 3 ins, but the innovation this time was the provision of a 'trap' that could be installed within the shield to prevent the flow of water in the case of a failure.˙ The C&SLR had used an airtight screen fitted to the tunnel roof behind the shield to prevent the tunnel from flooding completely if water broke in, but the innovation on the BS&WR moved this protection to within the shield. The aperture in the partition was made in its lower half, and it was accessed from a vertical metal shaft fitted behind. Handrails and steps were placed inside and outside the shaft, so that the workers would climb the outside and then lower themselves into the shaft to access the tunnel face. A hinged lid allowed the shaft to be closed. An additional vertical partition divided the working face of the shield into two halves.

If the tunnel face collapsed and water came rushing in, the workers would evacuate the front part of the shield via the shaft. As soon as the water level rose to the top of the opening in the main partition it would cease to enter, as it would have sealed the opening in the shaft. The lid could be closed and screwed shut for additional protection if required. This was put into action on four occasions,˙˙ which demonstrated the benefit of this type of shield construction.

Once the men had evacuated, there was little to do but wait until the tunnel face had slumped. The shaft would then be opened and the sand was carefully mined out little by little, applying timbering to the face until the front of the shield was clear and the face contained. The vertical partition allowed the work to be completed in two separate tasks. However, despite these aids, this would have been one of the most difficult and dangerous operations for those working in the shield.

---

*   This was not pioneered by the BS&WR, but this was the first use of a shield with a trap for making a tunnel on the Underground in London.

**   These occurred on 21 July, 20 and 21 August, and 14 September.

The crossover tunnel to the north of Lambeth North station, with a southbound train about to disappear into the station. The tunnel mouth on the right is different because it is another large crossover tunnel, in which the track leading to the BS&WR depot at London Road diverged. *(Page's Weekly)*

Another innovation used on the BS&WR shields was the provision of horizontally sliding metal shutters to cover the tunnel face. It was thought that these would be more efficient than the timbering used on previous tunnels, and they had proved effective in the shields used to bore the Blackwall Tunnel in London, and the Hudson River Tunnels between New York and New Jersey in the USA. Unfortunately, both these tunnels were substantially larger, and in the smaller BS&WR tunnels the shutters proved to be more of a hindrance. They were removed shortly after the shields entered the gravel section beneath the Thames, and conventional timbering used in their place, with steel struts used to hold the planks firmly in place.

At the rear of the shields fourteen hydraulic rams were placed in an uneven distribution, with eight at the tunnel invert and the remaining six placed in pairs around the crown. An intensifier in the tunnel behind each shield was fed from the hydraulic mains on the Victoria Embankment at 800 p.s.i., and generated the 2,400 p.s.i. used by the shield.

The western tunnel (for the northbound line) was constructed first, starting on 19 March 1900, with the engineers waiting until this was completed under the river before starting on the eastern tunnel. Less than a month after starting, on 2 April, work ceased for one month so that an airlock could be built between the shaft and the shield. This had a diameter of 5 ft 9 ins, and was 13 ft 6 ins long. Once work resumed

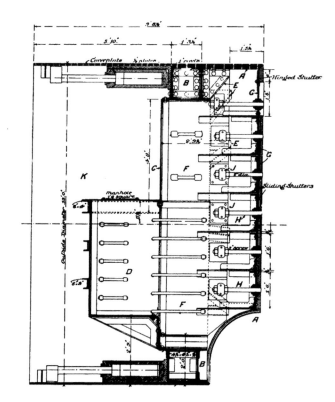

A cross-section along the shield used under the Thames, showing the trap fixed in place to the left of the partition (under the 'manhole' labelled in the drawing). *(Copperthwaite)*

it continued through clay towards the gravel pocket, and less than three weeks later a change in the consistency of the clay caused the workers to fit the trap into the shield. The airlock was closed two days later and compressed air working started, and three eight-hour shifts replaced the two 12-hour shifts operated until then. The company maintained a medical staff to deal with cases of compression sickness, of which a few occurred during the under-river tunnelling. Fortunately most were not serious.[128] Of the 117 men working in this section of the tunnel, there were 47 cases of sickness. Staff welfare was high by the standards of the day, and when workers finished their shift the company provided a change of clothing (into dry clothes) and hot coffee. It was on the recommendation of the company doctor that the compressed air was released into the tunnel immediately behind the airlock, allowing it to flow through the workings and thus provide better ventilation.[129]

The loose nature of the gravel allowed air to escape through it into the river. The tidal range of the Thames in central London is around 6–7 m, and this required the air in the workings to be in the range of 24–32 p.s.i. The pressure of the water in the gravel therefore varied considerably depending on the tide. This affected the pressure of air required in the workings. In a neat piece of automation, a float was fitted to the staging which was coupled to the valve on the air compressor, thus controlling the pressure of the air automatically. If the pressure in the tunnel was too great then the escaping air would cause waterspouts up to 3ft high on the surface of the river. One of these apparently disrupted the Doggett's Coat and Badge boat race by upsetting one of the boats, for which damages were paid by the railway company.[130] The paper about the under-river tunnelling read before the Institution of Civil Engineers noted that when the use of compressed air ceased:

> The waterspout at the river-surface over the tunnel-face, which for some months had been a feature visible from either bank, had now ceased to rise. It had sometimes risen to about 2 feet 6 inches above the surface, forming a picturesque cap to the invisible column of air ascending through the ballast and water from the working face.[131]

While the tunnel was built in compressed air the technique pioneered by Dalrymple-Hay on the W&CR was used, namely excavating pockets around the edge of the shield and inserting clay to form a watertight layer through which the shield could cut. Through this under-river section shorter tunnel rings were erected, being 18 inches long; this allowed the shield to advance in shorter increments. Typical progress was three rings per day, or one ring per shift. The shorter rings continued in use until the tunnel re-entered clay completely; two days later, on 8 October, the conventional 20-inch rings were being installed, and on 27 October the compressed air and airlock were taken out of use. The trap was also removed from the shield.

Work started on the second under-river tunnel in compressed air on 17 May 1901. This was arranged to run at a different gradient so that at the far side of the river it was directly above the first tunnel. This arrangement allowed the railway to pass under the narrow College Street without having to purchase either property or easements. Despite this difference in level, the soil through which it bored was slightly easier, and the compressed air was generally maintained at 5 p.s.i. lower than in the first tunnel.[132] During the work on this tunnel only 21 men fell sick, 12 of them with the bends. They were treated by the medical staff in a decompression chamber provided for this purpose on the staging. The shield was modified slightly based on experience with the first under-river tunnel, this providing slightly more room for the tunnellers within.

Further shafts for constructing the railway had been made at the station sites for Piccadilly Circus and Baker Street. When the first tunnel from the river shaft met that coming south from Piccadilly Circus they were aligned to a tolerance of around ¾ inch – a very creditable achievement.

The northbound tunnel was complete between Waterloo and a point under Regent Street, and the southbound between Regent Street and the bed of the Thames when the company financing the BS&WR collapsed at the end of 1900. Tunnels had also been made between Baker Street and Park Square (southbound tunnel) and Portland Place (northbound tunnel). The larger platform tunnels had been created at Piccadilly Circus and Trafalgar Square, and one platform tunnel completed at Embankment and Baker Street. Work slowed to a crawl, funded by calls on non-institutional shareholders, and was focused on the section between the river and Oxford Circus.

In March 1902 the deal was signed for Yerkes to take over the BS&WR. Once the railway was in his hands work restarted, as finance was again available. About 80% of the tunnelling was reported as being complete a year later.[133] Work continued to push ahead, and in July 1903 a large group of French engineers from the Association des Ingénieurs des Ponts et Chaussées et des Mines were able to visit several of the workings. Some of the party descended the shaft at the Victoria Embankment and then travelled through the tunnels to Oxford Circus on wagons pulled through the tunnels by a works locomotive. Once back at the surface, the group went on to Knightsbridge to inspect a rotary excavator at work on the Great Northern, Piccadilly & Brompton Railway (see next section).[134]

The original intention had been for the BS&WR to have a depot at Waterloo, beneath the main-line station. An Act of 1900 had authorized the southern extension to Elephant & Castle, and included a depot site adjacent to St George's Circus. The site was occupied by the School for the Indigent Blind, which was in financial difficulties and was happy to relocate to the countryside.[135] The purchase of the school for £140,000 was completed in January 1901.

John Mowlem & Co. were given the contract to construct the depot, and work started in 1904 with the demolition of the school buildings. The site was then dug down to around 20 ft below street level and a heavy retaining wall was constructed around the boundary. Sidings were laid covering much of the site, and these joined together to enter a single track tunnel at the western extremity of the depot. This connected the depot with the northbound running tunnel just north of Lambeth North station, and was on a gradient of 1 in 30. To the right of the tunnel entrance a second tunnel was made, 176 rings in length, to provide additional space for shunting trains. A ramp led down from the street entrance to the level of the tracks, and was used for delivering the rolling stock. At the foot of the ramp a hoist lifted the cars from the horse-drawn low-loader wagons and lowered them onto the rails.

The BS&WR was opened to the public on 10 March 1906, rapidly becoming known as the Bakerloo Tube.

The Great Northern, Piccadilly & Brompton Railway

The next of the three Yerkes tube railways to open was the GNP&BR. This had been formed when Yerkes amalgamated the Great Northern & Strand Railway (GN&SR), the Brompton & Piccadilly Circus Railway (B&PCR), and part of a proposed deep-level line for the MDR. Today the result is better known as the Piccadilly line. The GN&SR and B&PCR were joined together by a section of line between Piccadilly Circus and Holborn, leaving the section of the GN&SR south of the latter station as a short spur line.

Like the CLR, three separate tunnelling contracts were let, plus one for the section of line in the open air at its western extremity, 0·76 mi long:

Section	Engineers	Contractors
Hammersmith – Barons Court (open air)		Bott & Stennett
Barons Court – South Kensington	Cuthbert Brereton	Walker, Price & Reeves
South Kensington – Holborn	Szlumper Brothers	Walker, Price & Reeves
Strand – Finsbury Park	Alexander Ross	Walter Scott & Middleton

The tunnels are the same in size as those of the BS&WR and where possible followed the same profile with inclines either side of the stations to accelerate departing trains and decelerate trains arriving. Work commenced in April 1902 at Knightsbridge station, and by the end of September all three contracts were under way. Much of the tunnelling work was made with conventional Greathead shields, but about one-third used an improved version of the Price rotary excavator, first tried on the CLR. These machines were made by Markhams of Chesterfield.

The rotary excavator was, in essence, a Greathead shield without the partition and with rotating radial arms at the front fitted with cutting teeth. The arms were rotated about the central horizontal axis of the shield by an electric motor. The problem encountered by the CLR was that it could not excavate around curves, as the slight flexing in the driveshaft allowed the cutting face to remain flat against the tunnel face, rather than cutting more from the outside of the curve. This fault was due to the machine having a central driveshaft. For the GNP&BR, the drive was moved to the edge of the shield.

The arms were each made of two metal channel bars, connected at one end to the central axle, and at the other to plates that encircled the cutting face within the skin of the shield. These plates had a rack fitted inside them which was driven by a set of gears (partially enclosed to protect them from dirt) powered by the motor. These were all located on the left hand side of the shield (when facing the direction of travel), and the motor had a rating of 60 h.p. The gearing reduced its rotation from 500 r.p.m. to around 1½ r.p.m. for the cutting face. The teeth were removable, in case of breakage, and positioned on the arms so that one revolution of the cutting face would clear the tunnel face completely.

Metal buckets were fitted to the circumferential plates in the spaces between the cutting arms, positioned so that the clay cut from the tunnel face fell into them. As they reached the top of the shield they emptied into a steeply inclined chute. This took the spoil back from the cutting face and could deliver it directly into wagons, or onto a conveyor belt for removal.

The shield operator sat towards the rear, and had the controls for both the cutting face and the hydraulic rams at hand. The cutting face was not run whilst a tunnel ring was installed. Then the cutting face motor, conveyor belt, and hydraulic rams would all be switched on. Resistances allowed the speed of the motor to be adjusted, and valves performed the same function for the rams. These pushed the shield forward as the cutting arms removed the clay of the tunnel face. An ammeter showed current rises caused by the motor being overloaded, in which case the pressure at the rams was reduced.

The rotary excavator could bore tunnels at the rate of 180 ft per week, or about three times the rate of the conventional Greathead shields. The size of the team needed to work it was also smaller; only two miners, six labourers, and a boy were required, together with a ganger. In a discussion a few years later, Dalrymple-Hay noted that from a slow start, the contractors reached a peak of 109 tunnel rings in a single week using a rotary excavator, on the line to Strand. Accuracy was poor, with 25% of rings needing realignment. However, with experience the accuracy was greatly improved, and between Dover Street and Down Street all of the 102 rings installed in one week were aligned to within ½ inch.

A rotary excavator at an unknown location. *(LTM)*

At Earl's Court station the spoil was removed by conveyor belt, instead of the more usual spoil wagons. The belt was driven by a 10 h.p. motor connected to the local electricity board supply.[136]

When completed, the running tunnels had a concrete lining installed to a height of 2 ft above the level of the ballast. Although the W&CR had proved that lining the tunnels had little effect on noise, the BS&WR had discovered that track in an unlined tunnel occasionally suffered from short circuits when the collector shoes on the trains passed too close to the tunnel segments and arcing started as the current escaped to earth. A layer of concrete over the segments at the level of the track prevented this.*

The slum clearance scheme between Holborn and the Strand, and the creation of the new Kingsway thoroughfare between the two, led to delays in building the section of line south of the station at Holborn. The London County Council took an antagonistic approach to the new railway, blocking plans to make the spur line south of Holborn more useful by providing interchange with the MDR at Temple. It was only at the end of October 1903 that the site for Holborn station was acquired, and the sinking of shafts began at once. Tunnelling started, but only in the northbound direction whilst negotiations continued for a site for the southern terminus at Strand.

---

*   Rather than apply a concrete lining to the BS&WR retrospectively, the company instead switched the polarity of the current rails. The negative rail was then closer to the tunnel and as this was at a lower voltage, the earthing risk was substantially reduced.

The front and rear of a rotary excavator in factory-fresh condition. Only three of the metal buckets to guide the cut spoil are in position in the front view. The rear view shows the chute down which the spoil would be deposited. *(Cassell's Railways of the World)*

This was perhaps fortunate, as the layout for the junctions at Holborn was still unclear. It was only in the 1905 Parliamentary session that new powers were obtained for the required tunnels. A new terminal bay platform was to be provided for the Strand branch on the eastern side of the station. However, to make the platform arrangements easier for passengers, this platform was moved to the angle between the main northbound line and through Strand line platforms.[137]

All of the platforms except for the bay at Holborn were completed in early 1906, at which point tunnelling operations started from the site of Strand station, excavating northwards. The bay platform was completed just after the GNP&BR opened on 15 December 1906 (although some stations on the main line were incomplete and opened in 1907). The tunnelling on the spur line continued, and was finished in February 1907. Work to lay rails and cables, make the platforms ready for use, and complete the station at Strand took much of the rest of the year, and the branch finally opened on 30 November.

The Charing Cross, Euston & Hampstead Railway

Walker, Price & Reeves were also appointed as contractors to the CCE&HR, which ran from Charing Cross to Camden Town. Here it split into two, with one branch leading to Golders Green and the other to Highgate (which was renamed Archway in 1939). The construction work started in September 1903, and much of the tunnelling was through London clay. The Price rotary excavator was used extensively for the work. The manufacturer of the shields, Markhams, had suggested an improvement which was adopted. This was for additional cutters at the end of the radial arms which were moved outwards by cams and so could be set to excavate the tunnel wider on the outside of curves, thus giving the shield more room to rotate into and further improving its ability to be steered.

A comparison between the rate of tunnelling by hand and the rotary excavators was made between South Kentish Town and Kentish Town stations, where the two methods were used for adjacent tunnels. In a week the hand tunnellers averaged a length of 17·4 yds, a little over half the 32·9 yds achieved by the rotary excavator. The maximum dug in any week was 23·6 yds by hand, and 46 yds by machine.[138]

The only problems that the rotary excavators encountered were beneath Hampstead Heath. Here the tunnels were up to 250 feet below the surface and the pressure of the clay above the excavator caused distortion, preventing it from working.[139] The only solution was to excavate these tunnels by hand. Further problems occurred when the boring of the second tunnel under the Heath caused several of the segments in the first tunnel to crack.[140] To the south, at the site of Hampstead station, springs had flooded the workings when the shafts were started, and led to fears that the tunnels would drain the Heath of water and kill all the trees.[141] Pumps were needed to drain off the water, and the springs had to be diverted.

Compressed air working was required at Euston, where the water-bearing sand of the Woolwich and Reading beds was encountered. It was also used at Charing Cross, but here it was as a precaution against any ground movement damaging the main-line station.[142]

Charing Cross was to have been the site of a particularly difficult piece of construction work. The South Eastern & Chatham Railway, which owned the main-line station,

Opening the forecourt of Charing Cross station to excavate the CCE&HR ticket hall. The base of the Eleanor Cross can just be seen in the background, and many of the girders forming the ticket hall ceiling appear to be in place. *(The Railway Times)*

forbade any work that would disrupt their station or its forecourt, and it was beneath the latter that the CCE&HR intended to place their ticket hall following a 1905 agreement between the companies. It seemed as though the station would have to be constructed from below, with the workmen excavating the passages from the platforms to the lower lift landings, and then excavating the lift shafts upwards before underpinning the forecourt and mining out the ticket hall area.

However, on 5 December 1905 the wrought iron roof spanning the main-line station collapsed, after an undetected flaw in one of the metal tie-rods finally gave way. The station closed until March 1906 for reconstruction, and during this time the CCE&HR company was granted use of the forecourt for 6 weeks. They lost no time, excavating one lift shaft to its full depth of 73 ft, forming the walls around the ticket hall, and then placing girders over this area so that the forecourt could be put back in place. This was sufficient to allow the rest of the tunnelling work for the station to take place under the forecourt without further disturbance.[143]

The CCE&HR used exactly the same sizes of tunnel as the BS&WR and the GNP&BR. The largest types of running tunnel, on sharp curves, had to be used at two places: between Euston Road (now Warren Street) and Euston, and north of Charing Cross where it curves around the Garrick Theatre. Otherwise the curves on the line were all fairly gentle. It was not possible on the line between Camden Town and Golders Green to provide the humped line profile at stations, as the line was on a steep gradient for most of the way northward.

When it opened on 22 June 1907, the line was billed as 'The Last Link', and it soon became known as the Hampstead Tube.

Providing the power

The MR and MDR were powered by coal, loaded into the tenders of their steam locomotives hauling the trains through their tunnels. Gas was used for lighting the stations. There was no need for any centralized form of power generation until the C&SLR rejected cable haulage and made the daring choice of electric traction.

A site for a power station was quickly purchased near Stockwell — by 1890 the growth of London meant that this was about as close in as they could find for a large enough site. As well as a power station, carriage sheds were erected and a connection with the running tunnels was made via a steeply sloped single tunnel on an incline of 1 in 3½.* The power station was in two buildings: one housing the boilers, and the other containing generating equipment. The two buildings were separate, with ducts installed just below the ground to transfer steam from the boilers to the turbines, which were coupled to the dynamos. These had barely enough capacity to power the trains, and yet it was the world's largest power station when it opened.

The W&CR was similar, in that it constructed its own power station within the confines of its depot, which was to the south of the Waterloo terminus. Coal was supplied via the L&SWR, and brought down to the W&CR level by the hydraulic carriage lift that connected with a spur from the City-bound line. From here the wagons were shunted back into the depot, and then lifted via a hoist to be emptied into coal bunkers — a rather convoluted route. The boiler house and engine house were adjacent, squeezed onto the edge of the cramped depot site.

The CLR erected a large power station at its depot site at Wood Lane. This consisted of an adjacent boiler house and engine house, both constructed of brick with tiled roofs. Space was less of an issue for the CLR, and the buildings had room for additional equipment if required. They were the largest power station buildings yet erected for an underground railway in London, but there was nothing particularly innovative about their construction.

Lots Road power station

In order to supply the huge amounts of electricity that his burgeoning railway empire would require, Yerkes had to commission the world's largest power station — in London. The site his company chose was at Lots Road, alongside Chelsea Creek, which would enable coal to be brought in and ash to be removed by barge, the cheapest form of bulk transport. Work began on the 3·67-acre site in late 1902, with the land being cleared, and the construction of heavy foundations. The contractors, Perry & Co., employed around 450 men working around the clock to sink the foundations through the gravelly layers near the surface down to the clay at a depth of 35 ft. One of the walls also formed the edge of the creek, replacing a dilapidated timber structure with a more robust wall formed of blue Staffordshire bricks.

---

* The rolling stock was moved up and down the tunnel using a capstan and ropes, as there was no way that any locomotive could move on such a gradient under its own power without the aid of rack and pinion.

A view along Lots Road showing the steel framework for the power station rising alongside in 1903. The angled structure at the top of the right-hand building is the support for the coal bunkers. *(The Tramway & Railway World)*

Once the works were ready alongside the creek a large electric travelling crane was installed, so that heavy equipment could be unloaded from barges. This was supplied by Jessop & Appleby of Leicester, and had a maximum load of 35 tons.

The main building was designed by the UERL's chief engineer, James Chapman, who had come to London with Yerkes. It was 453 ft 6 ins long, 175 ft wide, and 140 ft high to the roof apex. All of the building work was contracted to the British Westinghouse Electric and Manufacturing Company, who promptly subcontracted the manufacture of the steel framework to Hein, Lehman & Co. of Dusseldorf. This was one of the first steel-framed buildings in Britain, along with the Ritz Hotel and Selfridge's department store.[144] The larger part of the building, housing the boilers, was placed on the southern edge of the site, adjacent to Chelsea Creek. This had the advantage that the smaller engine house was alongside Lots Road, and loomed over the houses on the opposite side rather less than had they been the other way around. The building wall along Lots Road was also pierced with frosted windows for most of its length, running from first floor height up to arches below the roof level. These lightened the façade, which would otherwise have appeared as a massive brick wall, but there was no other reason for allowing light into the generator building.

The London firm of Mayoh & Haley were engaged to erect the 5,800 tons of steel-work and the surrounding brickwork. As the steel frame progressed at the rate of about 800 tons per month, work began on the brick walls around the building; these were not load-bearing. Floors within the building were made of concrete. At the top of the boiler house a set of coal bunkers were created, capable of holding 15,000 tons of coal which could be fed by gravity into the boilers. A series of belt conveyors brought the coal to the bunkers, and were themselves loaded by a travelling crane used to remove the coal from barges at the adjacent wharf.

The four chimneys were built of brick and work started on their concrete foundations shortly after the site was cleared. These were each 42 ft square and 36 ft deep. The foundations, as well as the chimney structures to a height of 75 ft, were also built by Mayoh & Haley. Above this height, the Alphons Custodis Chimney Construction Company used their patented process to take them to their full height; this involved constructing them from the inside, as external scaffolding would have interfered with the work on the rest of the building. German bricklayers were specially employed for this work.[145] There were two chimneys on each side of the building, each about one-quarter of the way along from the building end, and when completed they stood 275 ft high with an internal diameter of 19 ft at ground level. During the erection of the building and chimneys almost 800 men were on site.[146]

Beneath the site an artesian well was sunk to a depth of 575 ft to ensure that there was a continuous supply of water for the boilers. The well, 8½ inches in diameter, was to supply water to the boilers. Also below the building were 220 concrete piles that supported the concrete bases for the heavy plant and equipment that was to be installed. A pair of 66 inch diameter pipes was laid between the engine house and the river wall for the intake and discharge of water for the condensors.*

Within the power station buildings, 64 boilers arranged in eight groups of eight on two levels burnt the coal to create superheated steam. This was fed to eight turbines directly connected with the generators; each produced 5·5 MW of power at 11,000 V AC, whilst running at 1,100 r.p.m. Each of these generating sets (turbine and generator) occupied a floor space of 50 × 29 ft. The building was designed with capacity for another two generator sets and their sixteen boilers and associated plant.

Cabling under the streets

Whilst the work on the power station building progressed, other workmen laid the ducts through which the supply cables would run. For although the power station was conveniently located to receive a steady supply of fuel, it was over a mile from the closest point on any of the railways that Yerkes controlled. The high-voltage supply of electricity from the power station to the many substations that were required along the route of the MDR and the three tube railways had to pass below the streets.

A substantial trench was excavated between Lots Road and Earl's Court station. Its size varied, but was no less than 4 ft wide and 10 ft deep throughout. Into this the stoneware ducts made by Doulton & Co. were placed. These were laid in eight layers, with eight 4-inch pipes to a layer, forming an 8×8 grid. Each layer was cemented into position to form a watertight block through which the cables could be fed. Regular

---

* In 1928 a tunnel was excavated from the power station site, 33 ft beneath Chelsea Creek to the centre of the Thames, where intake and discharge openings were made for the condensing water. This would allow the power station to have a steady supply of water even when the tide was low. The construction works for the tunnel were inspected by Lord Ashfield in August 1928.

An unusual view directly up inside one of the chimneys. *(The Tramway & Railway World)*

A drawing from 1904 showing the generators (dynamos) being installed within the power station. *(The Graphic)*

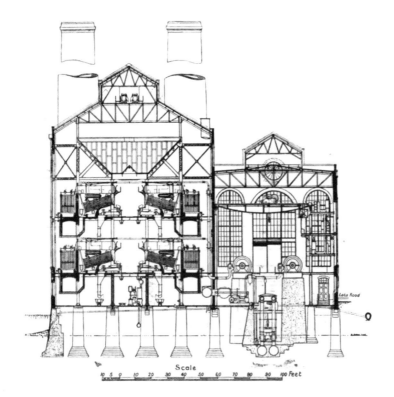

A cross-section of the power station buildings. The boiler house is on the left, with the coal bunkers under the roof and two levels of boilers below. On the right is the engine house (or turbine hall) in which steam from the boilers was used to make the electricity. *(The Engineer)*

A view along Lots Road in 1923 with the power station buildings on the left.

The ducts being constructed along a residential street in 1903. *(The Tramway & Railway World)*

manholes were set into the street opening onto cable access chambers below the surface, and from these the thick feeder cables were hauled through the ducts. Each was to carry 11,000 V to the substations.

From Earl's Court station, the feeder cables diverged to connect with the 23 substations that had been constructed for the MDR and the Bakerloo, Piccadilly, and Hampstead Tubes. Each substation was supplied via at least two cables, providing a primary and backup connection of three-phase AC power. The six feeder cables for the Piccadilly Tube descended a shaft just to the west of Earl's Court station, and were then supported by brackets on the tube tunnel walls to the substations at Hyde Park Corner, Russell Square, and Holloway Road. The feeder cables for the Bakerloo and Hampstead Tubes continued in the MDR tunnels to the substation at Charing Cross, together with those for the MDR itself. The Bakerloo cables descended to its tunnels, and fed the high-voltage supply to substations at Baker Street and London Road depot. Meanwhile, the feeder cables for the Hampstead descended a shaft and then passed along a cable tunnel constructed underneath Villiers Street before reaching its southern terminus. They were then carried on brackets through the running tunnels to substations at Euston, Kentish Town, Belsize Park, and Golders Green.

Substations

Although the electricity was distributed at 11,000 V from Lots Road, it had to be reduced to 600 V to power the trains. Substations were located at intervals along the route of each railway to transform the electricity. The CLR had placed its substations into the base of the lift shafts at Notting Hill Gate, Marble Arch, and Post Office, but a fire at the former in 1905 demonstrated that this location was awkward to access, particularly in an emergency. The UERL constructed its substations on the surface, in buildings adjacent to the stations, or just below ground level.

Hyde Park Corner and Charing Cross substations were both located below ground, because the cramped station sites did not allow for the erection of a separate building. Many of the other substations were placed in substantial brick buildings, designed to hold the heavy rotary convertors and other equipment that converted the high-voltage from Lots Road into the lower voltages required for traction current and supplies for lifts, lighting, and signals. Most of these buildings had some slight decoration through the use of different brick colours around the windows, which were metal-framed and typical of industrial buildings of the time. However, the shape of the windows and the style of decoration differed between the buildings, giving them a trace of individuality. Skylights were provided for many of the buildings to give additional illumination.

The substation building at South Kensington was more unusual, being of Portland stone with red brick bands. It was designed by Leslie Green, the architect for the UERL stations, and was intended to be a four-storey building in a Baroque style with the substation on the ground floor with flats above. The flats were never built, but in the 1920s two storeys were constructed (to a different design) above the substation to provide a dining club for the railway company.[147]

The substation building at Russell Square station is typical of the early 1900s substations constructed by the UERL. The large metal ventilation duct is not original. *(Author)*

Stations and equipment

Station buildings

The first station buildings on the MR seem to have been designed by the engineers, with limited decorative features.[148] There was nothing particularly innovative about them, or those that followed as the railway was extended. Brick, stone, and wood were used variously at the different locations, together with the wrought iron and glass in the elliptical arched roofs over the platforms that have been mentioned previously.

The C&SLR stations were made of brick, with stonework detailing. The most unusual feature was the large lead-covered dome, topped by a small cupola. It has been assumed by some that this was to house the lift equipment, but being hydraulically operated this was located at the bottom of the shafts. As the cross-section of Oval station shows (p 75), the dome contained the pulley wheels and nothing else.

The buildings of the other early tube railways were conventional in their manner of construction, and it was only the UERL with their American finance and management that decided to do something rather different. Like the power station at Lots Road, the stations were built with a steel frame. The lifts were electric, with the equipment placed on the first floor of the buildings above the shafts. In order to potentially get some return on their investment in property, the company hoped to sell the air rights above their stations to developers who could erect taller buildings above, with the strength of the steel frame allowing this. The buildings were all given flat roofs for this reason too.

Stockwell was typical of the C&SLR stations (except for King William Street). Kennington is the only one of these stations that has not been rebuilt, and retains its dome. *(LTM)*

Almost all of the station buildings were designed by the architect for the UERL, Leslie Green, and had a consistent appearance made of standard architectural components. This would have enabled people to recognize a UERL station anywhere in London. At ground level, pillars were placed between openings that could be wide or narrow. These provided access to the booking hall and lifts, shops, doorways for stairs to the first floor, or blank walls. At first floor level glazed arches were positioned above wide openings; smaller windows were used above the narrow openings, and in some cases, over the wider openings, in groups.

The station walls were of brick, with the main external façades clad with glazed terracotta blocks, in a colour called 'sang-de-bœuf', or 'ox-blood'. These had been chosen as a result of a competition, in which three manufacturers each erected a short section of wall (consisting of two pillars and an arch between) at the UERL depot at Lillie Bridge so that its quality could be assessed. The Leeds Fireclay Company won, and agreed to provide the terracotta blocks of what was known as Burmantoft's Faïence at "a flat rate of ten shillings per foot super of the elevation, openings deducted".[149]

The advantage of the steel frame was the flexibility that it provided for the station sites. Some were neat, rectangular sites, such as that at Oxford Circus on the Bakerloo line. Some façades were narrow, squeezed between existing buildings, as at Knightsbridge. Elephant & Castle had an irregular, almost trapezoid shape, whilst Chalk Farm was a long triangular site tapering to an acute point. The steel frame handled all of these sites whilst maintaining sufficient strength to support any oversite development, without requiring internal space to be wasted or constrained by load-bearing walls. The repeating panels of the façade could be placed along the edges of the building to allow the best use of internal space. The cast terracotta allowed the benefits of mass-production, as well as giving the ability to add small decorative details that distinguished the stations, such as:

- UERL monograms (still in place at Oxford Circus)
- Decorative cartouches (at least 15 different designs used, many unique to individual stations)
- A sign for Wisden & Co., above the doorway leading up to the offices that they leased above Leicester Square station
- *Art Deco* flourishes on the (since demolished) façade of Knightsbridge

It was only by adopting standardization of design together with a structure that could be put together quickly that the UERL was able to open 37 of these station buildings in the space of just over 16 months.

Station layout

There was little consistency in the layout of the original C&SLR stations, as noted previously (p 73–4), in part because of the original intention to use cable haulage. The CLR established the general convention on the Underground, namely having the platforms in two separate but adjacent tunnels with the platforms linked by cross-passages. Two of the cross-passages had stairwells descending to them, parallel with the platforms, which connected with the lower lift landings, providing separation between flows of passengers walking to and from the platforms. The lifts ascended directly to ticket hall level.

Covent Garden station, just before opening, was typical of the stations designed by Leslie Green. *(LTM)*

This arrangement was a result of the easement system, described in the Introduction (p 11). By effectively forcing the tube railway companies to follow the line of the streets above the platforms too had to be beneath the streets. Since the station buildings were at the side of the streets it was not possible to get the lifts to descend to provide level access to both platforms; they would always be to one side of the platforms, and so required passageways, footbridges, and stairs. It was not unusual for the station building to be in a side street, as this made the site cheaper to acquire; this was at the expense of longer, and sometimes more convoluted passageways at low level. At Notting Hill Gate, Chancery Lane, and Post Office the narrow streets forced the company to place the platforms at different levels so that they overlapped on the plans. The lifts here descended to an intermediate level with stairs up and down to the two platforms, which were both placed on the side closest to the lift shafts. Bank was the only station with a sub-surface ticket hall, and the opportunity was taken to place the lower lift landing between the platforms, which could be spaced further apart because of the wide road junction.

The BS&WR was unusual in that its standard practice was to place the platforms on the outside of the running lines. This avoided the need for the running tunnels to diverge on the approach to stations, and therefore reduced the likelihood of the tunnels needing an easement beneath private property. With the lifts to one side of the platforms, as with the other tube railways, it did mean that the access to the further platform was longer and needed four footbridges over the platforms (two over each platform). It also had the distinct disadvantage that the single tunnel to each

Cartouches featured in the glazed terracotta exterior of the buildings designed by Leslie Green. Top row: Oxford Circus, Down Street, Leicester Square. Bottom row: Covent Garden, Tufnell Park, Belsize Park, Chalk Farm. *(Author)*

platform had to serve as both entrance and exit, making for congestion and conflict between passenger flows. It seems that the company might have been aware of this, because Baker Street, Regent's Park, and Waterloo had platforms at different levels, and adopted the same approach as the CLR with separate entrance and exit passages. Both Kennington Road (now Lambeth North) and Elephant & Castle had their platforms between the tracks. This might have been because they served as termini, and cross-platform access makes it easier for passengers when trains can depart in the same direction from either platform. Trafalgar Square (now Charing Cross) also had the same arrangement.

The other two UERL tube railways, the GNP&BR and the CCE&HR, followed the CLR approach as far as possible. There were, inevitably, exceptions. At Caledonian Road, York Road, King's Cross, and Earl's Court the layout allowed the lifts to descend to platform level, with the platform tunnels further apart than usual. Russell Square, Strand (later renamed Aldwych), and Euston Road (now Warren Street) had outside platform arrangements like the BS&WR; at the latter station this eased the sharp curve north of the station. Because of junctions nearby, Camden Town, Holborn, and South Kensington had their platforms at different levels, and therefore had unique layouts. The lower landing of the lifts at Holborn and Camden Town were placed at a level between that of the platforms, with stairs needed to reach any of the platforms (some up, and some down). At South Kensington the lifts had two lower landings, one for each platform level, and provided step-free access to both platforms. Finally, Tufnell Park and Kentish Town both had platforms at different levels, with the platforms on the side closest to the lifts.

Tracks for the tubes

The C&SLR, W&CR, CLR, and GN&CR were all provided with tracks in which there was little foundation installed below the sleepers. The sleepers spanned the tunnel invert and had chamfered ends to fit against the tunnel segments. They supported the rails, but between the sleepers there was open space down to the tunnel lining, instead of the ballast that passengers would have been expecting to see based on their experience of railways on the surface.

The first tube railway tracks, on the C&SLR, were formed of transverse sleepers made of pitch pine spaced at 3½ ft intervals (2½ ft where rail joints occurred) with flat-bottomed steel running rails spiked to them. The rails were 24 ft long, with a conductor rail made of channel-section iron and supported by glass insulators on every other sleeper. This was placed between the running rails but offset from the centre to prevent it from being short-circuited by the coupling chains on the rolling stock.* For the same reason it was placed below the level of the running rails, and wooden ramps were required to lift the collector shoes at pointwork. Struts fitted to the ends of the sleepers and braced against the horizontal segment flanges kept the sleepers from moving.

The W&CR had a similar arrangement, but used longitudinal sleepers (again of pitch pine) in the tube tunnels, and a heavier running rail fixed to the sleeper by cast iron chairs. It used a steel channel rail as its central conductor rail supported on porcelain insulators at the same height as the running rails; these were fixed to transverse sleepers. Beneath the tracks a concrete gully ran along the tunnel, sloping towards the centre from both sides. Drawings indicate that the longitudinal sleepers would have been fixed to the concrete. In the stations and the depot the tracks were supported on transverse sleepers.

The track on the CLR also used longitudinal sleepers, made of oak or jarrah wood — sources differ on this point — but with an even heavier running rail of bridge section secured to them using fang bolts. Transverse sleepers and porcelain insulators were used to support the conductor rail, which was 1½ inches above the height of the running rails, but in other respects was a copy of the W&CR conductor arrangements.[150] A walkway was placed to one side of the conductor rail, made of wooden planks across the transverse sleepers.

The open spaces beneath the track were left because of concerns that ballasted track in a confined tunnel would lead to a build-up of dust.[151] Unfortunately it provided a place for rubbish and detritus to accumulate, thus increasing the risk of fires. As a result of a catastrophic fire on the Paris Métro in 1903, the Board of Trade (BoT) in the UK made a list of requirements for underground railways, which included the following stipulations in the original draft:

- Sleepers to be of hard wood, not creosoted, to be laid in ballast and covered with a layer of gravel or finely-broken stone free from dust
- The ballast to be formed with a level surface so as to form a convenient roadway for passengers in case of emergency.[152]

Discussions with the railway companies ensued, with some of the main objection being the requirement for ballast. Both the C&SLR and CLR cited dust from the ballast getting into electrical equipment as a reason for not using it, and also noted

---

*   It was positioned towards the right-hand rail for northbound trains, and the left-hand rail for southbound trains, so that the collector shoes on the locomotives did not need to be altered. This had the undesirable consequence of placing the conductor rail close to at least one platform at every station except for Oval and Borough.

Inside a CLR running tunnel, showing the rails supported on longitudinal sleepers, and the wooden walkway for use by workmen or during an evacuation. To the other side of the central conductor rail is a void down to the tunnel lining. *(Cassell's Magazine)*

that ballast would make the job of cleaning the tunnels more difficult. As a result of these objections, the BoT agreed that ballast could be omitted if the space between the rails was completely covered with "granolithic slabs, or slabs of a similar material". This would provide a safer walkway in the event of a train being evacuated in a tunnel, and would prevent the build-up of litter in the tunnel invert.

Unlike the three aforementioned railways, the GN&CR used two conductor rails, both positioned outside the running rails. The location of the rails prevented couplings and other equipment on main-line railway carriages from coming into contact with an electrified rail. The use of two rails was to provide an insulated return path for the current, rather than it returning via the earthed running rails. It had been found that the use of earthed returns allowed some current to flow via the soil and nearly conductors, such as gas pipes and telegraph cables; this unintended current could cause interference and electrolytic corrosion.

The track was fixed to longitudinal pitch pine timbers with regular transoms. The timber was treated to prevent decay, but nothing was done to render it non-flammable. Like the CLR, a stone pathway was laid between the rails, but this did not meet with the approval of the inspector from the BoT. It was only 18 inches wide, and laid adjacent to one of the rails. On the other side was an opening into the tunnel invert; the inspector felt that this would be a serious safety risk in the event of passengers being evacuated along the tracks, and gave the company three months to remedy the problem.* He proposed that either the walkway be widened to the width of the space between the rails, or the invert be filled with ballast or gravel (the latter being his preferred solution).[153]

The three tube railways opened by the UERL were ballasted, and thus had a more conventional appearance. Two conductors were used: as with the GN&CR it was thought that this would reduce the risk of corrosion from stray earth currents if the running rails were used as a return. These rails had a large, almost square cross-section to minimize resistance. The track was designed by James R. Chapman, together with J. Harrison, another of the engineers whom Yerkes brought over from the USA. Transverse sleepers of karri wood were used in every other tunnel ring, onto which cast iron chairs were screwed; the rails were clipped into these chairs. To reduce vibration, felt pads were placed beneath the chairs. Porcelain insulators made by Doulton supported the conductor rails, and were fixed to the sleepers using metal brackets. For both conductor rails the insulators were about 5 inches square, with channels through them parallel to the rails, which sat between projecting lips to hold them in place. The insulators that supported the positive conductor rail outside the running rails were angled because the short sleepers used in the tunnels would not otherwise hold the conductor sufficiently far away from the running rail.

Three types of sleeper were used (all 5 inches deep):
* Normal sleeper: 6 ft 6 ins × 14 ins
* Sleeper with insulator for outside conductor rail: 7 ft 0½ ins × 14 ins
* Sleeper at rail joint: 6 ft 6 ins × 10 ins

Two of the latter, narrower sleepers were placed in adjacent tunnel rings either side of a joint in the running rails. Each sleeper was supported on a bed of concrete beneath its centre section, and crushed granite ballast under the ends. They were fixed to the concrete by means of a metal angle iron spiked to the underside and set into a layer of cement above the concrete. More granite ballast was placed between the concrete sleeper supports, which had 3 inch tubes set towards their bases to enable drainage.

	Rail	Weight	Length	Type
C&SLR	Running	58 lb/yd	24 ft	Flat-bottom
	Conductor	10 lb/yd		Channel
W&CR	Running	87 lb/yd	30 ft	Bull head
	Conductor	46 lb/yd	30 ft	Channel
CLR	Running	100 lb/yd	60 ft	Bridge
	Conductor	85 lb/yd	30 – 42 ft	Channel
GN&CR	Running	85 lb/yd		Flat-bottom
	Conductor	80 lb/yd		Channel

---

* The GN&CR had argued that the tunnel invert would provide a refuge for any member of staff in the tunnel in the event of a train coming along, and that the space beside the walkway would allow them access. The BoT inspector dismissed this idea, stating that staff should not be in the tunnels when the trains were operating.

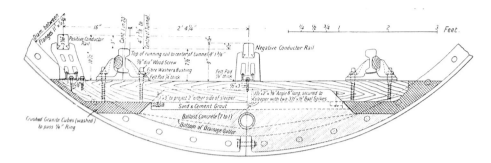

A cross-section through the track used by all three of the UERL tube railways. Note the different shapes of the two insulators supporting the conductor rails. *(The Railway Gazette)*

	Rail	Weight	Length	Type
BS&WR	Running	90 lb/yd	35 ft	Bull head
GNP&BR	Conductor	85 lb/yd	42 ft	Square
CCE&HR				

Table 1: Types of rail used on tube railways

On the Metropolitan and District Railways, and probably also on the short sections of the tube railways that were in the open air, the insulators had a 'mushroom' shape, which kept the lower part of the insulator dry. This reduced the risk of arcing if the insulator became wet. This became the standard style of insulator across the Underground for many decades. It is only in recent years, with the advent of lighter aluminium conductor rail that needs to be held down and in position, that new types of insulator with a more cylindrical profile have been used.

Stations and platforms

The large tunnels constructed at stations needed substantial work to equip them with station platforms. A wall was constructed along the length of the tunnel below the platform edge, and then the platform spanned the gap between this and the tunnel lining. The C&SLR and CLR platforms were made of wood (as were the City platforms on the W&CR).

The space beneath the platform was sometimes left empty, as it provided a useful conduit for pipes and cables. At some stations it was filled in; for example, the Bakerloo line stations between Paddington and Kilburn Park had the spaces below the platforms and beneath the lower escalator concourses packed with clay (presumably from the tunnel excavation).[154] The track was constructed in the same way as in the running tunnels, with space beneath on the earlier tube railways, but with concrete down to the tunnel lining on those of the UERL. At the handful of C&SLR stations which featured an island platform in a single tunnel, there was a large concrete arch at the bottom of the tunnel which supported the platform and one side of each track bed (see diagram on p 155).

A typical section of tube track in the platform area at Regent's Park station. The first and third rails from the top are square-section conductor rails, resting on mushroom-shaped porcelain insulators. The small, angled insulators on the top rail are rail anchors; these stop the current rails from being pulled in the direction that the trains travel. The central conductor rail runs over the anti-suicide pit. Bullhead rail is used for the running rails, which are held in heavy iron chairs secured to wooden 'pit blocks'. *(Author)*

The headwalls of the platform tunnels were brick, rendered with cement, and then tiled. The brick tunnel walls of the C&SLR were also tiled directly; the tunnel segments on the platform walls of the other railways were first infilled so that tiling could also be affixed. From the days of the C&SLR glazed white tiles had been used from the platform all the way around the tunnel vault as they were hard-wearing and maximized the reflected light in the tunnels. This was particularly important on the gas-lit stations of the C&SLR. The decoration varied between the companies. A chocolate brown stripe with a *fleur-de-lys* motif was used along the platform and passageway walls of the C&SLR. Both the W&CR and the CLR adopted plain white tiling, and this would have been used on the BS&WR had it remained independent.* Instead, each station on the BS&WR, as well as those on the GNP&BR and CCE&HR, was provided with an attractive coloured geometric design along the length of its platforms, but only up to a height of about 7 ft 6 ins; above this was white-painted plasterwork.[155]

---

*   The northbound platform tiling at Charing Cross was completed in plain white tiles before the line was acquired by Yerkes.

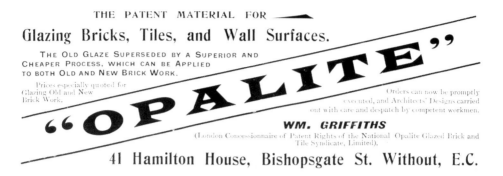

An advertisement for the Opalite tiles used on the CLR.

Gas lighting was used on the C&SLR platforms because the electrical generating station for the railway was too small to be able to power electric lamps, although electric lamps were installed as a backup. The electric lighting of the other lines was very dim by today's standards. Incandescent bulbs were placed regularly along the platforms of the W&CR, whilst the CLR, GN&CR and UERL railways used arc lamps. All of them ran the cables for the lights across the surface of the tiling. This looked untidy, but there was no alternative given the cast iron tunnel segments lying just beneath the tiles. Photos suggest that the main wiring ran along the length of the platform, probably in metal pipes, with connections leading off to each lamp. The Maxim arc lamps used by the UERL were fitted onto curved metal bars running vertically down the curve of the platform wall, allowing them to be lowered for maintenance and cleaning. The GN&CR used a pulley arrangement to lower its lamps.

The UERL stations supplied power to the arc lights via the same circuits that fed the lift motors. If these circuits failed switches allowed the lights to be fed from the conductor rails. In addition to the arc lamps, their stations had incandescent lamps along their platforms, fed from two different supplies. The majority were powered from the Lots Road power station, but via separate transformers in the substations to those that fed the arc lamps. The bulbs were suspended from the cables running along the tunnel walls. The others were fed from the local electricity supply company, ensuring that even if the main power station suffered a major failure some lighting would be maintained. This was in accordance with BoT fire regulations (see next section for more detail on these).

Improvements in lighting technology meant that no more arc lamps were installed after about 1908, and those in use were gradually replaced. Better lighting could be achieved with closer-spaced incandescent bulbs, typically around 100 candle-power. Hexagonal glass shades were used for the UERL lights.

Fire precautions

The Board of Trade requirements for preventing the risk of fires have been mentioned previously in regard to the ballasting of track. Other requirements applied to tunnels and stations, as follows:

- Tunnels to be provided with lights capable of being turned on from the stations at either end of each section and, if necessary, at some intermediate

The platform at Trafalgar Square (now Charing Cross) on the BS&WR, showing the decorative tiling, arc lights, and cabling along the wall with emergency incandescent bulbs illuminated. *(LTM)*

points. The lighting circuits to be independent of the traction supply.

- Separate entrances to and exits from each platform of the stations to be provided, and to be situated as nearly as possible in the middle of the platforms.
- All stairways, passages, and exits from the stations to be conspicuously lighted. Not less than 25 per cent. of the lights in these places to be supplied from independent source. If necessary, the exits to be made more conspicuous by the use of coloured lights in addition to white lights.
- Platforms not to be made of wood, and woodwork to be eliminated as far as possible from signal boxes, lifts, offices, &c., below ground.
- Efficient hydrants, hose, and fire prevention appliances to be provided.
- Ventilating ways to be provided wherever possible from the station and the tunnels to the surface.[156]

The CLR and C&SLR increased their efforts to replace their wooden platforms with concrete as a result of these regulations, and the three UERL tube railways were opened with concrete platforms. The Metropolitan Railway agreed not to make any further platforms from wood, but made no promises about replacing the existing ones. The MDR resisted the call to replace its wooden platforms, pleading its poor financial state and noting that it would cost £1,250 per station for the work.

The GN&CR was the first tube railway to open after the requirements had been issued (albeit in draft form), and decided as an experiment to install lights to guide passengers from the platforms to the exits at Moorgate and Finsbury Park. These had yellow filters fitted on their fronts, and notices on the platform walls informed passengers that following the yellow lights would lead them out of the station.[157]

Wood on the Underground

Given the effort that has been expended in removing all flammable materials from the Underground, it might seem surprising just how much wood was used by the underground railway companies in the early 1900s. Platforms on the MR and MDR were mostly made of wood, even on stations that were completely in tunnel. The C&SLR and CLR followed suit; the evidence is unclear for the GN&CR. Signal cabins were often of wooden construction too. The sleepers beneath the rails were invariably of wood, and the walkways provided in the running tunnels on the C&SLR and CLR were wooden planks across the sleepers.

The pitch pine used on the C&SLR and W&CR for its sleepers was seen with as much disfavour by the BoT as the creosoted wood used by the MR and MDR. The only wood that the BoT would countenance was hardwood, such as the karri wood and jarrah wood used by the UERL (and supplied by Millar's Karri & Jarrah (1902) Ltd). These were both types of eucalyptus wood imported from Western Australia, well regarded for their resistance to rot as well as fire. This continued to be the preferred sleeper wood used by the UERL and its successors for many years.

The lifts at GN&CR stations were primarily wooden, with mahogany used for the sides and top, and the floors made from Oregon pine covered with oak strips (for grip). Teak, which has a good resistance to fire, was used for much of the rolling stock on the line.

Fire hydrants on the UERL lines were placed in teak cabinets, teak being another hardwood. The floors of the lifts were made of karri wood, and jarrah was used for the signal cabins. Despite the cost, the UERL was keen to ensure that there was as little flammable material as possible in its stations.

As a slight aside, in 1936 the escalators at Moorgate, King's Cross, and Post Office were fitted with panels of different woods from around the British Empire. Moorgate was the first, receiving a selection of test panels. King's Cross was then given Queensland walnut, and the Post Office panels were of Indian laurel. LT apparently hoped that "greater interest will be stimulated in the fine woods of the Dominions and the Colonies".[158]

All of the wood used on escalators was removed after the devastating fire at King's Cross on 18 November 1987. A major programme of work saw the remaining wooden panels and steps replaced by metal.

A long debate ensued between the railway companies and the London County Council (LCC — which was in charge of the London Fire Brigade) over the size of water main required for fire-fighting purposes, with the LCC insisting on 4-inch mains. The railway companies objected, pointing out that the additional pressure present because of the depth of the stations would allow a 2-inch main to be adequate. The C&SLR already had mains of this size at each station, and presumably wanted to avoid replacing them; the UERL had been originally informed by the LCC to use 2½ inches, and had set this size of main in the concrete floors of the BS&WR stations by the time that the LCC changed their minds.

At UERL stations the fire mains ran from the surface, down the stair shafts at each station, beneath the passageway floors to platform level. The main was fitted into the void beneath each platform with pipes leading up through the platform surface to the two hydrants, one towards each end of the platform. Given the close interest being taken by the LCC, the arrangements for the other companies were probably similar, although the number of hydrants varied at some stations — for example, the C&SLR placed one hydrant near the middle of each platform, which was just acceptable with 200 ft platforms. All of the other companies provided at least two hydrants per platform.

The requirement for separate entrances and exits came too late to influence the BS&WR, as construction work had largely completed by the time that the regulations were published. That the GNP&BR and CCE&HR were compliant is probably the consequence of good design practice, as their design had been largely finalized (and in the case of the former, were under construction) when the BoT published. One change that seems to have been made was at Oxford Circus, where a single passageway connected the lifts with a point where the separate passageways to the platforms joined. Not only was there only one access point to each platform, but all the passengers would be forced to use one passageway for both directions. The UERL quickly arranged for this to be modified by extending the passage to the northbound platform closer to the lifts. This left an undesirable 'crossroads' junction near to the lifts, but this was probably unavoidable.[159]

The regulations were mandatory for new railways, but were not initially enforced retrospectively on the existing lines. The CLR, for example, took several years to replace its wooden platforms, and the C&SLR continued with its ballast-free track. A fire at Moorgate on 16 July 1908 started in rubbish beneath the tracks, and produced thick smoke that forced firefighters to walk along the tunnel from Bank station in order to reach it. As a result the LCC asked the BoT to apply the regulations retrospectively to all the underground railways.

Ventilation

The early tube railways were ventilated through their stations, for the most part. It was expected that the trains moving through the tunnels would force air through and prevent it from becoming stale. This was found not to be the case — the air just tended to move back and forth — and the CLR in particular gained notoriety for the smell of its tunnels. A fan was installed at Bond Street station in 1902, and later that year consideration was given to piping compressed air through the tunnels, and releasing it between the stations.[160]

The following year an unusual attempt was made to change the air in the tunnels each night. A firm specializing in mine ventilation, Walker Brothers of Wigan, was brought in to help. A fan 20 feet in diameter, capable of moving air at the rate of 100,000 ft^3 per minute, was installed at Shepherd's Bush station, wooden doors were closed over the nearby tunnel portals at the depot, and doors in all the stations except Bank were closed. The Shepherd's Bush fan was then run to pull air all of the way through the tunnels from Bank. Even this was not a cure for the smell, although the public was perhaps slightly reassured by a scientific investigation instigated by the LCC which concluded that there was nothing deadly or noxious in the atmosphere of the CLR. After analysis of 118 samples of air collected from the tunnels, they announced that carbon dioxide levels were satisfactory, and there were no harmful germs. It was just a musty, earthy smell, perhaps due to the low humidity in the tunnels.*

Unpleasant underground atmospheres

The ventilation problems experienced by the Metropolitan Railway when running steam locomotives through their tunnels have been described in Chapter 2, along with details of their various experiments to improve the situation. Removing the steam and smoke did not always result in a pure atmosphere though, as the CLR demonstrated. Factors such as humidity, temperature, CO_2 content, and dust all affected how the stations and tunnels smelt.

The CLR was not alone in its problems. In 1905 the Sanitary Engineer for New York ran a study of the air in the New York Subway for six months and declared it to be "a hotbed of deadly disease. The germs of pneumonia are nurtured in the foul air."[161] In Paris, where the underground railways were operated by two separate companies, a 1914 study showed that the atmosphere of one, the Nord-Sud, was markedly better than that of the other, the Métropolitain. Investigation suggested that the use of softer rails and cast iron brake blocks by the latter company led to significantly more dust in the air, so much so that it was considered to be a danger to public health.[162]

The solution adopted by the Paris Métro to the smell of the system (as opposed to the dust) has been to scent it with perfume, which has been tried regularly since the 1920s. In 1959 the scent of carnations was sprayed into the stations by one train in every six, by fitting the perfume dispenser to the brake system so that the air pressure used for braking would dispense the fragrance. The latest attempt was in 1998, with a new perfume called *Madeleine*. London Underground tried a similar perfume at three stations in 2001, but abandoned the trial after just one day amid claims that passengers were feeling sick.

In the 1980s, London Underground developed a five-car vacuum cleaner train which would pass slowly along the tunnels at night. High-pressure air was used to dislodge dirt from the tunnel lining and tracks, and a vacuum used to suck up the dirt and filter it out into collection wagons. A newer tunnel cleaning train is currently being constructed.

To avoid a similar problem the UERL installed fans at nearly all of its stations to extract air via ducts in the station and through a pipe up the centre of the spiral staircase. It was discharged at roof level, with fresh air entering via the stair and lift shafts. The fans could move 18,500 ft^3 per minute, which was sufficient to provide "the equivalent of a strong breeze" and prevent "musty smells" in the tunnels.[163] Part of

---

*   The following year a study was carried out on the air of the C&SLR by the Public Analyst of Southwark. This air was found to have similar levels of CO_2, but rather lower levels of bacteria than were found in the air of the streets outside the stations.

the problem seems to have been with the Parliamentary approvals for tube railways, as one of the underground railway engineers of the time, Douglas Fox, noted to the BoT that "Companies are generally prohibited from putting in Ventilation Shafts except at Stations."[164] There was probably a reluctance on the part of the companies as well to spend money on acquiring permanent sites for ventilation, given the cost of land in central London and their belief that the movement of trains would be sufficient to ventilate their tunnels. It was only in the 1920s and 1930s that ventilation shafts were provided between stations, by retaining shafts used for construction and equipping them with fans and shafthead buildings.

In May 1911 it was reported that the CLR had ordered a new ventilation system to be installed at all of their stations except Shepherd's Bush (which was felt to be too close to the tunnel portals to require equipping), manufactured by a company called Ozonair Ltd.[165] This consisted of equipment to filter and wash incoming air (the filters were apparently made from coconut fibre),[166] and then add a small quantity of ozone. The ozone was created by applying a voltage of 5–6 KV to a set of plates made of mica with thin wire gauze covering both sides.[167] The high voltage was generated by a transformer, fed from a rotary convertor which generated alternating current from the direct current drawn from the conductor rails. A cubicle in the ticket hall was the chosen location for the equipment, as it needed to be at the surface to pull in fresh air. Some of the cleansed air was pumped into the ticket hall and toilets, but the majority was passed through galvanized steel ducts to platform level. The ducts were often run down the spiral staircases and along the ceilings of passageways to reach the platform tunnels; here they continued into the void beneath the platforms. Vertical ducts led from the pipe under the platforms to release the air at a height of

A demonstration with the aid of a handkerchief of the flow of ozonized air coming from the platform duct, overseen by a rather sinister-looking member of staff. (*Ozonair brochure*)

The ventilation plant installed at Euston, on the Hampstead Line, in a disused station building. *(Operating Manager's Personal Letter No. 7: 1929)*

around 7 ft. The under-platform ducts continued into the tunnels for about 40 ft at the departure ends of the platforms, to allow the ozonized air to circulate throughout the tunnels. According to the publicity posters for the CLR, every trip on their line would "invigorate" passengers.[168]

At most stations the equipment could supply 5,500 to 6,500 ft^3 of ozonated air per minute. At Holland Park three times this amount could be supplied, to compensate for the lack of equipment at Shepherd's Bush, and British Museum station was fed with 10,000 ft^3 per minute, presumably because it was about half-way along the line. In total, the equipment at all of the stations could supply around 80 million ft^3 of ozonated air each day.[169]

Ozonair equipment was also installed at several UERL stations around 1914, including Euston, Edgware Road, Goodge Street, and Embankment. Posters highlighted the fresh scent which it brought into the tube stations, claiming that it was reminiscent of the seaside. Studies 'proved' the benefits of ozonated air to the public, and there appears to have been no adverse reaction in the press.*

By the 1930s the LER had discovered that the most effective way to ventilate their tube railways was by blowing fresh air *into* the tunnels (the plenum system), rather than sucking vitiated air *from* them (the vacuum system). The benefits were explained in a letter to staff:

> ...the force of the descending currents of air cause rapid ascent of the heated air below. It also drives the air before it to the next exit to street atmosphere. [...] The plenum system has a further advantage, namely, that of facilitating the addition of ozone and of the washing of the air, also that the air can be delivered to the point where it is most required.[170]

---

*   In his 2011 book *London Under*, the historian Peter Ackroyd notes that the ozone "made commuters slightly ill", but offers no source for this assertion.

A view of the track at Kilburn Park station around the time of its opening in 1915, showing the flat concrete track bed. *(LTM)*

Anti-suicide pits

The confined space in a tube tunnel meant that extricating the bodies of people who had fallen (or jumped) in front of a train was an awkward operation. A decision was made in the late 1920s to form a pit between the running rails throughout the length of the station platforms, into which people might fall and thereby avoid being crushed under an incoming train. The C&SLR stations which had both tracks and an island platform in a single 30 ft diameter tunnel appear to have had pits provided, but this seems to be unique to them (see cross-section on p 155).

The next stations to benefit from the anti-suicide pits were those on the Morden extension of the C&SLR, in 1926 (see p 193 for more details). The Southgate extension of the Piccadilly line was given a different design of pit (p 215). These two experiments were judged to add a worthwhile safety improvement to the stations, and so in 1934 work began on constructing pits 2 ft deep at the existing tube stations, starting with the eastbound platform at Hyde Park Corner.* In place of sleepers, jarrah wood pit blocks were set into the concrete either side of the pits, and the cast iron chairs for securing the rails were screwed to these.

The initial work was completely manual, with teams of three men breaking out the concrete beneath the track. One held a metal point with tongs, whilst the other two took turns to hammer the point. Each team could break out the concrete between three sleepers in a night, so the process was fairly slow. It was sped up by the introduction of pneumatic hammers, powered by petrol-driven air compressors placed in the street outside the station to keep the exhaust fumes out of the tunnels.

The sleepers had to be retained to keep the track in position as the concrete was broken out. The pit blocks were therefore installed in the space between the sleepers, except near rail joints when the position of the sleepers was adjusted. The

---

* This work might have been an experiment, as in early 1935 a Traffic Notice records that the teams were back at the station lengthening the pit.

South Wimbledon in 1926, showing the shallow anti-suicide pits provided on the extension to Morden. *(LTM)*

anchors for the pit blocks were then cast into the concrete forming the pit, the track positioning rechecked, and then the pit blocks were concreted into position. New insulators for the central rail were set into the pit, and finally the track was secured to the pit blocks and unclipped from the sleepers, which were removed and often cut up to form new pit blocks.

The work to construct the pits continued through 1934 and into 1935, taking longer than the 6–8 months that had been expected originally. Works trains consisting of flat cars coupled between two motor cars proceeded through the tunnels after the last passenger trains, dropping off equipment to the teams and then collecting it back together with rubble before the next day's service began. The work focused on different lines in turn: for example, the work on the former C&SLR was started in May 1935 and continued throughout the year. It proceeded from south to north, starting at South Wimbledon, Colliers Wood, and Tooting Broadway, and reached Angel in November. The stations on the Morden extension were included in the work, presumably because the original pits needed to be deepened from 1 ft 4 ins to 2 ft.

Anti-suicide pit construction work at Hampstead, showing the highly manual nature of the work. *(LTM)*

The first tube extensions

Early extensions of the C&SLR

After being the pioneering tube railway in London, it is not surprising that the C&SLR also constructed and opened the first tube railway extension. The problems with the terminus at King William Street have already been described, and from the moment it was opened the company looked for solutions. It rapidly realized that the only viable option was to abandon the station and build a new line; even if the line had been practical to operate, the eastern-facing tracks did not point in a useful direction for the railway to proceed.

Following the usual procedures for getting Parliamentary approval, work started on an extension in late 1896. The extension was to branch off from the existing line just north of Borough station, and through new under-river tunnels continue to Moorgate Street, with intermediate stations at London Bridge and Bank – the latter being the replacement for King William Street. The original line from King William Street as far as the junction would be abandoned.* It was recognized by the company that their tunnels were too small, and so the extension was constructed with tunnels having an internal diameter of 11 ft 6 ins. The tunnelling work was completed by the end of 1898.

John Mowlem & Co were appointed as contractors, and they began work at all of the new station sites apart from Bank. A delay occurred at this site because the station was to be built below, and in the crypt of the church of St Mary Woolnoth. The vestry forced the railway company and its contractor to get possession of the site via the Board of Trade, which finally occurred on 12 May 1897.[171] Much of the interior was carefully removed and stored, including carvings and the stonework floor. The work to underpin the church was complex, worsened by the poor construction of the church (described by the company chairman as "poorly built and flimsy"[172]), and delays soon ensued at this location.[173] Large iron girders 53 ft long had to be inserted under the structure to support it before the original foundations were removed so that the station could be built. A large rectangular lift shaft was also sunk, accommodating five lifts, with the machinery located at the bottom of the shaft below the lower lift landing.

At Borough a new shaft was dug above where the new route would diverge, to allow the junctions to be constructed. These were made by mining out the soil by hand around the existing tunnels. At one end of the junction the new tunnel was side-by-side with the old; here, the diameter of the junction tunnel was almost the same as the two tunnels, having a diameter of 21 ft 2½ ins (that this was the same diameter as the new platform tunnels was probably not a coincidence, as it avoided the need to cast another size of tunnel ring segment). Several rings of this size tunnel were installed. The next section was made of a few rings of a smaller diameter, and so on

---

*   An attempt was made to reuse the terminus by a company called the City & Brixton Railway. An inability to raise the necessary money led to this scheme being abandoned.

Inside the step-plate tunnel at Borough Junction, on the northbound line. The left-hand tunnel is the original line to King William Street, and the right-hand tunnel leads north to Moorgate Street. *(LTM)*

until a stepped conical tunnel was formed: this was termed a 'step-plate junction', and this appears to be the first time that they were used on the Underground. This whole process was delicate work, as trains were continuing to run through the original tunnel during the excavation. Finally the original running tunnel, which had been carefully supported whilst the excavation proceeded, would be dismantled.

The extension to Moorgate was built concurrently with a southward extension to Clapham Common. This had been approved back in 1890, and the powers used in 1893 to provide sidings south of Stockwell along the authorized line of route. For this reason the extension was made using the smaller 10 ft 6 ins diameter tunnels. No particular difficulties seem to have occurred on this extension. The stations at Clapham North and Clapham Common were each provided with island platforms in a single 30 ft diameter tunnel, at the time the largest bored tunnels in the world. These were constructed with shields and used cast iron segments, the lessons of the original masonry platform tunnels having been learned. Both stations opened on 4 June 1900.

North of Moorgate the line was extended onwards to the Angel, at Islington, via stations at Old Street and City Road. These tunnels were also of 10 ft 6 ins diameter, but this was to reduce their cost. The station at Angel was in a single 30 ft diameter tunnel like those in Clapham, but the other two both had their platforms in separate tunnels of 21 ft 2½ in diameter. Apart from cutting into some of the sands and gravels below the clay near Old Street, this extension was constructed without significant engineering difficulties and opened for use on 17 November 1901.

The final extension of the C&SLR as an independent company was from Angel to Euston, via King's Cross. Shafts were sunk for the latter station outside the main-line terminus in 1905, with tunnelling starting in August of that year. Both Greathead shields and rotary excavators were used for this work, starting out driving the tunnels

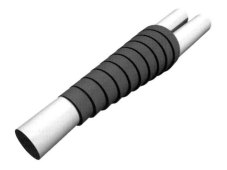

An illustration of a step-plate junction, seen from the outside. *(Author)*

towards Angel, and then back towards Euston. Again, the running tunnels had an internal diameter of 10 ft 6 ins. In clay good progress of up to 12 yards per day was made at each tunnel face.[174]

King's Cross had two separate platform tunnels, spaced further apart than usual because the large open area in front of the main-line station allowed them to do this without building under private property. This had the advantage for passengers of allowing the lift shafts to descend to platform level, rather than needing the usual stairs between the lower lift landing and platforms. At Euston a single 30 ft tunnel with island platform was built, the last of these on the Underground. A cross-section of the tunnel shows the amount of wasted space below the tracks and platform, which are supported on a massive concrete arch. Beyond the platform tunnel the running tunnels continued a short distance before joining in a single large tunnel of 25 ft

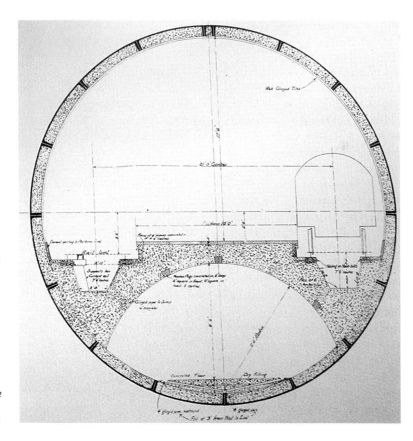

A cross-section through the large platform tunnel at Euston, showing the void beneath the arch that supports the tracks and platforms. *(The Tramway & Railway World)*

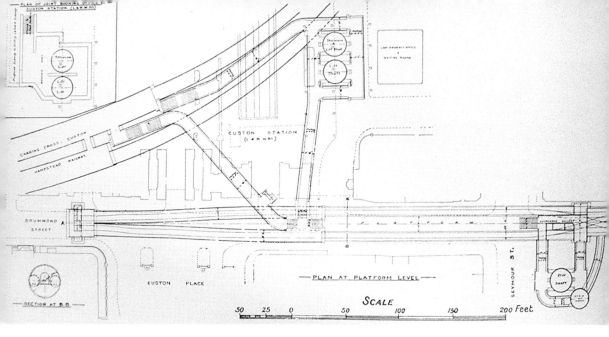

A plan of the tube stations at Euston in 1907. The C&SLR platforms are at the bottom, entering from the lower right corner, where the lifts and access passages can be seen. The Hampstead Tube platforms curve across the top left of the plan; the original lifts are not shown, but would be off the left-hand side. The passageways linking the two sets of platforms at low-level are in between, and a tiny ticket office was provided for passengers interchanging between the two tube railways (on the diagonal passage, below the label for Euston). The C&SLR locomotive traverser is at the end of their tunnels, in the bottom left of the plan adjacent to the Drummond Street label. *(The Tramway & Railway World)*

diameter that was fitted with a locomotive traverser (a section of track that could be slid sideways, allowing a locomotive to move from one track to another). To the east of the platform tunnel was a 23 ft diameter tunnel containing a crossover. A further 23 ft diameter tunnel was built beyond this for a junction with a siding to the south of the running tunnels in which trains could be stabled.

One of the challenges faced by Walter Scott & Middleton, the contractors, was water-bearing sand near Euston. From the point that the sand was met, all of the tunnelling work at Euston was carried out in compressed air not exceeding 14·5 p.s.i. When the tunnel was first pressurized the flow of water from the sand stopped, but started again as soon as the pressure stabilized. When the pressure was increased the flow stopped, but upon the pressure stabilizing it flowed once more. The engineers concluded that it was a large pocket of wet sand completely surrounded by clay, and that when the pressure increased the air escaped into the sand and drove the water back.[175] The station was built below Euston Street, which has long-since disappeared beneath the enlarged main-line station, but the front edge of the current station building marks its course.

The other construction challenge was the discovery of large boulders in the clay between Weston Street and Angel. These are not uncommon in the clay, but at this location they bent and broke the cutters on the rotary excavator and so the tunnellers had to resort to pneumatic rock drills.[176]

The tunnelling for this extension was completed by October 1906, and the line opened to the public on 11 May 1907.

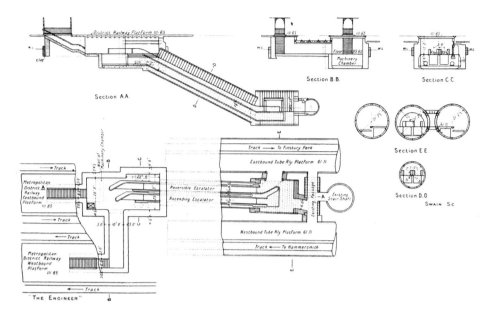

A plan (below) and several cross-sections of the escalator tunnels at Earl's Court. The 'shunt' landings are clearly visible on the plan at both ends of the reversible escalator, and the top of the ascending escalator. As the latter machine could only operate upwards there was no need for the shunt landing at its lower end. *(The Engineer)*

The first escalator

Until 1911, access to all tube stations was either via lifts or stairs. With a single exception,[*] shafts were made at stations during construction, and were used to access the tunnelling works. After the tunnels were completed either lifts or a spiral staircase (sometimes both) were placed into the shafts. So long as sufficient lifts were provided, passengers would rarely have to wait too long in order to ascend or descend.

Moving staircases allowed a continuous flow of people, unlike lifts. Various passenger conveyors had been tried in the early years of the twentieth century in Britain, but these were inclined conveyor belts usually with handrails. The escalator, which implies a machine with steps that move, had appeared in some American department stores, but it seems that the first to be installed in Britain was at Earl's Court station.[177] This linked a new concourse beneath the District line platforms with the platforms of the Piccadilly line, 50 ft below. The shaft was at the unusual angle of 26° 23' 16½"; the reason for this has never been satisfactorily explained, but it remained the standard for escalators on the Underground until the installations of the 1920s.

The early escalators had flat steps (the more familiar cleats which engage with combs at the top and bottom landings were not introduced on the Underground until 1924). To avoid the risk of passengers getting their feet trapped at the end, 'shunt'

---

[*]   Gillespie Road station on the Piccadilly line was close to the surface, and only conventional staircases were provided.

landings were installed. These were diagonal walls placed across the level section of the escalator which forced passengers to step off sideways. The steps continued beneath the shunt and only then curved back round beneath the machine.

The works were started by constructing the lower concourse. The side wall of an existing cross-passage was dismantled and a heading formed into the chamber. This was subsequently enlarged and a further opening made into the side wall of the eastbound platform. One month after these works started, construction began at the upper level with excavation from the District line platforms in an area fenced off from passengers. As this area was enlarged, timber props were placed beneath the tracks and replaced by brick walls that would enclose the upper concourse. The excavation immediately below platform level was in water-bearing gravel, and a clay lining was inserted behind the brickwork. Spoil was stockpiled in the area and removed at night by works trains.

The escalator shaft was 16 ft 4 ins diameter, and driven from top to bottom. A 6 ft × 5 ft heading was first created all the way to the lower concourse, and supported by timbering. By creating this first, spoil from the rest of the works could be dropped down to the Piccadilly line level for removal by works train (with no need for lifting). As the tunnel was completed, the cast iron segments were winched up this heading, avoiding the need to stockpile them in the small worksite on the District line platforms.

Once the shaft was completed, two parallel escalators were constructed within it. At the upper level stairways connected with both District line platforms. At the lower level the shunt of the descending escalator directed passengers straight onto the eastbound platform (as this was the most likely direction for them). Passengers transferring from the Piccadilly line needed to use the cross-passage and original opening to reach the ascending escalator.

The escalators were placed 7 ft apart (between centre lines), and had steps that

An early photograph of the escalators. On the left, the steps of the ascending escalator have been removed to show the central drive chain and the supports for the step boards. The balustrade has been removed from the descending escalator, on the right, and clearly shows the arrangements for the 'shunt' landing, which forced passengers off to their left.
(*Meccano Magazine*)

were 4 ft wide, and 18 inches deep, with an 8-inch riser. The vertical rise was 38 ft, and when stationary 57 steps would be on view. Moving handrails were provided on both sides of each machine, as would be expected. The steps were made of fire-proofed American oak, and the balustrades were of teak. All of the rest of the equipment was made of metal.

A single chain centrally located under the steps connected and moved the steps, and was driven at 90 ft/minute by a 50 h.p. motor, via reduction gearing. Each escalator had two motors: one for regular use, and one for back-up purposes. The motors were located in a machine room under the upper landing. Power was supplied from the District Railway current rails, and changeover switches allowed this to be taken from either the up of the down lines.

The BoT inspected the escalators on 29 September 1911, before they were brought into public use on 4 October. They suggested that three people could stand on each step, allowing a maximum flow of 10,800 passengers per hour – rather more than would be achievable in practice! In the event of an emergency switches were provided at the top and bottom of each escalator which, when operated, would stop it immediately. Restarting could only happen from the machine room.

The BoT was impressed with the equipment, describing it as "exceedingly ingenious...executed with the greatest possible care" and noted that "every precaution has been taken to avoid any risk of accident". However, they gave permission for them to be used for a period of one month, after which another inspection would be required. The LER was asked to record the number of passengers using the machines daily, and keep the lifts and stairways available for passengers who preferred to avoid the new devices.[178]

The LER made much of their new machines, erecting large signs directing passengers to their newest marvel. Apparently many people visited Earl's Court for the sole purpose of a ride.

A workman pushing a spoil wagon into an airlock on the CLR extension. The points just visible in the foreground suggest that the narrow-gauge railway used by the contractors was double tracked except through the airlock. (LTM)

The report of the second inspection was issued on 4 November. It recorded that in the first week of operation nine dresses had been torn, one finger had been pinched, and a lame passengers had fallen from his crutches. No accidents occurred in the following three weeks. In part this was due to dress guards being installed along the length of the descending escalator and at the ends of the ascending machine.

In the first month some 550,000 people travelled on the escalators, averaging 18,000 per day with a maximum of 24,500 on one day. The BoT Inspector, H. A. Yorke concluded in his report that the machines were safe (amended to "reasonably safe") and approved their use on a permanent basis.[179]

Central London to Liverpool Street

The CLR finally achieved its long-planned extension east to Liverpool Street in 1912. The extension was only half a mile in length. The reversing sidings originally built to the east of Bank were on the alignment for the extension, thus reducing the amount of tunnel required. However, the tunnels were of 12 ft 5 ins internal diameter due to the sharp curves forced on the company by the street pattern above.

John Mowlem & Co were appointed to build the extension, and work started in July 1910. The tunnels were all dug by hand from Greathead shields in compressed air. This was deemed to be necessary to avoid subsidence to the heavy city buildings above, even though the tunnels only pass through clay. The pressure was maintained at 12 p.s.i throughout the work. As well as the running tunnels, the extension included the two 21 ft 2½ inch diameter platform tunnels below Liverpool Street station, and two 25 ft diameter crossover tunnels at either end of the station. Two sidings were provided to the east of the crossover for reversing trains. Progress was usually 15 ft per running tunnel per day, with eight men working at the tunnel face. In the crossover tunnel a team of 16 at the face achieved about 10 ft per day.

Spoil was removed from the worksites via a working shaft at the far end of the new sidings beyond Liverpool Street, allowing the tunnels to proceed in just one direction without interference with the existing CLR. The shaft emerged on the surface on the eastern side of the main-line station, on a site south of Skinner Street and west of Bishopsgate. As usual the running tunnels were made first and then the segments were dismantled to allow the crossover and platform tunnels to be excavated. A report of the work noted that dismantling the running tunnels was not at all easy, and the segments had to be broken up to get them out, demonstrating the solid construction of tube railways. When the segments were finally removed the grout was found to extend in cracks though the clay up to 15 feet away from the tunnels.

Electric locomotives running on an 18-inch-gauge track in the tunnel pulled up to 25 wagons of spoil back to the shaft as the shields made their way towards Bank. It was powered at 210 V DC from an overhead line, but with a bow collector (similar to a pantograph) running under the wire rather than the trolley collector of the W&CR. The tunnels were lit electrically, and were drained automatically by compressed air. Water used at the shield was drained into a sump in the tunnel, and the higher pressure in the workings ejected the water out.

One unusual problem that the engineers faced was underpinning Liverpool Street main-line station. Much of this work was similar to previously described underpinning work, but some of the metal columns supporting the station roof were found to

Work proceeding on the excavation of one of the platform tunnels at Liverpool Street. The white tube that is almost horizontal on the left-hand side is an hydraulic segment erector, which helped to lift the cast iron segments into position behind the shield. A second erector is on the right, but is less obvious. The level of illumination is greater than on previous tunnelling work sites. *(LTM)*

The new tunnel from Liverpool Street meets the end of the original siding tunnel leading east from Bank, with the Greathead shield at the meeting point. The hydraulic controls are on the left. The rotation of the shield is noticeable from the inclined aperture in the partition. *(The Tramway & Railway World)*

be exerting a load of up to 110 tons on the soil. As they were found to be standing on fine loose gravel it was not possible to provide proper support by underpinning, and so interlocking steel piles were driven into the ground around them to hold the gravel firmly in place and retain the support.[180]

This was the first tube station in London to be constructed with escalators from the outset, each machine placed into a separate shaft. Two escalators and a parallel staircase ascended to the GER Liverpool Street main-line station, and two escalators and two lifts (in a single 21 ft diameter shaft) linked to the North London Railway station at Broad Street.

The Embankment loop

One of the shorter extensions built on the Underground was that bringing the Hampstead tube southwards to form an interchange with the District line at Embankment.* This would close an annoying gap in the connectivity of the Underground network in central London.

The extension was in the form of a long, single track loop. This was designed to avoid the delay of reversing trains in a terminus; instead, they would just pass around the loop and continue northbound. It also allowed the construction of a single platform, rather than the pair that a terminus would have required. As the loop was partially under the Thames, it was built in compressed air by the contractor, John Mowlem & Co. The clay layer beneath the soft river bed was shallow – less than two feet in places – so the air pressure was carefully adjusted in accordance with the tide. The clay pocket method of construction first used by the W&CR was again utilized to protect the tunnellers within the shield. An alteration to the process was made this time, in which cast iron tunnel segments were inserted into the pockets above the clay to resist the force exerted by the compressed air, and thus help prevent a 'blowout'.[181] The platform was built on the western side of the loop, both to avoid being beneath the river or heavy embankment wall, and to place it as close as possible to the Bakerloo line tunnels to facilitate interchange.

The loop was sharply curved, with a radius down to 231 ft. Because of this, the tunnel was constructed with an internal diameter of 12 ft 9 ins. There was concern about subsidence where it passed beneath the District line and the adjacent heavy substation building. Excavations were made from the surface to below the level of the foundations of the buildings, and brick arches were built beneath them, through which the new loop was constructed. This prevented the weight of the buildings from being exerted directly upon the new tube tunnels, which were excavated through the arch, with grouting subsequently injected between the cast iron and brickwork.[182] Some 4,000 tons of cast-iron segments, held together by over 105,000 bolts, were installed as 50,000 tons of earth was removed in the making of the loop.[183]

---

* The stations around Charing Cross have changed their names a bewildering number of times. For the sake of simplicity, the current names are used here.

Bakerloo extensions

The first extension of the Bakerloo line was one station southwards, to Elephant & Castle. This both a major road junction with good interchange potential for bus and tram passengers, and also an interchange with the C&SLR. John Mowlem & Co. were the contractors. The work started before the line opened, and the extension opened less than five months after the rest of the line. South of the platforms the running tunnels continued to form a pair of sidings curving to the east beneath the New Kent Road.

Baker Street did not remain the northern terminus of the BS&WR for long. The tunnels had already been constructed as far as Marylebone station when Baker Street opened in 1906, and trains ran empty into the unfinished northbound platform to reverse.* The station was completed and opened in 1907, by which time the line had become known to all as the 'Bakerloo'. Later that same year a further short extension opened to Edgware Road, but beyond this any extension was delayed by debate about the intended direction. This was finally agreed in 1911, when the London Electric Railway Act authorised a sharply curved line to Paddington that terminated facing north-west. In 1912 further powers were obtained for an extension beyond Paddington to Queen's Park, where the line would join the surface tracks of the LNWR. Although the CLR station at Liverpool Street was the first London tube station built with escalators from the outset, the stations from Paddington to Kilburn Park on the Bakerloo line were the first to be built with escalators and no lifts.

Work on the tunnels to Paddington started in June 1911. Because of the curvature of the line, all of the tunnels were either 12 ft or 12 ft 6 ins diameter. The platform tunnels were positioned with space between for escalators to descend to platform level. Two escalators either side of a fixed staircase were placed into the 21 ft 2 ½ in inclined shaft. There were no complications with the tunnelling work, which was all in good clay. Excavation of the platform tunnels finished in January 1913, by which time track-laying was already well under way from the western end of the extension. Beyond Paddington short stub tunnels were constructed to facilitate the work on the next part of the line, up to Queen's Park.[184]

The extension beyond Paddington was very straightforward to construct, with the tunnel works contracted to Walter Scott & Middleton. Trial boreholes along the route showed that it should be in clay throughout. It was built in conjunction with the extension to Paddington, with work starting in November 1912. Shafts were sunk at the sites of each of the three underground stations, with a further shaft to the north of Paddington between the Grand Junction Canal and the Harrow Road. Three of the shafts were sunk to the side of the line of the tunnels, with 8 ft heading tunnels linking them to 15 ft diameter shield chambers from where the tunnelling started. The shaft at Warwick Avenue station descended between the line of the two tunnels.

Most of the extension was constructed with 11 ft 8¼ in diameter running tunnels, apart from a few curves where a 12 ft tunnel was used. However, for the most part the line was made with gentle curves, as it was recognized that these reduced the

---

*   The platform tunnels at Baker Street were not at the same level, so it had not been possible to provide a crossover. Instead, one was constructed just east of the platform tunnels at Marylebone, controlled by a temporary signal cabin located above the tracks and within the crossover tunnel.

wear on the wheels and track, and increased the speed of the trains. Platform tunnels had a diameter of 21 ft 2½ in, and were arranged so that a central concourse tunnel could be placed between them. This meant that the station took up a greater width below ground, but careful location of the stations minimized the amount of private property that was affected.

The central concourse tunnel at each station was, for the most part, 19 ft 6 ins diameter, with three passageways on each side connecting it with the platforms. At one end it increased to 25 ft diameter to allow for the lower machinery chamber of the two escalators provided. These, together with a staircase between, ascended to the level of the ticket hall in a shaft the same diameter as the platforms. The concourse and escalator shafts were hand dug, not being long enough to warrant a shield.

At the north end of the extension the railway was brought to the surface at Queen's Park. South of the station an incline just over 800 ft long was dug out by John Mowlem & Co. After digging out the ground, a layer of concrete 2 ft thick was laid. Side walls up to 5 ft thick were cast *in situ*. The southern section of the incline, 164 ft 6 ins long, was covered over by a roof. This was formed of rolled steel joists 24 inches deep, 7½ ins wide, and between 27 ft and 30 ft 2½ ins long spanning the cutting between the concrete walls. The joists were spaced at intervals of 7 ft, and the spaces between them formed into concrete jack arches. This was waterproofed by being covered in a one-inch-thick layer of asphalt.

Company consolidation

In 1910, the GNP&BR changed its name to the London Electric Railway Company (LER), and absorbed the BS&WR and the CCE&HR. This reduced the administration; no longer were three companies being operated, with their own boards of directors and accounts. From a railway operations viewpoint the three had shared a common rulebook and sold tickets that allowed journeys using more than one of the railways since opening.

From 1 January 1913 the UERL took control of the CLR and C&SLR, although they continued as separate companies and were not merged into the LER. In the same year, the MR purchased the GN&CR, which was also operated as a separate railway, albeit with through ticketing to and from the MR.

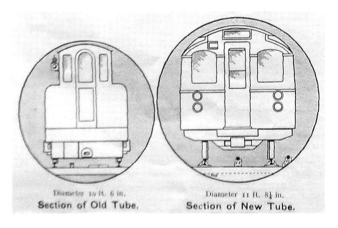

Diameter 10 ft. 6 in.
Section of Old Tube.

Diameter 11 ft. 8¼ in.
Section of New Tube.

A comparison of the 10 ft 6 in diameter C&SLR tunnel (left) and the standard 11 ft 8 in diameter tunnel used by the LER (right). *(The Tramway & Railway World)*

Rebuilding the C&SLR and joining with the Hampstead

Many improvements were made to the C&SLR after its opening to increase the number of trains that it could operate. In 1912 the UERL announced that it had made plans for a dramatic improvement to the railway, as part of their purchase of it. They realized that whilst the tunnels remained smaller than those on their other lines they would always be constrained, and it would require its own special design of rolling stock. The idea was to re-bore the tunnels and lengthen the platform tunnels from 200 ft to 350 ft, operating larger and longer trains and effectively doubling the capacity of the line. This would allow the line to be connected to other railways so that a wider range of services could operate. Extensions of the C&SLR and Hampstead Tubes were also planned to allow the Underground to serve a wider area and more passengers.

Tunnel enlargement

The plans for enlarging the tunnels and making connections with the Hampstead Tube (the public name for the CCE&HR) were approved by Parliament in 1913. They were put on hold the following year with the outbreak of World War I, and it was not until 1922 that they resumed. Prior to this an experimental enlargement was carried out on 180 yards of tunnel near to Stockwell. This proved that the enlargement was practical and allowed techniques to be agreed and costs confirmed. It also enabled the engineers to find out that the enlargement of each tunnel ring, 20 inches long, would take around two hours to complete, and thus helping them plan the effort that was required.[185]

The railway was closed between Moorgate and Euston, and the contractors took it over. With the trains out of the way they had complete access to the tunnels, and the work was performed with standard Greathead shields. The railway tracks and equipment were removed, and airlocks were built on the platforms at King's Cross so that the works towards Euston could be undertaken in compressed air. The air compressors were placed in the platform access passageways at Euston, and the lifts here were removed so that cranes located on the station building roof could use the shafts to raise and lower materials from the tunnels. These could load vehicles in the road directly as the pavements around two sides of the building had also been closed. Around 30,000 tons of material passed through these shafts in the course of 12 months: segments going in, and spoil coming out.

South of Moorgate the intention was to keep the railway operational throughout the works. Frank Pick, the Assistant Managing Director of the Underground, later noted that they

> had to try and keep the railway working while the enlargement took place, because while the line was unprofitable, the goodwill—the only thing left—might

The airlock constructed at the end of one of the platform tunnels at King's Cross. The white tiling (with a double band of dark brown) can be seen on the left, with a pile of spoil on the platform. Through the open door the cylindrical shape of the airlock interior is visible. Compressed air was not in use when the photograph was taken, as the door at the other end of the airlock is also open. It is likely that this shows the first stages of the airlock being removed, as it was published in September 1924 when the enlargement work was largely complete. *(Cassell's Railways of the World)*

have been lost if the railway had been closed during the enlargement, and then there would have been nothing at all of the original railway.[186]

Specially designed Greathead shields were manufactured by Sir William Arrol & Co. Externally they were 7 ft 3 ins long, 12 ft 10 ins diameter, and had central openings large enough for the trains to pass through. This allowed them to be left in place during the day. Ten equally spaced hydraulic cylinders were used to drive them forward. The work took place from a number of sites simultaneously, to maximize the rate of progress. At its height, 14 of the new shields were in use at the same time, although there were also many more hand-worked faces opened as the work progressed, leading to a situation in November 1923 with 62 separate worksites being operated. The operating hours for the railway were also reduced slightly to 06.20 – 20.00, allowing work to take place for almost ten hours each night.

Stockwell and Borough stations were closed and converted into depôts for the works, with platforms and lifts removed. Sidings were laid on the site of the plat-forms and works trains (one locomotive and 12 wagons) parked in these during the day. Wooden screens were installed between the sidings and running lines to protect passing passenger trains. At Borough a further track, of 20-inch gauge, was installed between each siding and the tunnel wall, and small wagons of one-half cubic yard capacity used for the transfer of spoil to the lift shafts. A trolley hoist transferred the wagons from the northbound platform along the passageway to the lift shaft. As the southbound platform was at a lower level, a trap-door was made in the ceiling of the passageway (which was below that from the northbound platform), and the hoist lifted the wagons from one level to another before moving them to the lift shaft.[187]

Borough station in use as a worksite. On the left is the track used by the passenger trains, with a wooden screen separating it from the siding laid on the site of the platform. A narrow-gauge railway has been built along the platform wall at a height that allows the small wagons to be easily emptied into the larger, standard-gauge wagons that were in the siding. This appears to be the southbound platform. *(Cassell's Railways of the World)*

The depôt at Stockwell was also used for removal of much of the spoil, as it had a large hydraulic lift from the tunnels below. Seventy-two wagons, each taking up to 7 tons of spoil were provided.[188] A fan of four new sidings was constructed 3 ft 6 ins above ground level, allowing the wagons to be emptied into carts that could be placed on the roads between them; a total of 66 wagons could be accommodated in these sidings. Three tank wagons were also constructed to remove water that filtered into the tunnels during the work. The C&SLR locomotives were used to move these trains, fewer being required with the services suspended between Moorgate and Euston, and up to 16 works trains operated each night. Additional shafts were sunk along the route, and to save costs they were lined with redundant tunnel segments removed from the old tunnels.[189]

Points were installed in the old step-plate junction tunnels north of Borough station, and sidings were laid in the disused tunnels to King William Street, allowing surplus rolling stock to be stored out of the way. In order to increase the pace of work by allowing more wagons to operate, Kennington station was also closed as from 1 June 1923, and converted into a third station worksite. The garden of an adjacent house was procured, and a new shaft sunk from the coal cellar below to provide a further access point to the tunnels.[190] Another set of 20-inch gauge tracks was installed, as at Borough, for the handling and removal of spoil. However, the passenger lifts were retained and used for moving the wagons to and from the surface.

After the last train of the day, works trains would be sent through the tunnels delivering three wagons to each work site. Two of these would be empty, for removal of spoil, and the third would contain the materials for the work.[191] Next the current would be switched off to the conductor rails and these and the running rails would be removed for a short distance in front of each shield. The rails had been cut into 15 ft lengths to reduce the length removed each night. Cables running along the tunnel (including one carrying 11,000 volts, which remained live throughout the work) would be unfastened and protected with a steel sleeve, and the workers would then break up the concrete tunnel floor with pneumatic drills and unbolt the segments forming the small tunnel ring directly in front of the shield. These would be taken to the rear of the shield for cleaning, and the hydraulic rams at the rear would push the shield forwards with a force of up to 300 tons. This was powered by an air-driven hydraulic pump, with compressed air being supplied via a main laid along the tunnel especially for the enlargement work. The cutting edge would trim the clay face, thus enlarging the tunnel, and the displaced segments would be re-erected at the rear and grout injected behind. Each ring of the smaller tunnel comprised six large segments, plus a key piece at the tunnel crown. Five new, small segments similar in size to the key piece would be added to the ring when it was re-erected, together with new wood packing, giving the new tunnel an internal diameter of 11 ft 8¼ ins. On curves the tunnels were made even larger, as was normal, to accommodate the rolling stock overhang. It would not be perfectly circular, but was adequate for the new rolling stock.[192] Hand-excavation, without the use of shields, was used for the

Stockwell Depôt during the tunnel enlargement work. The sidings are full of wagons, which would have been lifted from the tunnels. On the right is a tank engine, used for shunting the wagons, and a crane is just visible. In the background at the left is the Stockwell clock tower and war memorial. *(LTM)*

The special tunnelling shield used for the enlargement work, seen from the front (left) and rear (right), with the hydraulic rams clearly visible. *(The Engineer)*

sharper curves. In some areas the tunnel was reconstructed, the track was realigned, and then the tunnel was further enlarged in a second stage, which would not have been practical if a shield was used.[193]

At the end of a night's work the track was reinstated with the sleepers supported on wooden blocks. The spoil and other materials were collected by one of the works trains and taken to Stockwell or Borough for removal, and the track, signalling, and electrical connections were all tested; this was done by small teams of men who would visit four to five work sites each morning at the end of the engineering shifts.[194] Two trains were then run through the tunnels "at high speed" to ensure that all was well before the next day's service resumed.[195] Complaints were made to the contractors about their men not tightening the bolts properly. It was subsequently found that the problem was caused by the wood packing and the odd shape of the new tunnel rings causing the bolts to slacken after the rings were completed, probably when the tunnels were vibrated by passing trains.**

All new segments were used for the small length of 10 ft 2 in tunnel remaining between Elephant & Castle and Borough Junction, as the addition of new segments to the existing segments in such a small tunnel would have resulted in a decidedly irregular tunnel shape. North of the junction the tunnels to Moorgate had been built with a diameter of 11 ft 6 ins and so only a slight alteration was needed. This was done without the use of a shield; instead, the upper segments were unbolted, the clay removed, and the segments replaced with additional pieces to rebuild the larger tunnel. This was all achieved without the need to disturb the track, and has left these tunnels with their upper halves slightly larger than the lower halves.[196] The exception was in the water-bearing ground near Euston, where brand new lining was used;

---

*   It was also found that some of the men were neglecting to tighten bolts properly in the rush to complete the work though.

Enlargement work proceeding with the original, smaller tunnel behind the workmen, and the enlarged tunnel in the foreground. The controls for the hydraulic rams are visible within the shield on the left, and a single electric lamp illuminates the workers. *(The Engineer)*

this was also the case near Stockwell, also in wet ground. The work was especially tricky at London Bridge, where the presence of a crossover and siding necessitated the platform tunnels being extended at their north ends. This placed them just under the Thames, and much water was pumped out of the tunnels during this work. Compressed air working was used for the enlargement of 100 yards of tunnel at this point as a precaution.

The initial progress in the 10 ft 6 in tunnels was just two rings per face per night, rather less than the Stockwell experiment had suggested. Once the gangs became more experienced at the process, and a bonus scheme was introduced, the pace increased with some gangs achieving 24 rings per week (an average of four per night). As might be expected, the rate was less in the 10 ft 2 in tunnels, due to the slightly greater amount of excavation and the need to completely replace the lining. In this section progress reached 18 rings per week.[197]

The water-bearing gravels north of Stockwell gave problems again, but these were expected. The water table in the area had lowered considerably since the railway had been constructed, and so a rather lower pressure for the compressed air was required. The line was closed south of Oval between 25 April and 17 May following sand and water entering the tunnels, and upon reopening the operating hours were reduced to 07.00 – 19.40. Two new crossover tunnels were constructed beneath the

Clapham Road: one near South Island Place, and the other at Portland Place. These, together with the crossover immediately north of Stockwell, allowed single-line working to be operated from October 1923 around the four worksites, which could then be sealed off with bulkheads and airlocks. The crossover at South Island Place was of the 'scissors' type (i.e., two overlaid crossover tracks forming an 'X' shape) in a large cylindrical tunnel built around the two running tunnels. At Portland Place the crossovers were separate, and made by creating two new pairs of step-plate junctions; no reason for the difference in layout has come to light. Fortunately the installation of electric signalling on the C&SLR in 1922 made the alterations rather easier to implement than would have been the case with the original mechanical signalling. Five new shafts were specifically sunk to assist with the works on this section, in particular the new crossovers.

The shields used in these sections of tunnel were similar to those used for the rest of the enlargement, except that they had a hood fitted at the front, and a more conventional diaphragm with a smaller aperture, since trains would not be passing through. The work used the technique pioneered by Dalrymple-Hay when constructing the Waterloo & City line through waterlogged ground, using poling boards and clay pockets installed beneath the protection of the hood. The work was rather complicated because the original poling boards were still *in situ*, encased in

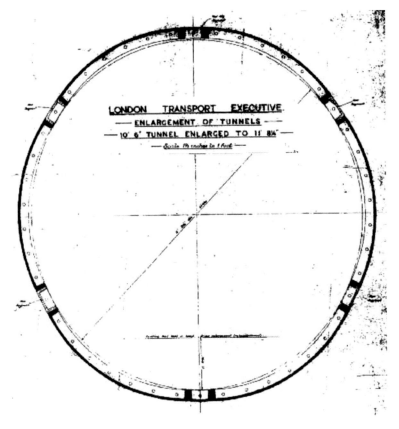

The irregular cross-section of the enlarged tunnels. The original key segment is at the top; between each of the six larger segments a new small segment has been introduced.

A recent view of the site of the facing crossover at Portland Place, showing the disused tunnel on the right, looking across to the northbound Northern line tunnel, with the southbound track on the left. The area for the crossover is now used for storage, as is the other crossover here, and also at South Island Place. *(Kim Rennie)*

grout, behind the tunnel lining. They were in good condition, for the most part, and resisted being pulled from the grout until the tunnel lining had been dismantled. A new process was developed, in which the tunnel ring was carefully supported by timbers fixed within the shield before the key piece was removed. As the ring was taken down the old poling boards were cut away.[198]

The careful work to enable trains to continue running whilst the reconstruction work progressed came to an end rather suddenly. A hand-worked face was in the northbound tunnel heading north from Elephant & Castle station, which was at a depth of just over 40 ft at this location. Advancing towards it in the opposite direction was another hand-worked face. Between them, a third hand-worked face had been established on 19 November, advancing north. This was because this section of tunnel was being enlarged in a unique way. Wet ground had been encountered when the tunnel was first built, and so the crown of the tunnel was remaining *in situ*, although the segments were temporarily removed during the work. The lower part of the tunnel was being mined away and the original invert segments replaced. Special side segments were fitted between the crown and invert, giving the tunnel an elliptical cross-section, 13 ft high and 10 ft 10 inches wide. This had an additional benefit in that it allowed the gradient in the tunnel to be improved.

The original tunnel segments had closed up tightly, and it was found to be impossible to remove and replace a single ring. Two rings were removed initially, and as each successive ring was rebuilt another was removed. This left a gap in the tunnel structure that needed support during the day. Wooden boards were pressed tightly against the exposed clay roof and wedged into place behind the tunnel rings on either side. The following night the tunnel enlargement would continue, and the boards would remain behind the segments encased in the new grouting. This avoided the need to remove the boards and risk a roof fall.

It was not possible to bring new rails into the C&SLR tunnels via any of its connections with the surface, as all were shafts. Rails lowered down would have to be manœuvred into passageways at the bottom, and this would restrict their length. Instead, a 4 ft diameter heading 50 ft long was bored at King's Cross to connect with the Piccadilly Tube. Through this, all of the rails and sleepers for the C&SLR work were brought in. The materials were brought in on works trains at night, originating at Lillie Bridge depot in west London, this also reducing the burden on the C&SLR depot at Stockwell.[199]

At 17.11 on 27 November 1923 a northbound train departed Elephant & Castle station. Its next stop would be London Bridge, as Borough was still closed. It consisted of locomotive no. 5 and six carriages, laden with around 60 or 70 passengers. One minute after departing it passed through the new worksite at about 15 mph and struck one of the wooden boards which had somehow been dislodged. The driver stopped the train to investigate, and found the remains of one of the boards on the track. Unbeknownst to him the penultimate carriage was now directly beneath the hole in the tunnel crown and two hundredweight of gravel was cascading onto the train. Fortunately he then pulled the train forward a short distance so that one of the guards could investigate behind the train. The guard reported that the track was obstructed and he could hear flowing water, and so after telephoning the controller at London Bridge using the tunnel telephone the driver set off again. As the train approached Borough station the power failed and it was coasted into the platform tunnel. The stationmaster here assisted the passengers and then went to investigate in the tunnel.

The night before, the usual two rings of tunnel roof had been supported by wooden poling boards. The key piece and both main segments forming the crown had been removed, and a 3 ft 3 ins length of the crown was propped, to a width of about 12 ft. Some water had been seen trickling from the roof when the work was inspected at 05.30. A large nodule had been found in the clay immediately above the tunnel segments, and had been broken to allow the enlargement. As the stones sometimes leaked water ('bleeding' in the tunnellers' jargon) they were not surprised and this was not seen as cause for concern. Some additional poling boards were placed in the gap to provide additional protection and clay was wedged into the gaps in an attempt to seal them and stop the water. Some time during the day at least one of the boards had slipped, and must have moved again shortly before the train came through. After the train struck the board 500 cubic yards of water-logged sand and gravel from a layer above the tunnels poured in: it was very fortunate that the train was not trapped in the torrent that had poured over the last two carriages. In fifteen minutes the tunnel was filled to the ceiling with a pile of material. Also fortunate was that the sand and gravel jammed the small hole in the tunnel so tightly that after the initial collapse very little water was able to pour in. The roadway above, Newington

Causeway, was undermined and the utilities beneath the surface left unsupported. A gas main fractured and the space under the road surface started to fill with gas, which at 18.05 ignited with a roar, causing the surface to collapse and reveal a crater 45 ft wide and 15 ft deep. At 18.30 the heat broke a 15-inch water main which then doused the flames.[200]

For the rest of the day trains operated two separate services, one between London Bridge and Moorgate, and the other between Elephant & Castle and Clapham Common. After an attempt to restart a limited service the following day using single-line working around the site of the damage,[201] the C&SLR decided to close the railway completely and finish the reconstruction work without the inconvenience of trains running. The increased pace of work allowed this section of line to open on 1 December 1924.* Beneath Newington Causeway airlocks were fitted to allow the damaged section to be repaired with reduced risk of further collapse. The road above was further excavated by the gas company in order to shut the broken main down and start repair work.

A statement was soon issued by the UERL, their engineers, and the South Metropolitan Gas Company to explain the cause of the accident and allay public concern. The most probable cause, they stated, was

> the excavation works coming in contact with what is probably an old storage well. This caused an inrush of sand and water into the tunnel leaving a crater-like empty space beneath the road.[202]

The replacement bus service operated between Euston and Moorgate was extended to Clapham Common, and additional vehicles procured for this. Southern Railway services were disrupted and its station at Elephant & Castle partially closed until 07.00 on 29 November whilst the railway bridge next to the crater was thoroughly inspected. The only damage was superficial (scorching to the side and underneath) and not structural, and so it was cleared for traffic use. The tramway along Newington Causeway was not so fortunate, as a section about 20 ft by 40 ft was damaged. Repairs began the day after the collapse, with workmen backfilling the hole with rubble. Cement was pumped into the cavity as well, both from the surface and from the C&SLR tunnel. The road was reopened on 12 January 1924.

The inquiry into the incident took place shortly afterwards, and was led by Lieutenant-Colonel A.H.L. Mount from the Ministry of Transport. He took evidence from the staff involved in the work, the train crew, and station staff, and then inspected the site. He concluded that the tunnel gang and inspectors should have been more concerned because the water was coming from the tunnel crown, which had not been seen before. Some of the poling boards were too short, and so provided insufficient support. The interruption of the work by the running of a passenger service was considered undesirable in future in areas such as this.

It seems likely that when the original tunnel was bored in 1888 that it stayed within the clay by a margin of a foot or two, because of depression in the clay which

---

* The Underground group's official account of the work makes no mention of the accident. It merely notes that services were withdrawn on 27 November 1923 and this allowed the work to be speeded up.

The scene at Newington Causeway after the surface had collapsed into the hole beneath the road, with repair work under way. The men peering into the hole are probably officials, with the public being kept on the pavement in the background. *(Illustrated London News)*

was overlain by the waterlogged sand and gravel. A lesson from the construction had not been learnt though, for the location of the subsidence was only about 28 ft north of where the roadway collapsed in 1888. In the intervening years it seems that the warmth from the tunnel had dried the remaining clay layer, making it less watertight, so when the support of the tunnel segments was taken away it was close to failure. Ten hours of trains vibrating beneath caused the shorter poling boards to work loose; without their support the thin layer of dry clay gave way, allowing the tunnel to fill. It was only the prompt action of the driver that prevented the incident from being far worse, for which he was duly recognized by the railway company.

During the course of the work, 14,000 tons of new tunnel segments were installed, 95,000 cubic yards of additional spoil removed, and 62,400 wagon-loads of material transported between the tunnels and the surface using the Stockwell Depôt lift.

Station reconstruction

Many of the stations along the C&SLR were rebuilt during the closure. Escalators were installed in place of lifts at Clapham Common, Clapham Road,* Stockwell, and Oval. At Stockwell new platforms were created just to the south of the old terminus by enlarging the running tunnels. This was necessary because the island platform of the station would have needed to be narrowed to a dangerous degree to allow the wider rolling stock to pass. A shaft was sunk just south of the existing station to tunnel level, and from this new platform tunnels were created around the running tunnels.[203]

At both Elephant & Castle and Kennington, surgery was performed to switch the position of the platforms and tracks in both of the northbound tunnels. At Kennington

---

*   Renamed Clapham North on 13 September 1926.

The short section of abandoned southbound tunnel immediately north of Elephant & Castle station. In the foreground is the enlarged tunnel, and in the background the tunnel with its original diameter of 10 ft 2 ins. The shield chamber is the large section of tunnel between the two. The far end of the tunnel has been blocked up, with the platform beyond, and behind the photographer is a concrete plug inserted where the new tunnel (to the right of the pictured tunnel) diverged. *(Printz Holman)*

A view down the escalator shaft at Oval. In the foreground is the shaft fully enlarged, with the smaller pilot tunnel visible behind. Planks are being used to support the tunnel face at the junction between the two sizes of tunnel. *(LTM)*

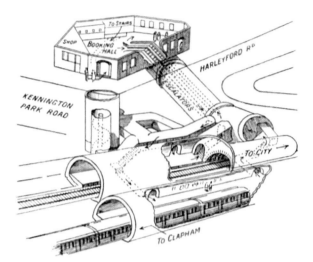

The layout of Oval station shows how new passageways at low level connected with the new escalator landings. These had to be in a different position to the original lower lift landings as the lifts descended vertically from the ticket hall, whilst the escalators were in diagonal shafts.
(The Railway Magazine)

this was to enable cross-platform interchange to be created with the Hampstead Tube extension from Charing Cross (see below), but at Elephant & Castle it appears to have been a realization that a rearrangement would allow the sharp curves north of the station to be eased – something that could be achieved with the line closed. Although the southbound platform remained in position, to the north of the station the southbound line was altered to follow the alignment of the siding, again to ease the curves. A section of the abandoned tunnels remains in place on both sides of the line. One of these even contains a shield chamber as the decision to rearrange the tunnels came during the enlargement work when one of the special shields was working on this part of the tunnel. Work ceased straight away, and the chamber was made so that the shield could be extricated (and presumably used elsewhere on the line).

Since the stations were closed and there were no passengers to be inconvenienced, it was more straightforward to make the changes to the stations. Some clever planning of the new station layouts enabled the stations to keep their existing ticket halls despite the fact that the connection with the platforms would now descend diagonally. Pilot tunnels for the escalator shafts were first sunk and lined, and these were then enlarged to full size ready for the escalators. Since the stations already had spiral stair shafts, these were retained and the escalator shafts were just equipped with a pair of escalators. At the lower end of the shaft new passageways were created to link with the platforms. The closely spaced platforms precluded the escalators descending to platform level, and instead passengers continued to use stairs between the escalators and the platforms.

All of the original platform tunnels, with the exception of those at City Road, were lengthened from 200 ft to 350 ft. The platforms from 1890, with a brick lining, were extended using cast iron tubes of 21 ft 2½ in diameter, whilst the later platforms were extended with the same size of lining used originally (usually 21 ft 2½ in or 30 ft). The enlargement was carried out by excavating another tunnel of 8 ft diameter from the existing platform headwall. Once this was 12 – 15 ft long, the remainder of

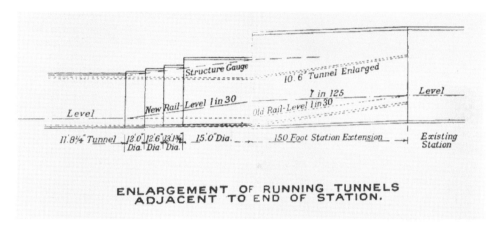

Structure Gauge

10' 6" Tunnel Enlarged

7 in 125

Level

New Rail-Level 1 in 30

Old Rail-Level 1 in 30

Level

Level

11'8¼" Tunnel | 12'0" | 12'6" | 13'1¾" | 15'0" Dia. | 150 Foot Station Extension | Existing Station
| Dia. | Dia. | Dia.

ENLARGEMENT OF RUNNING TUNNELS ADJACENT TO END OF STATION.

A diagram showing how the running tunnels were rebuilt adjacent to platform extensions to allow the ramp to be maintained. *(Curry & Jones)*

the headwall began to be removed, together with the tunnel segments for both the running and 8 ft tunnels. The track was carefully supported, and either a mechanical segment erector or air-powered winches were used to install the new platform tunnel lining. Temporary track supports remained in place until the concrete track bed was laid. The running tunnels at the extended end of the platforms were made with gradually decreasing diameters to allow the ramp away from the station to be 'moved' in line with the extension.

An extension to Edgware

Work started on extending the Golders Green branch of the Hampstead Tube in June 1922, at a ceremony attended by Lord Ashfield, the Underground group Chairman, and Sir Philip Lloyd-Greame, the president of the BoT. Although for the most part on the surface, this extension included some interesting engineering works.

North of Golders Green the line was a victim of its own success. Houses had been built across the most obvious route, and a new route curving around the rapidly expanding village. The railway needed to be elevated initially, as Golders Green station was on an embankment, and it was intended to extend it on an embankment too. However, the company decided to use a viaduct as this would take up less land. By remaining on a viaduct until it crossed Golders Green Road it minimized the number of houses that were in the way, and enabled the line to easily cross roads.

The level of the land meant that the line then descended into a section of cutting. This was not deep enough to pass beneath existing roads though, and so several smaller roads were severed by the railway. At Woodstock Avenue the road level was raised by 7 ft so that it could pass over the tracks; this left the road at first floor height outside the houses either side of the bridge. The largest bridge on the extension was at Elmcroft Crescent, fabricated from steel girders 129 ft 6 ins long and weighing 450 tons.[204] It was supported on large brick abutments, and the side girders were 'launched' at track level, supported from beneath by a wheeled scaffold that kept it up as it was pushed over the gap.

Construction of the viaduct to the west of Hoop Lane in September 1922. The small arches in the piers (right) were made using the wooden centrings on the ground in the foreground at the left. Piles of bricks for the bricklayers have been left along the line of the viaduct. *(LTM)*

Another large viaduct, 300 ft long and 34 ft high was built across the valley of the river Brent, between Brent and Hendon Central stations. This is a familiar sight for millions of users of the North Circular Road. As the land rose on the north side of the Brent valley the line entered the Hendon cutting. The cuttings were excavated using steam shovels, and the contractors laid temporary narrow-gauge tracks on which small steam locomotives hauled spoil wagons. The steam shovels were American, owned by the Erie Steam Shovel Company, and could each excavate a ton of earth per minute, or 750 tons per day. These were of particular use at Hendon, where the new cutting required the excavation of 70,000 yd³ of earth.[205]

Immediately north of Hendon Central station a pair of twin tube tunnels with diameters of 11 ft 8¼ ins were bored beneath a ridge of land known as The Burroughs. They were 5 furlongs long, up to 70 ft below the surface, and made on a gradient of 1

The launch of the first side girder for Elmcroft Crescent skew bridge in progress. The second side girder is waiting on the viaduct on the south side of the road. The tower is rolling along a surface made of wooden baulks, which is necessary because although the bridge is horizontal the roadway slopes down slightly (from right to left in this photograph). *(LTM)*

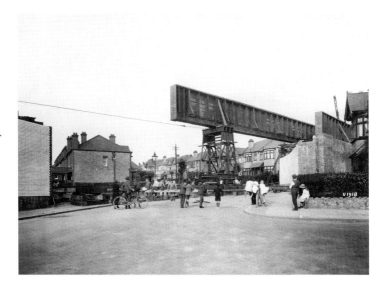

The tunnel face in this view under The Burroughs seems rather crowded, with six men on the platform and two more on the temporary tracks. The conveyor belt on the right runs along one set of tracks, making it easy for it to follow the shield along the tunnel. *(LTM)*

in 67. The northern end passed beneath the main-line tracks of the Midland Railway, and to minimize the risk of disruption the first 400 ft of both tunnels was mined by hand. The segments beneath the main line tracks were set into 6 ft of concrete as a further precaution. Beyond this length rotary excavators were used for the work all the way to Hendon. The tunnels took nine months to complete, working night and day, with the 30,000 yds^3 of spoil being removed to make embankments elsewhere on the line. In place of the spoil, 6,400 tons of cast iron segments were placed to form the lining of the tunnels.

The Camden Town junctions
The Hampstead Tube bifurcated at Camden Town; this was the only junction used by passenger trains on the tube railways (all of the other lines were simple end-to-end shuttles). Each of the northern branches had its own pair of platforms at Camden Town, with the junctions being to the south of the station. This generous arrangement was a legacy of the original plan, whereby trains would have operated between Camden Town and Highgate (now Archway) as a shuttle service, with the main line being from Charing Cross to Golders Green.

   Part of the UERL plan to improve the C&SLR was to link it with the Hampstead Tube. The C&SLR terminated at Euston; this would be extended in a long curving line to join the Hampstead Tube just south of the existing junctions. By means of some intricately designed connections, not only would trains from either southern branch (Charing Cross or Clapham) be able to serve either northern branch, but they would be able to do so simultaneously without conflicting.

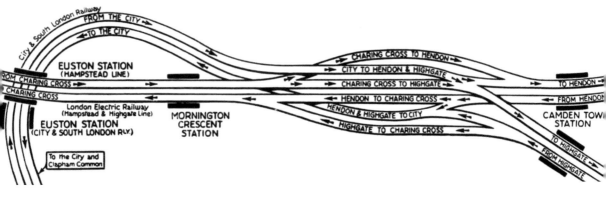

The complex of junctions immediately south of Camden Town station. *(The Engineer)*

The diagram shows the complexity of the tunnels at Camden Town Junction after the work was completed. The two new tunnels from Euston can be seen curving in from the left. They join the existing tunnels at the point where the original junctions were placed. There were two other new tunnels constructed, which were key to preventing conflicting movements. These are the top and bottom lines in the diagram, shown as 'Charing Cross to Hendon' and 'Highgate to Charing Cross', which act as by-pass lines to the main junctions.

Workmen excavating one of the new running tunnels between Euston and Camden Town, in the vicinity of Mornington Crescent station. *(LTM)*

A view from one of the work sites in the Camden Town Junction area, showing a passenger train passing through one of the larger tunnels. The juxtaposition of the two large tunnels suggests that this is on the northbound lines, looking northwards. The train, which is one of those dating to the opening of the Hampstead Tube, is on the line from Charing Cross to Hendon and about to enter the platform tunnel at Camden Town. *(The Engineer)*

The extension consisted of 1·8 miles of new line in the usual twin tunnels. Much of it was on a curve, and larger tunnel rings were used here as was normal. Where the new tunnels joined the old, step-plate junctions were formed, with their tunnel sections ranging from 12 ft to 25 ft in diameter. The work started at the same time as the line closure between Moorgate and Euston, and was conducted from two sites. At Ampthill Square a heading was driven across the line of both tunnels, two 15 ft diameter shield chambers were constructed, and two Greathead shields began tunnelling towards Euston. The only compressed air working took place on this section, when a length of grey sand was encountered and airlocks were installed for the construction of about 100 yards of tunnel. At Mornington Crescent, two shafts were sunk immediately north of the station. One descended to the level of the north-bound tunnel, the other to the southbound level.* Two shield chambers were built back-to-back at each of these shafts, so that four shields could be deployed. One pair worked south to Ampthill Square, and the other pair north to meet the Hampstead Tube tunnels at Camden. All six of the shields were manufactured by Markham & Co.

Once the latter pair of shields arrived at Camden Town, at the south end of the existing junction tunnels, headings were dug sideways from them and new shield chambers created outside the line of the tunnels. The shields were turned around and moved into these chambers and then began tunnelling southwards, creating the two by-pass lines described above. These tunnels changed level to meet the Hampstead Tube tunnels south of the station, where new step-plate junctions were formed. At the north end of each of these tunnels, they were extended to join the existing tunnels by hand, concluding with more step-plate junctions.

The existing junctions at Camden Town were both in large cylindrical tunnels the size of platforms – 21 ft 2½ ins diameter. These had to be enlarged to between 23 ft 2½ ins and 25 ft in diameter. This was carried out in a manner similar to the C&SLR

---

*   The tunnels are at different levels to allow the branches to cross at Camden Town Junction without the tracks having to physically cross each other, in line with Greathead's comments on the construction of 'flying junctions'.

enlargement work, by dismantling the tunnels ring by ring, digging out clay, and reinstalling the original segments with some additional pieces to increase the size. Extensive timbering was required to support the work – fortunately in clay – as the trains continued to run through the tunnels.

The extension reopened with the line as far as Moorgate on 20 April 1924. The rest of the line to Clapham Common was still being enlarged. Trains to Clapham Common resumed on 1 December 1924, but could now travel north to Edgware and Highgate. The tiny locomotives and their carriages had all been retired and replaced with the latest modern rolling stock as well.

The southern connection

A pair of new tunnels was constructed between the C&SLR at Kennington and the Hampstead Tube at Embankment. The loop at the latter location made the work more complicated to construct, especially as the Underground intended to keep trains running. There was no possibility of making a junction with the loop tunnel due to the shallow position of the tunnel under the Thames. The only solution was to branch off from the southbound tunnel further north, under land, and cut across the loop. This would not be possible without cutting through the loop tunnel though. The other issue was the need for a second platform at the station.

Before work started two trial borings were made in the Thames, using a pair of barges, to check the consistency of the river bed and layers beneath. Then, on 22 April 1924 construction work began. A shaft was sunk at Waterloo down to where the north end of the new northbound platform would be, and the running tunnel northwards under the river was started. Very soon after starting this tunnel, a cross-heading was made to the site of the north end of the southbound platform, from which the southbound running tunnel northwards under the river was started. The

A detailed plan showing how the new southbound tunnel cut through the existing loop tunnel at Embankment. The District Railway runs from top to bottom across the middle of the plan (dashed lines), and the River Thames is on the right. *(The Engineer)*

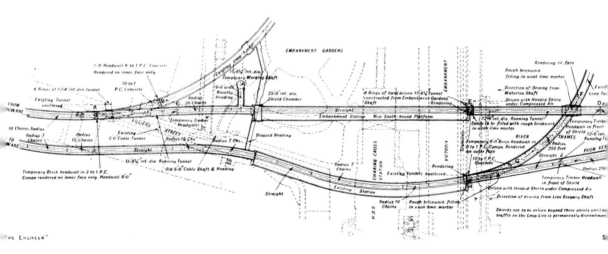

Tunnelling work in progress on the Kennington loop, with the Greathead shield visible in the background. *(LTM)*

tunnels were in clay throughout, but under the river compressed air working was used, with airlocks installed in both tunnels just under the southern shoreline. As happened previously, the pressure was varied with the tide, between 10 p.s.i at low tide and 20 p.s.i at high tide.

Southwards from the Waterloo shaft the two platform tunnels were formed. Further south two more shafts were sunk in the grounds of Bethlem Hospital (now the Imperial War Museum). Four shields started their work here, one pair travelling north to Waterloo, the other pair south to Kennington. When water was struck on the southbound line work stopped, and the rest of this tunnel was bored from the south. A final shaft on the south side of the river was dug in Kennington Park, from which a 1,800 ft long tunnel was created to form a reversing loop. A 400 ft length of this work was performed in compressed air due to the expected wet ground between Kennington and Oval stations, where the loop dipped into the Reading beds again below the existing C&SLR tunnels. The rest of the southbound tunnel was also driven northwards from this shaft. Beyond the site for the new platform at Kennington the work was under compressed air to join the tunnel from the Bethlem shaft. A 2 ft thick layer of rock was encountered by the shield making the southbound tunnel near Kennington, requiring hand excavation for a 903 ft length of tunnel. Sand, shale, and even oyster shells were found here, as the tunnel dipped from the clay into the Woolwich and Reading beds. At all the points where the new tunnels passed closely beneath the C&SLR tunnels (to avoid making any more tunnel than necessary in the Reading beds), the inverts of the old tunnels were dug out in advance and re-concreted with ten lengths of old rail embedded in each to strengthen the tunnels.

Kennington needed some internal rearrangement to make the new layout work. The existing platforms for the C&SLR were at different depths, and were both on the eastern side of their respective tracks. This had made access to the lifts and stairs, also to the east, straightforward. The intention was to have the new platforms on the Charing Cross branch flank those of the original C&SLR, but with the new northbound platform on the western side of the station it would be awkward to arrange the desired cross-platform connections.

The solution was to switch the position of the northbound track and platform. This allowed the two northbound platforms to be back-to-back with cross-passages between. Staircases from these passages led up to subways that crossed the station to the lift and stairs. The problem did not occur for the southbound platforms, but the original passageways would have been in the way of the new platform. By providing

Diagrams showing how the platform layout at Kennington was altered with the construction of the Hampstead Tube extension southwards to form two new outer platforms. The northbound City branch platform has been switched with the tracks, and a new access passageway has been made at a higher level, linking with stairs descending to a cross-passage between both northbound platforms. *(Underground News)*

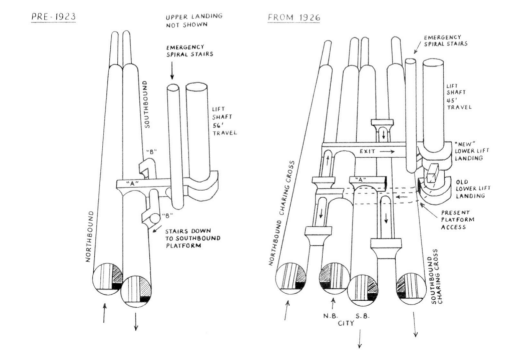

stairs up to the level of the new subways the old lower passages could be sacrificed as the new platform was built. A new lower lift landing was built 11 ft higher up the shaft to reduce the number of steps that might otherwise have been required. There are several relics of the platform alteration remaining at Kennington:

- a door in the trackside wall on the City branch platform, marking the original platform access;
- the very long staircase up from the southbound platforms (because of their extra depth); and
- when standing on the northbound City branch platform looking south, the track in the running tunnel is perfectly aligned with the platform, and kinks sharply upon entering.

There was a problem though. Both of the old platforms were on the eastern side of the tracks in the platform tunnels, with passageways leading to the lower lift landing on this side of the station. Whilst the new southbound platform could be adjacent to the old, the spiral stair shaft would be in the way

The original plan had been to construct a siding at Waterloo, just south of the

One of the cylindrical junction tunnels being excavated around the existing running tunnel at Kennington. A narrow-gauge railway is being used by the tunnellers (on the left), and wooden bracing has been placed between this railway and the running tunnel to keep the latter in position. The white inverted 'T' hanging from the tunnel is used to check the tunnel alignment. *(LTM)*

platforms, so that southbound trains could be reversed. The plans changed and the siding was moved to Kennington instead, where it would enable trains from the City branch to reverse (the loop being the primary means of reversing trains from the new West End branch connection). A number of junction tunnels were required: for crossovers between the West End and City branches just south of the platforms, and the to the south of these, for the reversing siding. All those on the C&SLR had to be constructed around the live railway tunnels with great care. The crossovers each comprised a pair of step-plate junctions linked by a short 12 ft 6 in diameter running tunnel. The northernmost of the two junctions (where the new line from Charing Cross branched to the reversing loop), and the running tunnel were built as part of the new link, but both of the southerly tunnels had to be excavated around the existing C&SLR.

The contract for the reversing siding was awarded to Charles Brand & Son, who commenced by sinking two shafts at a site in Kennington Park Road. There was only just enough space for the siding tunnel between the running tunnels, and the work was further complicated because the northbound line was 8 ft 6 in higher than the southbound. This was solved by making a step-plate junction tunnel around the southbound line. The siding tunnel led from the southern end of this, and climbed to the same level as the northbound tunnel on a 1 in 40 gradient. At this point another large cylindrical junction tunnel with a diameter of 27 ft 6 ins was made around both the siding and the northbound line, and the siding then continued south for 700 ft, long enough to stable two trains if required.[206]

The work at Embankment was carried out under compressed air from a shaft sunk at the north edge of Victoria Embankment Gardens. From a short heading at the base of the shaft a small piece of running tunnel was excavated southwards to the point where the north end of the platform was to be. This was dangerous ground, which tended to be saturated by water held back by the impermeable mass of the Victoria Embankment. At this point a large shield chamber was dug, in four separate stages. Firstly, a 25 ft length of tunnel just 14 ft in diameter was excavated southwards, comprising just eight tunnel rings. Secondly, two of these rings were then dismantled and the small section of tunnel face thus exposed was enlarged to 21 ft 2½ ins diameter. Thirdly, the next two rings were then removed and enlarged to 25 ft in diameter; lengths of steel rail were laid around the outside of this short section of tunnel. The enlargement of the final four rings at the north end to 25 ft diameter then proceeded in two stages, followed by a further short length that was filled with concrete to form the headwall of the tunnel. Finally the temporary pair of 21 ft 2½ in rings were removed and rebuilt as 25 ft diameter tunnel.

A 22 ft 6 in diameter shield was now erected in the chamber and driven southwards to create the new southbound platform tunnel; the existing platform on the loop was fortunately in a position that would enable it to be used for northbound trains. The remaining 230 ft of running tunnel north of the new platform was dug by hand towards the existing loop. The south end wall of the new platform was made of special metal castings designed to hold back the water in the rather wet ground of the embankment. Six rings of running tunnel were constructed here, and then bricked up to make this end of the station watertight until the shield arrived from Waterloo.

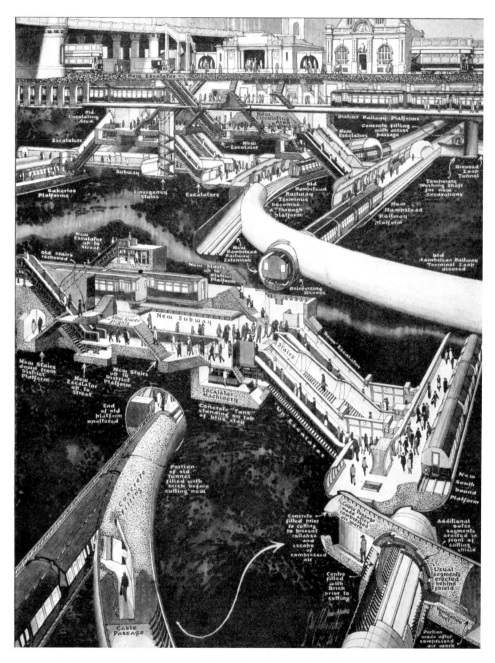

An isometric drawing of Embankment once the southward extension of the Hampstead Tube had been completed. The lower half of the drawing is a more detailed view of the Hampstead Tube station, showing how the new southbound tunnel cut through the old loop. The cable passages shown within the concrete infilling the loop tunnel were never made – this was fortunate as the loop was flooded by a bomb dropped into the Thames during the Second World War. *(The Sphere)*

On 25 January 1926 the loop was closed. Through some clever timetabling a train service was maintained to Embankment using single-line working. With no time to lose (the tunnels from Waterloo were already beneath the river and approaching Embankment) the work on the loop was carried out. The connection at the north end of the new platform was relatively easy. It was under land, and the tunnel was dismantled as the new tunnel was hand dug. The former entrance to the loop was filled with concrete behind the new tunnel lining, and a small passageway maintained for access.

South of the existing platform, on what was to become the northbound line, the cast iron tunnel was partially dismantled and filled with rough brickwork bonded with weak lime mortar. When the tunnel shield arrived from across the river the brickwork was dismantled as the shield advanced and new tunnel rings were erected to form a single unbroken tunnel.

The most complicated part of the work was where the new southbound tunnel cut through the old loop completely. Like the previously described connection, the cast iron rings were removed and rough brickwork filled the space. When the shield was about 3 ft from the tunnel work stopped and three rings of 14 ft diameter tunnel erected, partly cutting into the brickwork. Then a length of 15 ft diameter tunnel, eleven rings long was made almost completely through, followed by another three rings of 14 ft tunnel. Once this was all completed the shield was moved through this larger tunnel, constructing its tunnel behind it like a thread through the eye of a needle. The void between the running tunnel and the larger tunnel was filled with concrete. In this way a remarkably solid connection was made in poor ground. The section of old loop tunnel between the new northbound and southbound tunnels was also backfilled with concrete.

South to Morden

The final part of the massive scheme of works to connect, extend, and improve the Hampstead Tube and the C&SLR was the extension of the latter south from Clapham Common to a new terminus about 5¼ miles away at Morden. Charles Brand & Son were contracted to build the line between Clapham Common and Tooting Broadway, and The Foundation Company the remainder of the line to Morden. The intention was that both tunnels on all sections of line except the southernmost would be bored from north to south, with shafts at each station site. This was not quite the case, however, due to the ground conditions.

Work on the extension started on 31 December 1923, at the site of Clapham South station. Ten rotary excavators and four conventional Greathead shields were used for the work, between them excavating 1,400 ft of running tunnel each week.[207] From Clapham Common to a point between Trinity Road (now Tooting Bec) and Tooting Broadway the work was conventional tunnelling in good clay. The running tunnels had the standard internal diameter of 11 ft 8¼ ins except on one curve near Clapham South. Here special packing was used between the standard segments to increase the diameter to 12 ft, thus avoiding the need for a small number of different-size segments. Hydraulic segment erectors were used in the platform tunnels to hold segments in place whilst they were bolted up. Special carriages were provided that received the spoil from the chute on the shields and, using conveyor belt, transferred

The front (left) and rear (right) of the rotary excavators used on the Morden extension. *(The Engineer)*

it into the muck wagons. Works locomotives ran through the completed tunnels on a narrow-gauge railway with an overhead line for power (some locomotives were battery-powered), and hauled the muck wagons to the shafts.

The clay at Tooting Bec rises into a shallow anticline* and so the tunnels broke through into the Woolwich beds and compressed air working started. The Woolwich beds at this point consisted of a series of hard rocky mudstone layers containing a variety of shells, underlain by black clay, followed by hard brown and grey loams, then another thin shell bed, and finally mottled red clay. Occasional layers of wet sand were interspersed amongst these beds. The tunnels even cut through the bottom of the mottled clay at one point, into a bed of green sand containing some fish teeth.[208]

From this point on, towards Tooting Broadway the beds were encountered in the reverse order. The station was made in the layers of loam and mudstone. The whole of Tooting Broadway station, including a reversing siding to the south and associated step-plate junctions, was constructed under compressed air, between 15 and 18 p.s.i. Vertical airlocks had to be installed in the three shafts that were sunk until sufficient tunnelling had been completed for the more usual tunnel airlocks to be built. The vertical airlocks were then removed.

The station itself required special treatment because of the difficult soil. The escalator shaft was sunk as a 10 ft 6 in diameter pilot tunnel under compressed air, with the tunnel extended up into the future ticket hall area to accommodate an airlock. Once the shaft reached the lower level of the station grout was injected into the ground behind the shaft to consolidate it. Working from the bottom up, the pilot tunnel was enlarged to 22 ft 4 in diameter. In order to keep the working face vertical,

---

*   An anticline is a geological structure in which horizontal layers of rock have been deformed to create an upwardly-curving structure, as shown on the next page.

special oval tunnel rings were used which joined together in vertical slices to form the inclined escalator shaft.[209]

To allow the construction of the running tunnels to be completed quicker, two additional shafts were sunk at Trevelyan Road between Tooting Broadway and Colliers Wood stations, at a point where the tunnels would be completely within the lower level of London clay. From these shafts both tunnels were driven northwards, initially in free air, and then in compressed air once the Woolwich beds were reached. Two more shields bored the tunnels southwards to Colliers Wood. Here, although the work was in free air and cutting through clay, the consistency of the clay was not good enough for rotary excavators to be used. The excavator shields were therefore used as conventional Greathead shields until the clay improved.

The southernmost section of line was to emerge into a cutting to the north of Morden station at Dorset Road. The tunnels to South Wimbledon were bored from a shaft just north of the cutting. Rotary excavators were used, but initially without their cutting arms and with the addition of hoods. Compressed air was used until the tunnels had descended at a gradient of 1 in 60 through the upper layers of wet sand and gravel and into clay; some houses were tunnelled beneath with just 7 ft clearance to the base of their foundations. When the shields were fully in good clay the hood was removed, the cutters replaced, and then the excavators were used to make the tunnels to South Wimbledon.[210]

Although originally intended to be a cutting, the section between Dorset and Kenley Roads was constructed as a cut-and-cover tunnel because of the wet nature of the ground. A sump and pump-house was constructed at each end of this section to

A geological section along the line of the tunnels from Colliers Wood to Balham, showing how the tunnels cut through the clay and into the Woolwich beds below. *(Author, redrawn from Davis)*

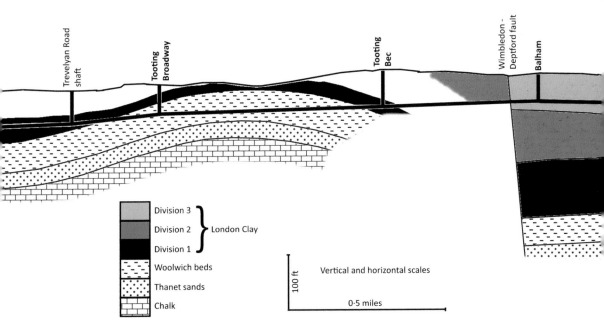

The pilot tunnel for the escalator shaft at Tooting Broadway was extended up to the surface and curved to the horizontal to allow an airlock to be constructed on the level. All of the tunnel visible in this photograph was temporary, and would have been dismantled once the escalator shaft and other tunnels were completed. *(The Engineer)*

capture water entering the tunnels in the event of heavy rainfall. The cutting itself was formed by driving interlocking steel piles into the ground along both long sides and then excavating out the soil between. A concrete base was poured in for the whole site, and reinforcing bars erected around the area of the tunnels. Temporary tracks were laid along the centre lines of the tunnels. A pair of travelling frameworks were rolled along these tracks, expanded to form the shape of the tunnels, and the concrete was cast around them. The size of the frameworks determined that the tunnels were cast in 20 ft sections, each taking about two days to make. The frameworks were collapsed and reused, and the tunnels were covered over with earth. This site now forms Kendor Gardens,* and has presumably been left without buildings because of the tunnel beneath.

Much of the spoil from the excavation of the cutting and the site of Morden station, totalling around 68,000 cubic yards, and another 14,000 cubic yards from the shaft at Dorset Road needed to be removed. The cost of this would have been high using trucks, and so the contractors installed an aerial ropeway to carry it about half a mile to a gravel pit for disposal. In total, the Morden extension involved the removal of 278,653 cubic yards of spoil, and the installation of 55,200 tons of cast iron tunnel and shaft segments.

---

*   The name presumably comes from the first three letters of the road names at the south and north of the tunnel.

The cut and cover tunnels being cast north of Morden station. The formers for the tunnels can be seen in each tunnel; in the left, the shuttering is being assembled. The right-hand tunnel appears to be waiting its turn. *(The Engineer)*

The stations were all provided with escalators descending from ticket hall level to a concourse at platform level. The platforms on the extension, together with those between Charing Cross and Kennington, and on the enlarged section of the C&SLR, were redecorated to give a fresh look. Panels of white tiles were framed with turquoise-green and silver tiles, with black tiles forming the outer frame. Bands of dark maroon tiles ran along the lowest edges of the walls.

At surface level the stations were designed by the architect Charles Holden. They were built from white Portland stone, and featured large, metal-framed windows above their entrances incorporating the Underground bulls-eye symbol. They were all based on a standard façade which was adjusted to suit the shape of the site, giving a consistency of appearance.

One other difference that passengers on the extension would have quickly noticed was the anti-suicide pits, 1 ft 4 ins deep, between the running rails. Sleepers would have prevented these from being effective and so the tracks were fixed to longitudinal sleepers along the edges of the pits. These do not appear to have been installed on the other C&SLR stations during the reconstruction of the line.

The extension to Morden was opened by Lord Ashfield, Chairman of the UERL, on 13 December 1926. The combined Hampstead Tube and C&SLR continued to be shown with their separate titles on maps issued by the LER, although were sometimes referred to as the Hampstead & City Line. It was not until 1937 that the title of the Northern line was adopted.[211]

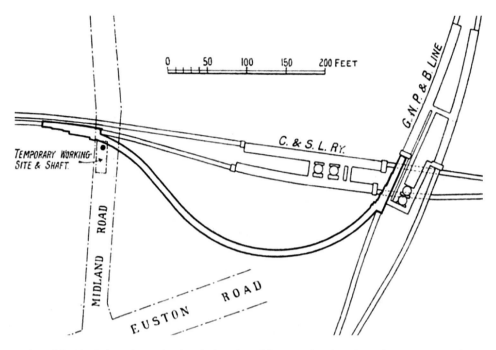

A plan of the King's Cross loop, showing the location of the step-plate junctions where it connected with the existing tunnels. *(The Railway Magazine)*

The King's Cross loop

One final piece of work on the C&SLR was a connection with the Piccadilly line at King's Cross. The LER had opened a large overhaul works for rolling stock at Acton, but there was no connection between the Hampstead & City line and the other parts of the network. Walter Scott & Middleton were contracted to build a tunnel 813 ft long at King's Cross, linking it with the Piccadilly line. A working shaft was sunk in the Midland Road, adjacent to St Pancras main-line station, and from this the step-plate junction was formed around the westbound tunnel of the Hampstead & City line. The single-track tunnel connection, with a diameter of 12 ft 6 ins, curved east and then north in a continuous curve, rising 15 ft as it did so to reach the eastbound tunnel of the Piccadilly line immediately south of the platform tunnel.[212] Another step-plate junction was excavated around this tunnel. The connection was brought into service on 27 March 1927.

From lifts to escalators

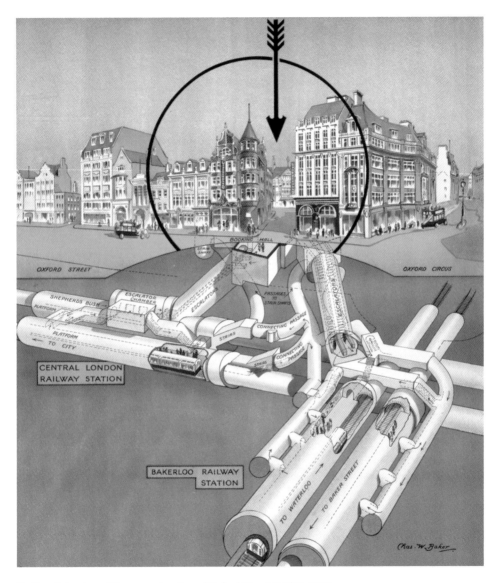

Sectional drawing of the reconstruction of Oxford Circus station, 1925.

The escalators at Earl's Court demonstrated their practicality at Underground stations. There was no waiting around for them to arrive, unlike with lifts, and a constant flow of passengers could be accommodated — particularly useful for the exit flows, where a large volume of passengers might arrive at once. Before the Earl's Court escalators had even opened for public use, the UERL had begun planning a series of further installations. Oxford Circus was to be the first station at which escalators would replace the lifts (unlike Earl's Court, where they augmented the lifts). Powers for the work were obtained in 1910, and on 9 May 1914 they were opened to passengers who were using the Bakerloo line. They descended from a new ticket hall constructed in the basement of the Bakerloo line station building, and the lift shafts were capped to provide a larger area for the ticket hall. The work included underpinning the existing station buildings on new girders and ensure that the piles supporting these girders would not obstruct the new sub-surface ticket hall. Water-bearing strata in the ground complicated both the underpinning and the work to sink the escalator shafts.[213]

The success of the Earl's Court escalators led to a number of new schemes being proposed. Exactly one month after they opened, plans were being announced for Oxford Circus, Baker Street, Piccadilly Circus, Leicester Square, and Elephant & Castle.[214] Of these, only the first two were achieved in fairly short order. Piccadilly Circus had to wait until the late 1920s (see below), and Leicester Square until 1935. Elephant & Castle is still waiting...

In fact, despite the excitement about escalators, few were installed until the 1920s, and only those at Oxford Circus were replacements for lifts. Liverpool Street already had two pairs. Baker Street received a pair in 1914, but no lifts were removed in consequence. Charing Cross (Embankment) received four, as a pair for the Bakerloo and a pair for the new Hampstead Tube platform, but there had never been lifts here previously. The stations on the Bakerloo extension between Paddington and Kilburn Park all received a pair, so by the end of 1915 there were just 22 escalators in service.

The First World War delayed any further plans, and once this was over the financial situation precluded any major works on the Underground until the Government introduced a Trade Facilities Bill in 1921, intended to relieve the high unemployment in Britain by providing a Government-backed guarantee for capital and interest that were borrowed for works that would boost employment. The Underground received backing for a £5 million programme of improvement works, which included the C&SLR reconstruction and extension described in the previous chapter.

It was not until 1924 that more escalators were installed, and all eleven (a 50% increase in a year) were replacements for lifts at Bank CLR, Moorgate, Shepherd's Bush, Stockwell, and Clapham Common. These were built at the more conventional angle of 30°, which has remained the standard ever since on the Underground.* Another eight were commissioned in 1925, of which seven were lift replacements (Oxford Circus CLR, Old Street, and Tottenham Court Road), and the other was an additional machine at Liverpool Street. The following year saw 13 new escalators

---

* The older shafts at 26° 23' 16½" still cause problems today, as the escalators and some of their components are non-standard. In 2011 LU was able to fit replacement 30° machines into one of these shafts at Oxford Circus, but this results in the ceiling headroom diminishing slightly (but noticeably) as passengers ascend.

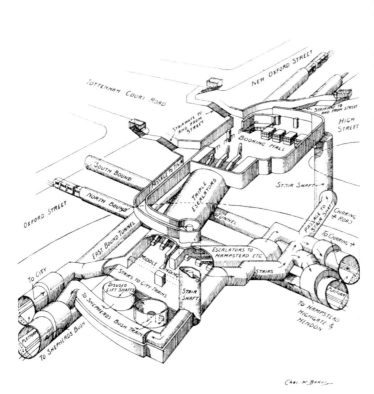

An isometric drawing of Tottenham Court Road station, looking north-east. The disused lift shafts for the CLR can be seen in the foreground; passageways were made across them, and these form the area known today as the 'rotunda'. The lift shafts for the Hampstead Tube have been omitted, but had their lower landings along the 'passage to stair shaft' shown in the drawing, and led up to the ticket hall. *(LTM)*

opened on the Morden extension, plus ten as lift replacements. Oval, Clapham North, Trafalgar Square, and Bond Street were each provided with a pair, and two final machines were commissioned at Tottenham Court Road.

A flagship station at Piccadilly Circus

Piccadilly Circus was seen as being the heart of London, and was described as being the "hub of the Empire". Something special was required when it was enlarged and modernized. Comprehensive reconstruction with escalators was essential to relieve congestion, preferably done in one go rather than the piecemeal approach taken at Oxford Circus. A subterranean ticket hall would give greater flexibility to the location of the escalators (instead of trying to squeeze them into the existing building), as well as giving access from all around the road junction. The new station was designed by the architect Charles Holden in conjunction with Harley Dalrymple-Hay as consulting engineer.

The road junction was part of the problem though. It would never be possible to close even a part of the junction for any length of time, which made the construction of a ticket hall beneath rather problematic. However, this was the type of challenge that the engineers, particularly Dalrymple-Hay, enjoyed meeting. They decided to perform all of the work from a single traffic island in the circus, which meant that

A night-time view of the cramped worksite on a traffic island in Piccadilly Circus. The illuminated window of the Swan & Edgar shop is on the far left, and the crane can be seen in the middle of the site. The gates to allow lorries into the site are to the left. *(LTM)*

its occupant, the aluminium statue known as Eros, had to be removed. It was found a temporary home in the Embankment Gardens. All of the subterranean work would take place from this one island: it was to be the civil engineering equivalent of keyhole surgery.

Once the hoardings had been erected around the site a service shaft was sunk, 18 ft in diameter and 92 ft deep. The location of the shaft fixed part of the new station layout, as it was to be used for a spiral staircase once the station was completed. The site on the island was tightly packed, with a single crane for managing materials in and out of the shaft, and a number of site cabins. The crane was placed on wooden staging, with an adjacent spoil hopper; this was placed above a lorry loading bay, accessed through gates in the hoarding around the site.

The planning for the new station culminated in the construction of a full-scale model of the ticket hall in the Empress Hall at the old Earl's Court exhibition site, using scaffold poles and cardboard; this could easily be adjusted to determine how passenger flows and construction might work, until a suitable layout was reached. This was a near-circular ticket hall with subways radiating out to stairwells at every street corner. From the ticket hall passengers would travel to and from the platforms

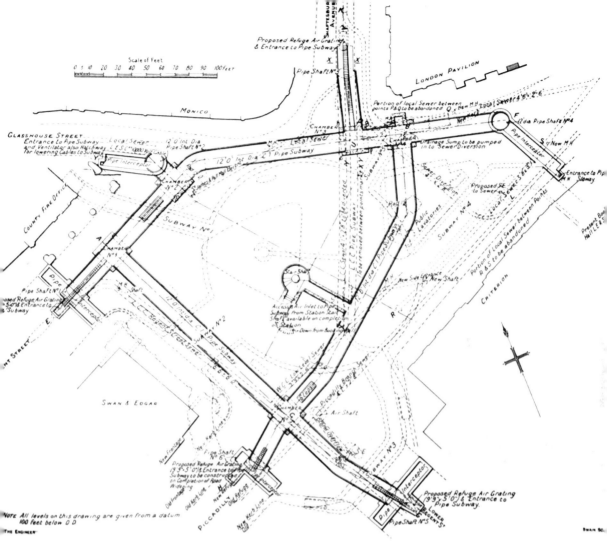

A plan of the pipe subway constructed beneath Piccadilly Circus. The dotted ellipse in the middle shows the extent of the new ticket hall, and other dotted lines mark the diverted sewers and the section of Shaftesbury Avenue pipe subway that was destroyed. *(The Engineer)*

using five escalators in two shafts. The location of the escalators was subsequently determined using the model, but laying them out as a horizontal plan only.

Beneath the surface of the road junction was the usual tangle of services and utilities. Some of these, leading up Shaftesbury Avenue, were already in a pipe subway to facilitate access. The rest needed to be diverted to make space for the new ticket hall. One of the first pieces of work was the construction of a pipe subway. Like that at Bank, it formed a loop 550 ft long around under the circus, with brick interceptor shafts at each street into which the existing service were diverted. Unlike the Bank pipe subway, it was constructed as a tube tunnel, with a 12 ft diameter and cast iron lining, and its layout bore little relation to the public areas constructed above. The section of the Shaftesbury Avenue pipe subway that extended into the circus was abandoned, and an inclined shaft made between the two pipe subways.

The pipe subway lies between 18 ft and 30 ft beneath the surface; the level varies as it has to pass beneath the pedestrian subways leading to the ticket hall, and above and below existing sewers. Its shallowest point is beneath the junction of Piccadilly and Lower Regent Street, where it was constructed in the gravel just above the level of the clay. Both the branches north-west to Regent Street, and north-east to Shaftesbury Avenue descend into the clay, with a sump at the latter point from where water entering the subway drains, and can be pumped into the adjacent sewer. Fortunately the geology of the area was good, and the ground was dry and easily tunnelled. A sewer that ran across the centre of the circus needed to be diverted to the north-east corner so as to avoid the new ticket hall. Within the subway metal hangers fixed to the walls supported the cables, an hydraulic main was placed in the tunnel invert, and two 24-inch water mains were supported on metal brackets and concrete piers. Around 60,000 telephone lines were diverted as part of the work.

From the single shaft, headings were created at different levels. At the bottom, a heading was driven from which the lower escalator landing, and the new passage-ways accessing the Piccadilly line were driven. A heading just over half-way down the shaft was used to create an intermediate level concourse. This was for the lower landing of the escalators descending from the ticket hall, and the upper landings of the banks of escalators to the Bakerloo and Piccadilly lines. It was from this level that these lower escalator shafts were driven at an angle of 30°. The spoil from the two tunnel faces was hauled up the shafts in skips pulled by electric winches, moved by hand to the main shaft, and then lifted up by the crane. This work proceeded 24 hours per day, but the spoil hopper was only emptied at night by a procession of lorries servicing the site. The loading bay was arranged with gates at either end, allowing a constant flow of lorries through the site without needing to manœuvre.

Four escalator shafts were excavated. Each of the two lower shafts, linking the two railways with the intermediate concourse, contained three escalators. The two upper shafts were parallel, one with three escalators and the other two.* The three triple escalator shafts were first bored as 'novelty headings', i.e., small shafts supported by just four segments of a tunnel ring with oak blocks at the corners. They were then enlarged out to their full diameter of 22 ft 4 ins, and the segments reused with additional segments added to make the full-size tunnel rings. The double escalator shaft was excavated with a diameter of 16 ft 4 ins.

At the intermediate level, the four escalator landings were arranged side-by-side in separate chambers, with the upper landings for the lower flights either side of the two lower landings of the upper flights. Between each adjacent pair of landings two passageways were excavated and provided with concrete walls, floor, and ceiling, strengthened by steel joists. These connected into the chambers through openings made by omitting segments from the lining and framing the holes with girders top and bottom, and stanchions to the sides.

The ticket hall had to be constructed whilst providing complete support to the roads and pavements above, and this could only happen once the pipe subway had been brought into use. A complex metal framework that would form the ceiling of

---

*   Presumably the planning for the new station had determined that five escalators were needed between the ticket hall and intermediate-level concourse.

The metal framework for the ticket hall ceiling, assembled away from the station to ensure that all of the components would fit. *(LTM)*

the ticket hall and support the road had to be inserted into the ground, together with 54 metal columns and their concrete foundations. The metalwork was fabricated by Josiah Westwood & Co., in Millwall, and was initially assembled in their yard to ensure that every component fitted perfectly. Each piece was then numbered so that it could be identified and installed correctly.

Back in Piccadilly Circus, two small circular shafts were sunk close to the existing shaft, but only to the depth of the ticket hall. From these, headings were tunnelled beneath the road junction, 6 ft high and 8 ft wide and about 40 ft long. These ran to the sites of the four central columns for the ticket hall, and were roofed with rolled-steel joists supported by temporary timbering. The column foundations were made, and the columns erected. Then the main girders spanning the ticket hall were inserted in the headings and on top of the columns, and steel packing was inserted to connect the joists to the girders. The weight of the ground above was now being carried by the girders and columns, and the timbering was removed. Then, bit by bit, further headings were driven and additional girders and columns were installed. All of the work to move the heavy pieces of metal was accomplished manually with the aid of rollers, jacks, and block-and-tackle gear.

Out of all the pieces that made up the metal framework, only two, girders G8 and G9, were not moved underground via the shaft, as it was considered desirable to get them into position as early as possible, and before there would be a clear path to their places from the shaft. The disused southernmost section of the Shaftesbury Avenue pipe subway passed diagonally adjacent to where they were needed, and this had an opening in a traffic island above. The girders would need to be placed in the road before they could be guided into the subway, and there was justifiable concern

The wide subway between the ticket hall and the Swan & Edgar shop under construction on 12 July 1928. A narrow-gauge railway has been installed for the removal of spoil. *(LTM)*

about the effect of them getting jammed and holding up traffic, even though the work was to be done on a Sunday. A trial run was held using a dummy girder made of wood; this did get stuck, and so the hole was enlarged by cutting away a little of the subway roof, and this was found to be sufficient when the process was tried again on the next Sunday. On the third Sunday the real girders were successfully moved underground.[215]

The outside wall of the ticket hall was constructed simultaneously with the metal-work. A circular heading was excavated along its length, and the brick and concrete foundations were made. A second heading was then driven above the first, and the height of the brick wall increased to a level where it would provide support to those girders that reached to the edges of the ticket hall. Because of the weight that it would bear, and the fact that it formed a retaining wall, it was built 4 ft 6 in thick.

With the outer wall built, and the metal framework of columns and girders installed, the structure of the ticket hall was complete. The soil remaining between the many headings was removed, revealing an elliptical space 155 ft by 144 ft, and 9 ft high. Six subways were constructed radiating out from the hall, by creating headings in which the side walls were erected, and roofing them over with girders supported by the walls.

Three ventilation plants were installed during the work. The largest was in the old station building and pumped 45,000 ft³ of air into the lower tunnels every minute. A second, also placed in the old station building, supplied 15,000 ft³ of air per minute into the new ticket hall via ducts placed 2 ft above floor level. The final fan drew air from the various escalator machine chambers and removed it from the station to prevent the smell of oil or machinery permeating the station.[216]

The reconstructed station was opened in a ceremony by the Mayor of Westminster on 10 December 1928. The work had cost around £550,000, and had taken four years to complete with around 150 workmen on site full-time, employed by John Mowlem & Co, who were the contractors for the work. The opening brochure noted that 950 tons of steel girders, 2,700 tons of cast iron segments, 3,600 tons of cement, and 1¼ million bricks had been used. To accommodate them, 34,000 cubic yards of London clay had been removed from the site, with 1,000 tons per month being removed from the tiny island worksite.

The lower landing of the upper escalator shaft at Holborn under construction, showing the enormous size of the shaft, which accommodates four escalators side-by-side. On both sides of the photograph the cross-passages are just visible, showing how much space will be beneath the floor, where the escalator equipment will be accommodated. The workmen are casting the concrete supports for this equipment. *(LTM)*

Holborn reconstruction

Plans to improve the interchange between the CLR and the Piccadilly line had been in existence since shortly after the latter opened. The CLR had a station at British Museum, about 170 yds away from the Piccadilly line station at Holborn. Unfortunately, those passengers wishing to make the connection had to ascend to the surface, cross a very busy street, and then use the lifts to return to platform level. In 1908 it was suggested that a tunnel containing a passenger conveyor was being planned,[217] but nothing came of this. It was not until 1930 that a Bill was deposited to resolve the situation.

The plan was to construct new platforms on the CLR to the east of British Museum station, and immediately to the east of where they passed above the running tunnels of the Piccadilly line. Escalators would connect the two lines, and a further bank of escalators would then connect to the ticket hall. Towards the end of the year John Cochrane & Sons Ltd were awarded the contract for the £500,000 project.

The upper escalator was, at the time, the largest escalator shaft ever made, containing four parallel escalators rising 76 ft 8 ins, which were the longest in the UK.[218] The shaft had a diameter of 30 ft, and was enlarged further to 31 ft 6 in at its lower end to accommodate the machine chamber.

The platform tunnel at Holborn has been completed, and the original running tunnel lining is now being dismantled. Passenger trains are still running through; one can be seen in the background. Health and safety would not allow this to happen now. *(LTM)*

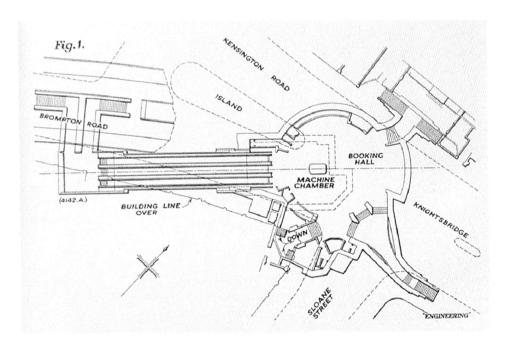

A plan of the eastern ticket hall at Knightsbridge, showing the escalators descending to new access passages. *(Engineering)*

The lower concourse of the quadruple bank of escalators was just over 10 ft above the height of the new CLR platforms. These had to be built on the outside of the tracks, as the tunnels were too close to allow a conventional central platform arrangement to be made. Both the entrance and exit passages from the two platforms crossed over both platform tunnels, with side stairs descending to the westbound platform. At the end of the passages stairs descended to the eastbound platform.

On the south side of the escalator landing was another concourse, this being at the top of a triple bank of escalators descending to the Piccadilly line platforms in a 22 ft 9 ins diameter shaft. This connected in with one of the existing lower lift landings, allowing the existing passageways to continue in use. Once the lifts were taken out of use a passageway and short staircase were constructed across the lower level of the middle shaft, forming additional access points to the westbound platform. One of the lift shafts was used to provide ventilation to the new CLR platforms.[219]

Possibly the most intricate work was the construction of the new CLR platforms. These were hand-mined around the existing running tunnels for a distance of 335 ft. As with similar work, trains continued to run through and the integrity of the old tunnels was maintained through the use of heavy props until it was time to dismantle the old linings.

Replacing lifts by escalators at Knightsbridge
Knightsbridge station, on the Piccadilly line, had been built with two lift shafts each containing two lifts, as well as a shaft containing a spiral staircase. The station

building was mid-way between the two current entrances, as because it was a long, narrow site, the lift shafts were some way to the south of the platforms, giving a longer-than-usual walk to passengers. To improve access a scheme was drawn up to provide separate entrances at each end of the station, using escalators. The new works were all completely separate from the existing access arrangements, making them more straightforward to plan than if temporary underground rearrangement was required.

The work to build the eastern end of the station was not straightforward. There were two separate operations: the ticket hall and the escalator shaft. The new ticket hall was placed beneath the road, and constructed in twelve separate sections to avoid disrupting traffic more than the bare minimum. Some of the girders that would form the ticket hall roof, and support the road above, had to be inserted into headings beneath the road whilst it was in use. In this way an elliptical ticket hall was formed, with stairwell access from three corners of the road junction above.

The escalator shaft was made almost independently from the ticket hall. A 12 ft diameter shaft was sunk from a traffic island to a depth of 30 ft. From its base, a heading was tunnelled at right angles to the line of the new escalator shaft. This was lined rather unusually by using four running tunnel segments and four key pieces. A ring of running tunnel used six segments, so four gave the tunnel a cross-section that was a square with sides that curved outwards, around 9 ft across. Where this tunnel passed over the line of the escalator shaft a second short tunnel was made, at right angles and above the line of the escalator shaft. At the intersection of the two the pilot tunnel for the escalator shaft was begun, of 9 ft diameter, again using rings

Work proceeding on the escalator shaft. The pilot tunnel (centre) has been filled (apart from a small passage left in its lower half), and the radial timbers can be seen towards the back. The cast iron rings 27 ft in diameter are clearly visible around the works. *(Engineering)*

made from four 11 ft 8½ in tunnel segments; the final shaft was to have a diameter of 23 ft 2½ ins.

The problems started during the construction of the shaft, when water was discovered just below the level of the access headings. Trial borings into the ground around the site showed layers of loamy yellow sand, clay, and gravels, with the top of the London clay about 36 ft below the ground. Compressed air working was started, with the airlock installed in the access heading, and a new tunnel driven from the bottom of the shaft to house the air compressors. However, the air tended to leak away through the porous ground, despite the joints between the tunnel rings being tightly caulked. Progress slowed to one-sixth what it would have been in good clay, namely one tunnel ring every 24 hours. The engineers were concerned that as the tunnel deepened and lengthened, proportionally more and more air would be needed, increasing the costs, and the risk to the buildings on the south side of the road (under which the lowest part of the shaft would pass) would increase. After the use of a hooded shield and the clay-pocket system (see p 91) was considered and then rejected, ground consolidation was decided upon, using the Joosten process.

The Joosten process

To chemically consolidate waterlogged ground using the Joosten process, two chemicals are injected separately. Sodium silicate is first injected via a 1-inch diameter steel pipe with its furthest section perforated for 2 ft; this is pressed into the ground so that the perforations are at a point that requires consolidation and the sodium silicate is pumped in to the tube in sufficient quantity to spread around the pipe for about 1 ft. The pipe is then pressed in by 2 ft and the process repeated until it is at the maximum depth. Calcium chloride is then pumped in, and the pipe withdrawn in 2ft stages back to the original depth.

The two chemicals react immediately to create a thick gel; this binds with the sand or gravel to form an "artificial sandstone" through which excavations can be made. The process was quite expensive, with pipes having to be driven at 2 ft intervals in order to consolidate a length of ground.[220] It is only suitable for use in ground consisting of ballast, gravel, or sand; it does not work effectively in clay, mud, silt, and peat.

Since there was no way of knowing whether the consolidation process would completely protect the workings, an alternative form of protection was installed first. A temporary larger chamber was formed at the top level of the escalator shaft, using thirteen 27 ft diameter rings. This followed the curve of the pilot tunnel from horizontal to the 30° slope of the shaft. A further nine half-rings of the same diameter were installed, making the top half of the shaft. These could not have been made as full rings as the tunnelling would have required too much compressed air; however, they formed a hood over the top part of where the escalator shaft was to be. Inside these half rings sturdy timber props were placed radially to provide support, and the pilot tunnel was filled with brickwork to create a solid core.

From here, 39 steel tubes 4 inches thick were driven into the ground just inside the temporary half-rings. These extended down and into to the clay, and the total length of 1,350 ft of tube was driven in four weeks. Between them, smaller injection pipes were also driven into the wet ground above the shaft, and the ground was consolidated in a curved surface over and around the tunnel, effectively forming a semicircular tunnel over the shaft, but of a larger diameter than the final escalator shaft. This would protect the workings against water ingress.

The full-size escalator shaft was now driven in compressed air, starting within the 27 ft tunnel rings and then continuing beneath the hood of consolidated ground and metal tubes. Concrete was used to fill the space at the top between the two sets of rings. The consolidation was found to be very effective, so much so that the steel tubes had not been necessary. The sand had been consolidated into "the equivalent of a soft friable sandstone" which was easily excavated by the pneumatic picks. Overall the work was seen as a success.[221]

The longest escalator in the world at Leicester Square

Another station in central London that was suffering acutely from congestion was Leicester Square. The station had been opened with five lifts descending to a level between that of the Piccadilly and Hampstead Tube platforms. From the lower lift landings stairs led down to the Piccadilly platforms, and up to those of the Hampstead. Traffic had increased to 27 million passengers each year, and something had to be done to fix the problem.

The reconstruction of the station created a smaller version of Piccadilly Circus, and many of the same techniques were used. Two pipe subways were constructed in the advance works, one beneath Charing Cross Road running north/south, and the other beneath Cranbourn Street running east/west. A connection was made between the two where they crossed at slightly different levels. Both subways were lined with standard cast iron segments as used for running tunnels. Services beneath the roads were diverted into the pipe subways so that a larger, sub-surface ticket hall could be made. A large sewer beneath Cranbourn Street was also diverted into a new alignment away from the new ticket hall site. The disused sections of pipe subway were found to be useful for the new work as they were used for creating the foundations on which the columns were secured that would support the new ticket hall roof.

Once the existing building was underpinned, work could start on mining out the new ticket hall. One side of Charing Cross Road was closed to traffic, the street was opened up, and the girders for the new roof inserted. This was a luxury not afforded to the builders at Piccadilly Circus! The side of the road left open to traffic was reinforced with metal grids (made from old rails), as the builders had to excavate small headings under the surface to accommodate some of the longer girders. The ticket hall was circular, under the junction of Charing Cross Road and Cranbourn Street (as well as partly beneath the original station building) with four stairways leading down from the different sides of the road junction.

The works at deep-level were constructed from a pair of 9 ft diameter heading tunnels, one above the other, which were driven from a 12 ft diameter shaft a short distance away from the station, at the junction of Upper St Martin's Lane and Long Acre. The site on this corner had been cleared so that a new substation could be built, providing power to the Underground. The heading tunnels would eventually be used for the power cables, but were constructed early so that they could be used

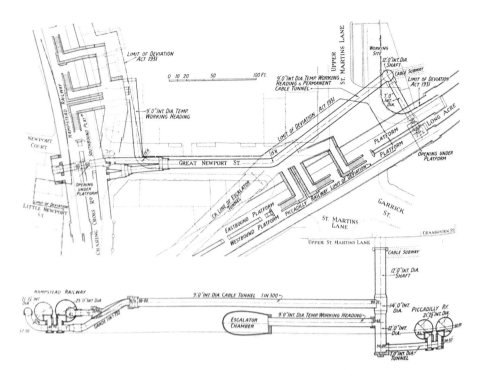

A plan and section of the low-level work at Leicester Square, showing the headings between the substation site (top right) and the Hampstead Tube (left) and Piccadilly Tube (bottom right). *(The Railway Gazette)*

in enlarging Leicester Square station. The upper heading was at the level of the Hampstead Tube platforms, and ran beneath Great Newport Street. Near the platforms a temporary heading curved off northwards to the site of the lower escalator landing, and from here the escalator shaft was dug upwards, under Charing Cross Road, to the new ticket hall. Beneath Cranbourn Street, and from the end of the lower of the two 9 ft headings, a similar escalator shaft was tunnelled upwards for the Piccadilly line. Both shafts had a diameter of 22 ft 9 in. A further heading, 7 ft in diameter, led from the base of the working shaft to the Piccadilly line platforms; this was to carry the cables from the substation when the station was finished. Since the pairs of platforms for both lines were back-to-back, and close together, it was not possible for the escalators to descend to their level. Instead, new passageways led from the lower escalator landings to new flights of stairs constructed between the platforms. In order to fit the stairs in, sections of the platform tunnel lining had to be carefully removed and replaced by vertical segments; this just made enough room.[222]*

Each escalator shaft was fitted with three escalators made by Otis, and of type 'MH'. This was a heavy-duty escalator designed for high rises. Those descending to

---

* The platforms were originally accessed from passageways that led from the headwalls, hence there had been no need to accommodate stairs between adjacent platforms. These passageways were retained after the reconstruction for passengers interchanging between the two lines.

Leicester Square substation building under construction. The steel framework can be seen at the top, with the brick walls being built upwards and around the frame. This is the Upper St Martin's Lane façade, with The Sussex just visible on the right. *(LTM)*

the Piccadilly line were proudly proclaimed to be the longest in the world, 161 ft 6 ins long with vertical rises of 80 ft 9 in. The new station opened on 4 May 1935, but with the north-eastern part of the ticket hall incomplete. This was still occupied by the lift shafts, which had been in use the previous day. With the escalators in use the lifts were removed and this corner of the new ticket hall was completed. One of the old lift shafts was retained and fitted with an exhaust fan to improve the station ventilation. More tunnels were excavated between its lower end and the two pairs of platforms.

Whilst the station was being reconstructed, work on the new substation continued. A large steel-framed brick building was constructed on the corner site and was largely completed by mid-1934. It had two brick façades, one onto each of Upper St Martin's Lane and Long Acre, which were largely blank brickwork with Portland stone bands above the ground and first storeys. The southern corner of the site was occupied by The Sussex public house. This was demolished around late 1935, and a replacement provided in a two storey building of a similar style to the substation (but with rather more windows). The substation was commissioned on 10 March 1935.

Escalator conversions: a summary

This list contains the details of all escalators subsequently installed at existing stations prior to the Second World War. It includes those installed as a result of new platforms being built: for example, when the Hampstead Tube was extended to Charing Cross (now Embankment) in 1914. It excludes completely new stations on new extensions.

Station	No.	Location	Date
Earl's Court	2	District – Piccadilly	4 October 1911
Charing Cross (Embankment)	2	Concourse – Bakerloo	2 March 1914
Charing Cross (Embankment)	2	Concourse – Hampstead	6 April 1914
Oxford Circus	2	Ticket hall – Bakerloo	9 May 1914
Baker Street	2	Metropolitan – Bakerloo	15 October 1914
Bank	3	Ticket hall – Central	7 May 1924
Moorgate	2	Ticket hall – City	3 July 1924
Shepherd's Bush	2	Ticket hall – Central	5 November 1924
Clapham Common	2	Ticket hall – City	1 December 1924
Stockwell	2	Ticket hall – City	1 December 1924
Oxford Circus	2	Ticket hall – Central	5 July 1925
Old Street	2	Ticket hall – City	19 August 1925
Tottenham Court Road	3	Ticket hall – Central	28 September 1925
Tottenham Court Road	2	Ticket hall – Hampstead	1 February 1926
Trafalgar Square	2	Ticket hall – Bakerloo	13 April 1926
Clapham North	2	Ticket hall – City	29 May 1926
Oval	2	Ticket hall – City	29 May 1926
Bond Street	2	Ticket hall – Central	8 June 1926
Waterloo	3	Ticket hall – Bakerloo	29 July 1927
Oxford Circus	1	Ticket hall – Bakerloo	2 October 1928
Charing Cross (Embankment)	2	Ticket hall – concourse	10 December 1928
Piccadilly Circus	11	Ticket hall – Bakerloo and Piccadilly	10 December 1928
Camden Town	2	Ticket hall – Hampstead	7 October 1929
Archway	2	Ticket hall – Hampstead	15 June 1931
Hyde Park Corner	2	Ticket hall – Piccadilly	23 May 1932
Marble Arch	2	Ticket hall – Central	15 August 1932
Kentish Town	2	Ticket hall – Hampstead	21 November 1932
Tottenham Court Road	1	Central – Hampstead	22 April 1933
Holborn	5	Ticket hall – Piccadilly	19 May 1933
Bank/Monument	2	District – City	18 September 1933

Station	No.	Location	Date
Green Park	2	Ticket hall – Piccadilly	18 September 1933
Holborn	2	Ticket hall – Central	25 September 1933
Warren Street	4	Ticket hall – Hampstead	27 September 1933
Knightsbridge	2	East ticket hall – Piccadilly	18 February 1934
Chancery Lane	5	Ticket hall – Central	25 June 1934
Knightsbridge	2	West ticket hall – Piccadilly	30 July 1934
Leicester Square	6	Ticket hall – Hampstead and Piccadilly	4 May 1935
Moorgate	2	Northern City – City	19 June 1936
Moorgate	2	Ticket hall – Northern City	2 October 1936
St Paul's	5	Ticket hall – Central	1 January 1939
King's Cross	5	Ticket hall – Piccadilly – Northern	18 June 1939

All of the escalators installed before 1924 were made by Otis, and were of the same type as those at Earl's Court (described on p 157), and were designated 'A'-type escalators. They were all made at an angle of 26° 23' 16½″. In addition to the ten listed in the table above, there were another four at Liverpool Street and two on each of the Bakerloo line stations between Paddington and Kilburn Park.

During the 1920s, all new escalators were an improved design (known as 'L'-type), and had an inclination of 30°. There was one exception: a new escalator at Liverpool Street was installed in place of a stairway parallel to two of the original escalators. The shaft was at an angle of 26° 23' 16½″, and so a one-off 'L'-type escalator was made at this angle.

In the 1930s all escalators were from the 'M'-type family. This included the 'MH'-type, for particularly long escalators, and the 'MY'-type, which were short escalators. These were all very solidly built machines which gave good service for many decades. It was not until 1955 that an escalator from a manufacturer other than Otis was installed on the Underground.**

---

*   This was at Alperton station, and was previously used in the Dome of Discovery at the Festival of Britain, opened in 1951. The escalator was made by J&E Hall of Dartford.

Tunnel works of the 1930s

The 1930s saw the largest ever scheme for the extension of the Underground network – the 1935/40 New Works Programme. This proposed, and largely completed, a number of extensions that would allow the Bakerloo, Central London, and Morden-Edgware* lines to join with existing lines on the surface and thus be extended into the suburbs. Before this occurred, the Piccadilly line was finally extended north from Finsbury Park.

The Southgate extension

There had been an increasing clamour since the 1920s for a northward extension of the Underground from Finsbury Park. Despite considerable opposition from the L&NER, who were concerned about loss of passengers to a tube railway, an extension of the Piccadilly line to the rural outpost of Cockfosters was approved in 1930. Later that year construction work began.

The first four miles of the extension were in twin tube tunnel of standard size. Beyond this the line ran on the surface and on viaduct to the terminus, except for a half-mile tunnel at Southgate. The tunnelling work was unremarkable, being conducted from 32 tunnel faces and nine 12-ft diameter shafts located at stations and intermediate points. Twenty-two Greathead shields were used, all made by Markham & Co., and the clay was excavated using pneumatic spades. The compressed air that worked the spades was also used to operate segment erectors working at the rear of the shields. On average one mile of single tunnel was built each month. The tunnelling was completed by the end of 1931, having used around 55,000 tons of cast iron segments.

At Wood Green a 14 ft diameter reversing siding was driven to the north of the station between the running tunnels, with three step-plate junctions making the connection. A fourth step-plate junction was built on the southbound line between the platform and the reversing siding, allowing the siding to be turned into the first part of a branch to Enfield at some unrealized point in the future.[223] At the tunnel portals, about halfway between Bounds Green and Arnos Grove, the southbound tunnel was increased in size to 16 ft diameter to form a bell-mouth, which would reduce the effect of the air pressure on passengers as their trains entered the tunnel (the 'popping' sensation). For aesthetic reasons the last three rings of the northbound tunnel were made to the same size so that the tunnel mouths appear symmetric. The same arrangement was made at the portals of the tunnel at Southgate.[224]

The tunnelling work was continuous, except for a maintenance period from Saturday afternoon until Sunday evening each week. Spoil was removed from the sites by a fleet of eighteen Sentinel steam lorries operated by the St Mary's Wharf

---

*   The merger of the C&SLR and the Hampstead Tube in the 1920s, as described in the previous chapter, had not resulted in a straightforward name for the combined line. In the 1930s it became the Morden-Edgware line for a few years before the adoption of the Northern line title in August 1937.

Tunnellers hard at work on the Southgate extension. This Greathead shield is just north of Finsbury Park station. The backs of the hydraulic rams can be seen next to the workman on the right, and the workman on the left is next to the controls. *(LTM)*

One of the dark blue steam lorries at the Turnpike Lane work site. It appears to be empty, so is probably returning to the site to be refilled. The crane to lift spoil up the shaft is just visible on the left. *(LTM)*

One of the platform tunnels at Manor House, with the structure complete but before any work on the platform or track bed has started. This demonstrates the size of the platform tunnels in a way that is impossible to see after the fitting out. A small works train is visible in the foreground, left. *(LTM)*

Cartage Co., which took it for landfill in the Lea Valley.[225] The same lorries were used to bring sand and gravel back to the work sites for the making of concrete.

Four stations were built in the main tunnel section and one (Southgate) in the short section of tunnel further north. Heading north from Finsbury Park the first three stations (Manor House, Turnpike Lane, and Wood Green) had larger tunnels than usual, 23 ft 2½ ins in diameter, as higher traffic was expected at these. Bounds Green and Southgate had standard dimensions for their platforms. All of the platforms were around 385 ft long, and the platform walls were made flatter to reduce the impression of being in a tunnel. This also allowed five ventilation ducts to be placed behind the walls on each platform, which were covered at the first three stations by decorative bronze grills. The ducts were fed with air from beneath the platforms. Each station had a 5 ft diameter ventilation shaft sunk, which was connected to a long duct at the rear of the under-platform space by heading tunnels of the same diameter. At the surface ventilation plant capable of pumping 20,000 ft³/minute of air to the platforms was installed. Further ventilation was provided through the retention of some of the working shafts constructed between the station sites. These were equipped with fans of even greater capacity: that at Finsbury Park Tennis Courts could supply 50,000 ft³/minute, whilst those at Colina Road and Nightingale Road were each equipped with two 70,000 ft³/minute fans.[226]

Following their trial on the Morden extension of the Piccadilly line, anti-suicide pits were constructed between the running rails in the platform areas. These were built at two levels, the half closer to the platform being deeper.[227] Arches in the side of the anti-suicide pits, leading to the space under the platforms, facilitated staff access to people who had fallen under trains.[228]

The other major work on the extension was the viaduct across Arnos Park, to the north of Arnos Grove station. This was constructed from approximately three million brindle Staffordshire bricks, and consisted of 35 segmental arches over a length of 1,500 ft, as well as a further five arches in a short section between Waterfall Road and Hampden Way, immediately to the north of the main viaduct. All of the

The Arnos Park viaduct under construction in January 1932. The arches on the right are being constructed over wooden centrings not dissimilar to that used for the tunnel arches on the original Metropolitan Railway tunnels (see p 21). Bricklayers can be seen at work on top of the arches. *(LTM)*

arches had a span of 25 ft, apart from two slightly shorter arches on the northern viaduct. Apart from the shallow, southernmost section, each of the piers was divided into three pillars below the level of the main arch springing, with small semicircular arches joining them. It was constructed in the conventional way for viaducts, namely by building the piers up to springing level, constructing a ledge to support a wooden framework for the arch, and then constructing the arch over the framework (see p 45-6 for more details about this type of construction). The upper levels of the viaduct were then completed. It has been alleged that this was the last brick-built viaduct in the UK, but this is clearly untrue as the extension of the Central line west to Greenford included a new three-arch brick viaduct over the River Brent, completed in 1937.[*]

Another 237 yds of brick viaduct was built between the north portal of Southgate Tunnel and the next station, at East Barnet (now called Oakwood). This consisted of nineteen semi-circular arches, of which eighteen had a span of 30 ft, and one near

---

[*]   The extension of the Northern line to Bushey Heath was to have a brick-built viaduct at Brockley Hill. This was never completed, and was subsequently demolished.

the centre of the viaduct a span of 50 ft, possibly to span a road, although this was never built and the arch remains above a footpath connecting two separate residential streets.[229]

The LPTB kept detailed figures about the construction of the extension and the amount of effort required. These were needed so that they could calculate costs for future work and justify the expense estimates. On the Southgate extension, they recorded that the contractor employed 100 men at the start in September 1930, rapidly increasing to 1,300 in March 1931, and up to a peak of 1,565 two months later. The split was as follows:

Skilled	996
Semi-skilled	350
Unskilled	138
Administrative	81

Over 1,500 men remained employed on the extension until July 1931, when the number fell to 1,200. They continued to drop as work was completed, reaching 800 in November and remaining at that level until November 1932.

Each running tunnel shield required two shifts to operate it, each shift comprising twelve men. Shafts each required another five men on duty for each shift (a banksman, crane driver, two gantry men, and a yard man). Three muck trains per shield, each operated by two men per shift, would employ a further twelve men, and in the tunnels behind each shield would be a carpenter and mate, fitter and mate, and electrician and mate, making another twelve men across the two shifts. If it is assumed that a single shaft can service four tunnel faces, this gives a workforce of 58 men. There would also be a team of about twelve workmen and maintenance staff per shift at the surface at each shaft, taking this total to 70 men employed at each worksite. Platform tunnels required around 25 men per shift because of the greater amount of excavation. Labour costs were, on average, £50 per man month, and this was roughly 50% of the total cost of the work.

An impressive quantity of materials was used for the extension, all of which boosted employment around the country, as recorded in the staff magazine:

Indirect labour is represented in the manufacture of: 55,000 tons of iron segments; 1,500 tons of steel rails; 2,000 tons of contact rails; 900 tons of girders and other ironwork; 2,000 tons of bolts and nuts etc.; 20,000 tons of cement; 12,000,000 bricks of all sorts; in the digging up of 60,000 cubic yards of sand, ballast, etc.; spoil is represented by 700,000 cubic yards of excavation.[230]

The stations on the extension were all designed by Adams, Holden & Pearson, the architectural practice co-founded by Charles Holden. Their style was summarized as being brick boxes with concrete lids, and had first been tried at Sudbury Town, on the western part of the Piccadilly line. The buildings on the extension to Cockfosters were similar in style, although a variety of shapes were used for the 'boxes': Oakwood has a rectangular prism, Southgate a shallow cylinder, Arnos Grove a tall cylinder, Bounds Green an octagonal prism, and Wood Green an elliptical cylinder. They were

A view along the former eastbound platform tunnel at Down Street, looking westwards. The tiled rings around the tunnel ceiling show that the points are within the old platform tunnel. The siding has been excavated through the platform tailwall, and is the left hand tunnel to the rear. *(Kim Rennie)*

constructed using a steel frame which was encased in concrete to form the main structure. Brick walls and large metal-framed windows filled in the sections between the concrete pillars; the pillars were left exposed at some stations, and clad in brick at others. Different types of bricks laid in different bonds were used to give variety between the stations. The concrete roofs were cast with the rest of the concrete frame where possible, although prefabricated concrete panels were used to save time at some of the later stations.[231]

One other piece of tunnelling work on the Piccadilly line in the early 1930s was in central London. The station at Down Street, between Green Park and Hyde Park Corner, was closed. It was located on a side street and was not greatly used. The latter station was reconstructed with escalators, which opened in May 1932, and Down Street was closed at this time, in part because the new entrances at Hyde Park Corner were now closer, making the closure less inconvenient for those few who did use it. With the station closed, work began on constructing a reversing siding between the running tunnels to the west of the platforms.* The western ends of both platforms were demolished along with the headwalls so that points could be placed in the platform area, reducing the amount of work to create the junction tunnels.

A tunnel 836 ft long was excavated almost as far as the platforms at Hyde Park

---

*   None of the tube railways constructed by the UERL had reversing sidings except at Highgate (now Archway), Finsbury Park, and Elephant & Castle, and all three of these were termini. There were several crossovers provided on each line, but these would not allow a disabled train to be cleared from the line.

Corner, which was long enough to hold two trains. It was larger than the running tunnels — 14 ft 6 ins diameter — to allow for a walkway alongside the tracks. An inspection pit between the rails and special lighting enabled trains to be examined. Trains that failed in service could be moved out of the way into the siding, and if the traffic from the Southgate extension proved to be heavier than that from the westward extension of the line (taking over tracks from the District line) then some of the service could be reversed at Down Street. As with all underground reversing sidings, foot access was provided from the dead-end of the tunnel, in this case via a 7 ft tunnel that linked with the crossover tunnel immediately east of Hyde Park Corner.[232] A walkway of wooden planks was laid in the running tunnel between the rails on the westbound line to make the access easier for staff. The siding was commissioned on 30 May 1933.

Realignment of the Central London Line tunnels

The first work to be started as part of the New Works Programme, following Royal Assent for the LPTB Act of 1936, was the realignment of the CLR tunnels through London. Although an impressive achievement in 1900, they were in need of adjustment if rolling stock as used on other tube lines (the so-called Standard Stock) was to be used. Their diameter was 2¼ inches less than the tube tunnels built by the UERL,

A selection of photographs showing the original lining being dismantled (top left), the grouting machine being prepared (top right), the completed and enlarged tunnel (foreground, bottom left), and checks being carried out by measuring the completed work (bottom right). *(Pennyfare)*

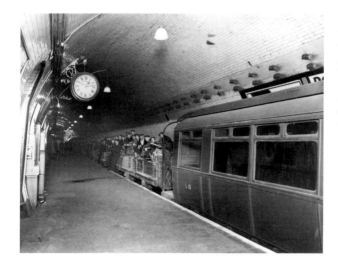

One of the works trains taking the workmen to their sites along the CLR, passing through Marble Arch station. The train includes withdrawn gate stock car L18 (now used by the engineering department) and a number of open wagons, in which the workmen are sitting. *(LTM)*

and the rolling stock on the CLR was slightly smaller than that on the other lines.* Had the CLR tunnels been perfectly aligned, it would have been possible to use the Standard Stock, but the misalignment of the tunnels was such that correction was needed. Also, the platforms needed to be lengthened so that eight-car trains could be operated to handle the heavy traffic on the line.[233] The final part of the work was the conversion of the line to use the standard four-rail electrification used by the LPTB, in place of the original CLR three-rail system.

The work started in August of that year between Bond Street and Marble Arch. It did not require the use of tunnelling shields, but instead the work used a detailed survey that showed which rings were out of alignment and adjusted these individually. The worst of the rings diverged by 8 ins from the true centre line of the tunnel.[234] After the trains stopped running at night works trains worked along the line from west to east leaving wagons at each work site. At each site a small team would dismantle part of a tunnel ring by unbolting the segments and using screw jacks to extract the key piece. The men would then excavate where necessary behind the ring using pneumatic picks and shovels to remove the clay and old grout and improve the alignment, typically at cant-rail level.** Compressed air was supplied from equipment on nearby station platforms. The ring was then reassembled, sometimes with small additional packing segments to fit the slightly larger space, and sometimes with replacement segments that had been adjusted to provide an improved alignment. The ring was then re-grouted to seal the space behind. If replacement segments were used then the old segments were loaded onto the wagon to be adjusted back at Wood Lane Depot and sent out on another night to be reused elsewhere.[235] Up to 29 gangs of miners performed the work each night.[236]

---

* The rolling stock on the CLR was 8 ft 6 ins wide and 9 ft 4½ ins high. The Standard Stock on the Northern, Piccadilly, and Bakerloo lines was 8 ft 8½ ins wide and 9 ft 6 ins high.

** The cant-rail is at the join between the body side and the roof on a railway carriage.

As well as the men who performed the work described above, the team included signal and electrical specialists who would disconnect and then reinstall any signalling or electrical equipment encountered. They would also protect cable using sacks whilst the work was done.

The station platform tunnels were lengthened from 325 ft to 427 ft by boring a new pilot tunnel from the platform ends, behind the running tunnel in the section for enlargement. This tunnel, of 8 ft 6 ins diameter, allowed the enlargement to take place without disturbing the running trains whilst removing much of the soil necessary to make the new platform area. Once completed, a new platform tunnel 23 ft 2½ ins diameter was formed around both the running and pilot tunnel and these two tunnels within were dismantled and the remaining soil was removed.

One problem in lengthening the platforms was the slope at each end of most of the platforms. The 'humped' profile of the line, with gradients to accelerate and decelerate trains, meant that the platform extensions would be at gradients of 1 in 60 or even 1 in 30; rather greater than the maximum of 1 in 264 recommended by the Ministry of Transport. The solution was to build the extension wherever possible at the end with the 1 in 60 gradient, and then to build it on a shallower gradient than the tunnel. The height of the running tunnel adjacent to the extension was then increased by up to 3 ft for a length of up to 80 ft, by replacing the segments at the tunnel sides by taller segments. This led to some steeper gradients in the running tunnels either side of the stations, but kept the stations more amenable to passengers.

Both the original termini for the line caused problems. At Bank, compressed air had to be used for the work, again to avoid the risk of subsidence in the soft clay. At Shepherd's Bush the escalator shaft prevented westward extension of the platforms, but at the east end there was a crossover tunnel, bringing the running tunnels too close together to permit platforms to be installed. The only practical solution was to build a large tunnel 35 ft in diameter around both running tunnels between the platforms and the crossover, and create an island platform.

The realignment work took two years to complete, involving work on around 10,000 tunnel segments. The result was that the standard four-rail current system could be provided, and rolling stock was transferred from other lines to replace the original CLR multiple unit trains. Although the realignment work had significantly improved the tunnels, had the positive rail, placed outside the running rails, been positioned at the same height as on the other lines it would have been dangerously close to the metal tunnel lining. Instead it was raised by an additional 1½ inches and was made with an inverted 'L' cross-section. To increase its conductivity copper bonds were run in parallel. The rolling stock was, and is to this day, fitted with special 'high-lift' shoe-gear to operate on the Central line.

East Finchley extension

North of its terminus at Highgate, the Morden-Edgware line was extended to join the surface tracks of the L&NER at East Finchley station via a single intermediate station at Highgate. In November 1936 work started on boring the four miles of running tunnel using a 13 ft 2¾ in diameter rotary excavator (powered by a 60 h.p. motor) and six 12 ft diameter Greathead shields.[237] One further Greathead shield was constructed for driving the station platform tunnels. The extension was on a gradient

A view out of the new tunnel portal on the northbound line, looking towards East Finchley. The wall on the right is a new structure to hold the embankment on which the original tracks lead south to Highgate. *(LTM)*

up to East Finchley, and one of the difficulties was in keeping the gradient manageable for underground trains whilst ensuring that the tunnels emerged at sufficient distance from East Finchley for them to pass over the Great North Road. The work was complicated by the need for the tunnels to emerge on either side of the existing railway, which was on an embankment.

Sheet steel piles were driven into the embankment to ensure that it remained supported during the construction work; these were linked together under the tracks by tie rods to help prevent the embankment from slipping. The earth was then dug away to form the tunnel approaches. The tunnels were bored as far as possible in reducing ground cover, the northbound tunnel being driven right through to the portal. The northernmost part of the southbound tunnel was constructed from tunnel segments within a trench and then buried in concrete to provide additional support. There was insufficient width to form a bell-mouth tunnel to alleviate the pressure increase, so instead a series of vents were made in the roof of the tunnel through which air would be expelled as a train entered the tunnel.

One new tube station was constructed on the extension, beneath the L&NER station at Highgate. This had the unusual feature of platforms 490 ft long, designed to accommodate trains nine-cars long. A congestion-relief plan from before the Second World War envisaged the operation of longer trains, and some surface stations received longer platforms. Highgate was the only tube station with longer platforms as it was comparatively cheap to make them longer during construction, compared with the cost of lengthening existing platforms. At each end of the platforms, three rings of 14 ft diameter were constructed at a slightly lower level, their axis being 1ft below that of the running tunnels. These provided a space to allow power and signalling cables to be crossed beneath the tracks.

The tunnelling work was substantially completed by the end of 1938,[238] and Northern line services were extended through the new tunnels on 3 July 1939. The new station at Highgate was not ready for traffic, and instead served as an air-raid shelter until 19 January 1941, when its platforms opened for rail passengers.

Bakerloo to Finchley Road

A bottleneck existed on the Metropolitan line with the tunnels between Baker Street and Finchley Road stations. North of the latter, there were four tracks – two in each direction. The tunnel section only had one track in each direction, which was a severe constraint for services. The solution was to build a new pair of tracks, but these could not be for the Metropolitan line otherwise the capacity problem would just be moved south to Baker Street and the services running over the north side of what is now the Circle line. By making the link an extension of the Bakerloo line, and connecting it with one of the pairs of tracks north of Finchley Road, all of the local Metropolitan line services south of Wembley Park could be moved to the Bakerloo, speeding up Metropolitan line services. Tunnels for the Bakerloo line would be cheaper as it operated tube trains, rather than the large 'surface' stock operated on the Metropolitan line. South of Baker Street the Bakerloo line also had spare capacity.

The majority of the extension was a straightforward pair of 12 ft diameter twin

The original plan for Baker Street omitted the lower escalator concourse between the southbound platforms, and would have included a further pair of escalators in another shaft linking the existing northbound Bakerloo line platform to the concourse under the Metropolitan line platforms. This would have meant switching the position of the track and the platform in the station tunnel, which would have been very disruptive to the train service. This plan also shows the unbuilt subway linking to the Circle line platforms, which would provide useful congestion relief today had it been constructed.

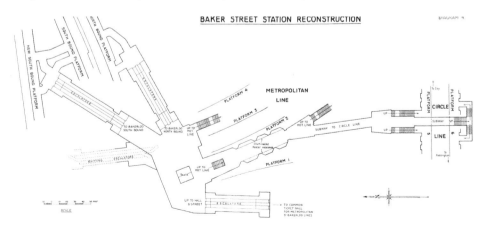

BAKER STREET STATION RECONSTRUCTION

tube tunnels 2¼ miles long, plus the platform tunnels for the stations at Swiss Cottage and St John's Wood. At both of these stations, a pair of escalators flanking a stairway descended from the ticket hall to a concourse tunnel between the platforms. Several cross-passages provided the connections between the platform and concourse tunnels. Large 'picture-frame' segments were inserted into the tunnels to form strong portals for the cross-passages. At each end of the platform tunnels three rings of 14 ft diameter rings were made. The crown of these was at the same level as that of the running tunnels, thus they formed a 2 ft enlargement in the tunnel invert. This was used to switch cables from one side of the tunnel to the other.[239]

The complexity on the extension lay at each end of the running tunnels, where it connected with the existing lines. At Baker Street a pair of step-plate junctions was constructed around the existing Bakerloo line tunnels. The larger ends of the junctions with rings varying from 31 ft 6 ins to 19 ft in diameter were dug by hand around the tunnels whilst the trains continued to run. The smaller ends, from 19 ft down to 14 ft were dug at night, with the old tunnel segments being dismantled as the work progressed, as space did not permit the work at this end of the junctions to take place without doing so.

An additional platform was also created at Baker Street, on the new southbound line. If two southbound trains were both approaching the station at about the same time this would allow either to wait in a platform, rather than a tunnel, while the other proceeded. For this reason the southbound step-plate junction was built to the south of the station whilst that on the northbound was to the north. A new shaft was excavated for a pair of escalators, descending from the area beneath the Metropolitan line platforms to a concourse between the two southbound platforms.

All the tunnelling works were the responsibility of Charles Brand & Son, who sunk shafts (from south to north) at Allsop Place (adjacent to Baker Street station), the goods yard at Marylebone station, Acacia Road, and Adelaide Road. That at Acacia Road was on the site of St John's Wood station, and those at Marylebone goods yard and Adelaide Road are now ventilation shafts.

If anything the work at Finchley Road was more problematic. The inner two tracks were being transferred to the Bakerloo line north of the station, but to the south the Metropolitan line tunnels were side-by-side. The first part of the work was therefore to build a new southbound tunnel, for which the contract was awarded to John Mowlem & Co. Property on both sides of Finchley Road needed underpinning as the tunnel was at shallow level beneath them. This work, and the tunnel construction, was performed from the basements of the buildings. Where it passed beneath the road it was constructed in small sections to avoid reducing the width of the road too much. Many services beneath the road required diversion to make the tunnel, which had brick walls supporting a succession of steel girders with concrete panels between them.

Once the Metropolitan line had been diverted into its new tunnel, the old tunnel was backfilled with clay with a covering of concrete. The northbound Bakerloo line tunnel was driven up to the surface through the clay, with the concrete ensuring that there was cover for the shield.

The southbound Bakerloo line tunnel descended from Finchley Road into a new covered way; once this was deep enough, the shield-driven tunnel began. A heavy

The step-plate junction under construction, with the lining of the existing tunnel crossing to the right braced with large timbers. The usual narrow-gauge railway leads from the new tunnel in the foreground to the workmen excavating the step-plate tunnel. *(The Railway Magazine)*

concrete retaining wall was constructed on the north side of the covered way, and a concrete invert beneath the tracks. Metal pillars were placed on the south side, between the two Bakerloo tracks. These supported a series of metal girders that formed the structure of the covered way roof.

The Ilford Tube

The eastern extension of the Central line ran from its terminus at Liverpool Street through to the L&NER tracks at Leyton, mostly in tube tunnel. A further tube tunnel was planned to run from Leytonstone to Newbury Park along the line of the Eastern Avenue. This work had a number of interesting tunnelling challenges to overcome, described below from west to east.

At Liverpool Street the pair of reversing sidings to the east of the station were lengthened at their eastern ends. A new crossover and junction tunnel was also built,

A view into a completed step-plate junction at Baker Street. The old lining has been dismantled and removed, and points and track have been laid. This was taken in August 1939, three months before the new tunnels opened to passenger traffic. *(LTM)*

The 7 ft pilot tunnel (background) being enlarged to full size, through the use of the Greathead shield in the middle of the picture. *(The Railway Gazette: Improving London's Transport supplement)*

also to the east of the existing crossover, and requiring sections of tunnel up to 31 ft 6 ins in diameter for the step-plate junctions.[240]

A rotary excavator was used to excavate the tunnels between Liverpool Street and Bethnal Green. It was reused from the East Finchley extension of the Northern line.[241] This was about the only section in ground good enough to allow use of this machine; the rest of the tunnels used Greathead shields and pneumatic picks and spades. The shields were fitted with 20 hydraulic rams, pressing forward with a thrust of just over 600 tons.[242] At Bethnal Green, large Greathead shields were used for the excavation of the platform tunnels.

At Mile End station the Central line platforms were to flank those of the District line, which was only about 23 ft below ground level. The new tunnels would have to rise up though the clay into the gravel layer above to achieve this, normally requiring compressed air working. It was decided that for the short length of tunnel this would be too expensive, and so an alternative approach was developed. A 7 ft diameter pilot tunnel was started whilst the shields were still within the clay, and this was driven using a smaller shield as far as the station. The wet ground above the pilot tunnel was then consolidated using the Joosten process, with the pipes being inserted into the ground via holes specially formed in the pilot tunnel segments. Additional consolidation was performed beneath the foundations of a theatre above the line of the tunnels. The pilot tunnel was then enlarged using the shield to its full 12 ft diameter.

Chemical consolidation was a repeated theme in the wet ground of east London, some of which was described by the engineers as having the consistency of pea soup.[243] Beyond Mile End station John Mowlem & Co. had to use compressed air for much of the tunnelling, and the alignment was kept below the main-line railway embankment to provide additional ground cover. The Greathead shields were hooded, and the clay-pocket process was used in all sections built using compressed air. Even with these precautions, where the main-line railway crossed the City Mill River on a bridge there was concern about the compressed air blowing a hole through the river bed. Ground consolidation was carried out below the river bed from barges moored below the bridge, connected to pumps and tanks on the towpath, and thereby forming an impermeable layer below which it was safe to tunnel. Sheet steel piles were inserted through the bed of the river for the length below which the tunnels would pass, to prevent the consolidation chemicals from spreading out too thinly.

A short distance to the east, where the line was to pass beneath the Waterworks River, the same approach could not be taken as a pier of the bridge carrying the main-line railway was in the centre of the river. After as much consolidation as possible was achieved from boats in the river, a 7 ft diameter pilot tunnel was bored and from this further consolidation chemicals were injected upwards to ensure a consistent layer above the line of the tunnels. As at Mile End, a shield was then used to enlarge the pilot tunnel to full size.[244]

The usual technique for constructing curved tunnels was to provide additional packing between adjacent tunnel lining rings, but there was concern that in soft, water-bearing ground this might increase the likelihood of leaks. For these tunnels it was decided to have some tunnel rings manufactured with a slight taper. By including these, curves of different radii could be constructed without the need for packing, as follows:

- two taper rings out of three: 20 chain curve
- one taper ring out of three: 40 chain curve
- one taper ring out of six: 80 chain curve

The taper rings were also used to correct the course of the tunnel where measurement shoed it diverging from the correct course. Other specialist castings were used at the junctions between tunnels to ensure watertightness, for example where side or cross passages joined with running tunnels. This increased the cost of construction, but reduced the long-term costs associated with pumping water from the tunnels.[245]

On the approach to Leyton station further use of the Joosten process was made beneath Loughton Branch Junction signal box, near Leyton. This had shallow foundations in the gravel layer, and the tunnels needed to rise to the surface beneath it as the location was constrained by housing on one side and the L&NER tracks on the other. By consolidating an area of about 30 ft by 50 ft under the signal box down to the level of the clay at 6 ft it was possible to bore the new tunnels without any disturbance. That many of the tubes injecting the chemicals into the ground were inside the signal box and threaded through the mechanical equipment without interfering with it made the feat even more impressive.

The new tube tunnels beneath the Eastern Avenue were built using concrete tunnel segments for 2¾ miles, because of a shortage of iron and steel as Britain began to arm itself for war. Cast iron was used for the remaining 1¼ miles. The

Concrete segments were also used for shafts. This segment, made by W.&C. French Ltd, was for the shaft at Cambridge Park Road. *(LURS Collection)*

tunnels made with the concrete lining were bored slightly larger than usual, at 12 ft 3 ins to allow for signalling equipment in the tunnel that would have tucked into the cast iron segments between the flanges. The reinforced concrete segments were 2 inches thick, and had steel-reinforced bolt holes. Six segments and a key were used for each tunnel ring, the same as was used for cast iron tunnel rings. The outside face of the segments was coated with a bituminous emulsion to protect the concrete against reacting with the clay, and Portland cement was injected behind them as grout.[246] The packing between segments was hessian coated in bitumen, and strips of creosoted timber ¼ inch thick were placed between adjacent rings. Progress with constructing these tunnels averaged 25 yds per week.

Testing the concrete tunnel rings

Tests had been conducted at Wood Lane depot prior to the decision being made to use the concrete segments, to ensure that they would have sufficient strength. A section of tunnel with a diameter of 8 ft 6 ins was constructed just below ground level, with 2 ft 6 ins of soil above. For half its length the tunnel segments were made from cast iron; the other half were concrete. Iron blocks weighing 175 tons were then placed above the tunnel, and it was found that the concrete bore this load even better that the iron, in which cracks were found. A second test was then performed, using a 12 ft diameter concrete tunnel. This time 228 tons of iron was placed on the ground directly above, and again, the concrete proved to be able to resist the load.

A further test was made to determine how the concrete rings would withstand the compressive forces of the hydraulic rams on a tunnelling shield. A single ring was erected in a tunnel under construction, and the shield was pushed forward. The earth had not been fully excavated in front of the shield, increasing the pressure required. The concrete ring failed when the pressure reached around 450 tons.[247]

> As a result of the tests, the segments were redesigned with thicker flanges, altered reinforcement, and fewer bolt holes. The new design was tested in the same way, and proved to be successful . An order for 48,000 concrete segments was then placed with Balfour Beatty & Co. and Kinnear, Moodie & Co. for use on the extension.[248]

The platform tunnels at Wanstead station were, like those at Bethnal Green, dug using large Greathead shields. At Redbridge the tunnels approached the surface and the station platforms were in a reinforced concrete box constructed using the cut and cover technique. The roof was supported by the side walls and by a line of columns placed along the centre of the island platform. Due to the shallow nature of the platforms a single stairway was provided for access, unlike the escalators installed at the other two tube stations on this extension. To protect the tunnels as they were bored eastwards from Wanstead station an embankment was built above their line on the surface, to increase the ground cover.[249] Compressed air was used as the tunnels approached the River Roding, just west of the station, as the soil in the valley around the river was waterlogged. These tunnels were constructed with cast iron segments.

Gants Hill was provided with a large vaulted concourse between the platforms, 140 ft long, and separated from the platforms by two lines of eight columns. This was constructed using a clever sequence of five tunnels being excavated in parallel.

In the first stage, pilot tunnels of 8 ft 6 ins diameter were excavated along the line of the platform tunnels, primarily to allow access to the western ends of both

The 228 tons of iron stacked above the 12 ft tunnel being tested.
(Pennyfare)

A view along the embankment built over the running tunnels, looking towards the River Roding. *(LURS Collection)*

tunnels, which were constructed conventionally using Greathead shields. Next, the tunnels adjacent to the platforms (called the erection headings) were bored, from opposite ends of the station, with the same diameter as a standard platform tunnel, 21 ft 2½ ins. As the shields approach each another, work ceased in one and the face was closed with boards. The other shield continued until it was safely past, at which point work resumed.

Once these two tunnels had been completed, eight cross-headings were made between them, in which large steel girders were fixed below the eventual floor level. A pair of steel columns was fixed to each girder, one in each of the two tunnels. At the same time, a 7 ft diameter pilot tunnel was bored above the centre line of the station, just outside and above the erection headings. This work was done in compressed air because of the presence of water-bearing gravels. The compressed air plant was installed at the top of the timbered shaft, and an airlock installed in a short section of tunnel constructed for this purpose between the shaft and the pilot tunnel.

An isometric drawing of Gants Hill station, showing the unusual shape of the concourse. *(The Engineer)*

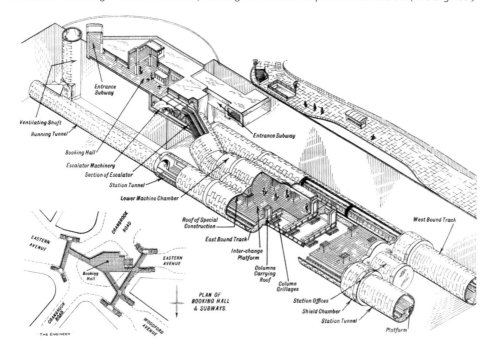

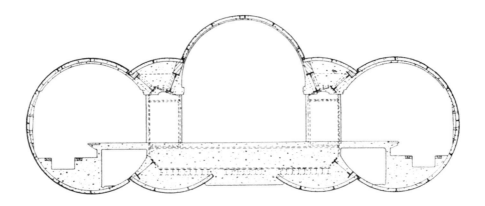

A cross-section of the platforms and lower concourse at Gants Hill, clearly showing the five overlapping tunnels that were used to create the complex shape. *(LT: Seven More Stations)*

In the next stage, the roofs of the erection headings were underpinned by the steel columns, through the use of steel joists, engineering bricks, and specially-cast concrete blocks. Grout was then injected into the structure thus formed to bind it into a single mass. Whilst this work proceeded the central pilot tunnel was enlarged to a diameter of 21 ft 2½ ins, with its lining being supported from below on the lining of the enlargement headings. Finally the platform tunnels were enlarged to full size, and the redundant segments from the erection headings were removed for reuse. Of the twelve segments that were used to form each of the rings originally, only five remained: two above, and three below. The concourse formed in this way was 50 ft between platform edges, and gives the impression of being formed from five parallel, overlapping tunnels. All of the work was carried out from a 15 ft diameter shaft sunk just east of the ticket hall, which was subsequently used for ventilation, and a temporary timber-lined shaft to the west.[250]

In total, forty different sites were used for the tunnelling of the various sections of the Central line east from Liverpool Street. In good conditions 200 ft of tunnel could be made in a week by an individual rotary excavator, but the work in compressed air averaged 60 ft per week.[251] In the summer of 1939 it seemed likely that tube trains would be running out to Leytonstone and beyond on the surface lines by the end of the following year, and through the Ilford Tube to Newbury Park in 1941. The start of the Second World War made the LPTB think again, but they decided to push on with the work until the declining situation in early 1940 brought it to a standstill.

Major station reconstruction work

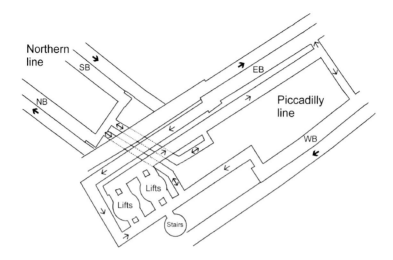

The original layout of the tube platforms and passageways at King's Cross St Pancras. Arrows indicate direction of pedestrian flow in subways. The bold arrows show the location and running direction of the tracks. Dotted lines show subways passing under other tunnels.

Rebuilding King's Cross[*]

Prior to the work starting in early 1936, King's Cross was served by three almost-separate underground stations. The Metropolitan Railway had opened their station on Pentonville Road in 1863, to the east of the main-line L&NER station (with which it was connected by a long curving pedestrian subway opened in 1892). The Piccadilly Tube opened their station further west, on the forecourt of the main-line station, in late 1906. Less than a year later, the C&SLR opened their station close to that of the Piccadilly; this is now the Northern line. Both companies each provided four lifts (in two shafts, with a pair of lifts in each) down to their respective platforms; interchange between the two tube lines was via two parallel staircases which linked the south-eastern headwalls of the C&SLR platforms (which were at a lower level) with the passageways connecting the Piccadilly lifts and platforms. Unusually the lifts for both lines had their lower landings at platform level, this being possible as the station sites were under the main-line station forecourt and so could place their platform tunnels further apart than usual.

At surface level the Piccadilly Tube had constructed a large building, clad in their signature ox-blood terracotta tiling, directly in front of the main-line station.

---

[*]   A version of this section was published in *Underground News*, January 2010

Contrary to their normal practice, the C&SLR provided no building, but instead had a sub-surface ticket hall near the Great Northern Hotel, reached via stairways in the street. The reconstructed station was to use this sub-surface ticket hall, but enlarged, as its main access point. It was subsequently named the Tube Ticket Hall.

No changes were made to the existing tunnels and passageways in the first stage of work. A 12-ft-diameter working shaft was sunk in the region of the Tube Ticket Hall, and from this a pilot tunnel for the main bank of escalators to the Piccadilly line was driven. The concourse between the Piccadilly platforms was created, together with the cross-passages to the platforms. Where the stairway to the Northern line was to be, another shaft was sunk, and a heading created beneath the tracks and platform of the eastbound Piccadilly line. The lower segments of the platform tunnel were removed during this work, to allow sufficient headroom in the subway. Steel joists across the concrete side walls of the subway replaced the segments. The subway turned left through ninety degrees after this point, and formed a passageway connecting with the eastern end of the southbound Northern line platform.

The connecting passage between the western end of the westbound Piccadilly line platform and the lifts was closed at the start of the second stage of work. In its place, a new tunnel was dug from the headwall of the same platform parallel with the lift shafts, and linking with the base of the spiral stairs. A widened section of this new tunnel was to form the upper concourse for the new Northern line escalators, together with the connection to the lower concourse for the Piccadilly line escalators.

The new concourse between the Piccadilly line platforms was opened to passengers, together with two pairs of cross-passages at the western end. Further work in this phase consisted of providing stairs in the subway to the Northern line, and constructing a very short connecting tunnel between two passageways to the north of the lifts.

For the third stage of the work, the two existing stairways linking the Piccadilly and Northern lines were closed, and the new subway passing beneath the eastbound Piccadilly line platform opened in their place. This allowed work to start on constructing a new concourse between the Northern line platforms, and south-eastwards to form the lower escalator landing. The upper escalator landing was enlarged as part of this stage, and a pilot shaft for the escalators was also sunk to link them. Part of the tunnel to the south of the lifts was opened to form a second route to the spiral stairs.

The fourth stage saw the Northern line concourse, together with its two pairs of cross-passages open. The shaft for the Northern line escalators was opened out to full size, to accommodate two escalators with a rise of 18 ft 6 ins, and a fixed stairway between.* The lower landing for the Piccadilly line escalators was also opened out during this stage. As this is located above the Northern line southbound running tunnel the latter was rebuilt using stronger iron segments; these replaced the tunnel that was enlarged in the 1920s, and which was as a result not completely circular.

The route between the Piccadilly line platforms and the lifts was also substantially altered. The original passageway from the lifts to the platforms was closed (probably because it was in the way of the new Northern line escalators), and instead

---

* This stairway was replaced by an escalator from 11 September 2002.

Workmen tightening a bolt between tunnel segments in a new escalator shaft at King's Cross, in December 1937. Behind the workman on the left can be seen the freshly cut surface of the clay. *(LTM)*

a new passageway was opened, running via the upper landing for the escalators that would lead to the Northern line. Hoardings were used to prevent access to the full landing. No indication is given of the passenger flow, but there was now a route from the north side of the lifts to the western headwall of the eastbound platform (the original exit from this platform), and another from the south side of the lifts, via the foot of the spiral stairs, to the western headwall of the westbound platform.

In the fifth and final stage of work, further changes were made to the passenger flows, with the route between the north side of the lifts and the eastbound platform closing. A clever rearrangement of the passageways to the south of the lifts, together with opening the connection between the upper Northern line escalator landing and the lower Piccadilly line escalator landing allowed this to happen, which in turn permitted the enlargement of the main escalator shaft to 18 ft 6 ins diameter. Part of this shaft passes close under the northbound single-line tunnel linking the City

Widened Lines to the main-line tracks at King's Cross, and was built with especially heavy iron segments. The shaft also trimmed the lower part of the Fleet Sewer tunnel, and a little concrete was required to protect this.

The diagram below shows the layout at this stage, with new works from all five stages in thicker black lines, and closed sections in grey. The closed staircases between the two lines are completely omitted for clarity. Three new escalators were installed with a rise of 56 ft 6 ins, linking the new ticket hall with the Piccadilly line.

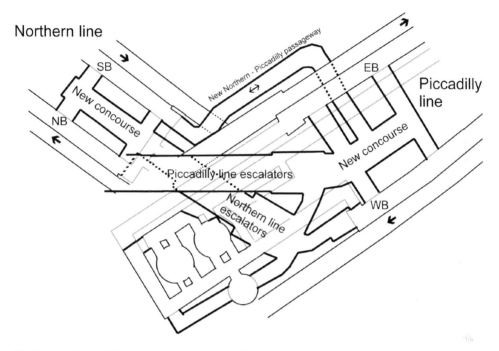

The layout of the additional passageways and escalators after the reconstruction work was completed at King's Cross St Pancras.

The two sets of escalators were opened on 18 June 1939, and the lifts were closed. The passageways to and from the lifts were closed off by closing up the two entrances on the upper landing of the Northern line escalators. Both original ticket halls were closed and replaced by a single elliptical hall beneath the station forecourt, to the west of the old GNP&BR building, and south of the C&SLR ticket hall. The steel and concrete roof of this hall was designed to take the weight of a four-storey building, as required by the L&NER. The new escalators were panelled with walnut wood from Queensland, as part of a new policy of decorating escalators with different woods from around the Empire.[252]

The Northern line lift shafts were to be capped off, and the booking hall was "to be let for other purposes", according to the Ministry of Transport Inspection Report. The same report noted that the basement of the Piccadilly line building was to be converted into staff accommodation and a buffet (the latter seems to have been dropped as an idea during the Second World War), and ventilation equipment was to be installed in one of the lift shafts.

After the war, two of the Piccadilly line lifts (in the same shaft) were returned to service to assist with the peak-hour ascending passenger flow. They re-entered service on 30 August 1947, and remained in service until 1953. The original GNP&BR building remained until 1963, and the site was for many years occupied by the unpleasant single-storey ticket hall building for the main-line station, and which was demolished as part of the main-line station's reconstruction in 2013.

As noted at the start of this section, the Metropolitan Railway station was to the east of the tube railway station, and featured four platforms under a glazed arched roof. The southern pair of platforms served the Metropolitan services, including those of the Inner Circle trains. The northern pair of platforms were for the use of main-line trains using the City Widened Lines.

When the London Passenger Transport Board came into being in 1933, the poor interchange at King's Cross was high up their list of items to rectify. The City Widened Lines platforms were to remain in position, but replacement platforms for the Metropolitan line services were planned to the west. Edmund Nuttall, Sons & Co. Ltd were appointed as contractors for the £250,000 project.

The most straightforward part of the project was the new eastbound platform. A tunnel already existed on the north side of the site for the new station, built in 1868 as part of an abortive attempt to connect the City Widened Lines to the main line at Euston. Between 1925 and 1935 this tunnel contained a single track eastbound connection between the Metropolitan line (at Charlton Street Junction) and the City Widened Lines, built to allow an improved Metropolitan line service to the City.* The eastbound (or outer rail) running line was now rerouted over the same path through this tunnel, but was linked back to the main tracks to the east of the station via a short length of new cut-and-cover tunnel. A 13-ft wide platform was constructed in the tunnel.

A new tunnel for the westbound line was needed, and this was constructed to the south of the main running tunnel. The work was complicated by the need to relocate a major sewer, and this was rebuilt into a new mass concrete wall on the south side, beneath the pavement of the Euston Road. This wall supported a series of steel arch ribs placed 5 ft apart and supporting pre-cast concrete panels forming the roof structure. The existing brick tunnel was exposed during this work, and temporary concrete struts were installed to take the lateral forces from its arch once the support from the soil was removed. The westbound (or inner rail) running line was relocated into this new tunnel, and a 12-ft wide platform provided. Construction was complicated by the position of the tunnel beneath the busy Euston Road, and small working sites were opened up through which materials and spoil had to pass. The road was slightly narrowed, and traffic inspectors were stationed at gaps in the fencing along the edges of the temporary pavements to marshal pedestrians across the road.

The two original brick tunnels needed waterproofing on internal surfaces to make them acceptable for passenger use. Firstly the walls were cleaned of the dirt and

---

* Services started using the connection on 15 May 1926, and ceased running on 27 April 1935.

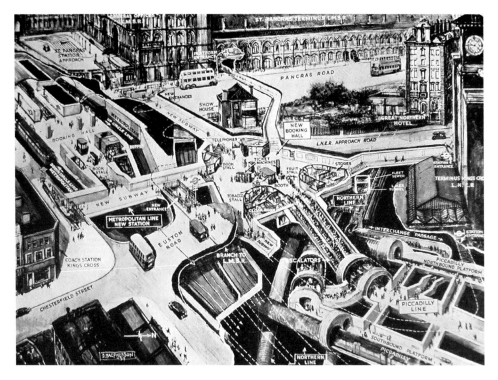

An isometric drawing of the station, published in 1941, showing the new escalators and Metropolitan line platforms. The bay platform is just visible in the top left. The Hotel Curve is also shown, passing in front of the Great Northern Hotel and beneath the L&NER Approach Road. *(Daily Telegraph)*

grime that had accumulated from decades of use as running tunnels. Bituminous sheeting was heated and pressed onto the brickwork, and then covered with steel mesh. Cement was sprayed over this to a thickness of 2 inches, and this was then covered with plaster onto which the tiling was fixed. Above cross-passages copper sheeting was formed into channels which directed any water to drainage at the side. All of the platforms and cross-passages were tiled in the standard square biscuit-coloured tiles used at Underground stations in the 1930s.

The original running line tunnel in between the two new platforms was equipped with a single track bay platform, with 9 ft 6 ins platforms either side, and connections to both inner and outer rail tracks at its western end. Cross-passages linked the bay platforms with their adjacent through-line platforms.* The work on the bay platform was not completed, and the track was not electrified. In 1952, when consideration was being given to a new service pattern for the Circle line which would make use of the bay platform, it was estimated that the work to complete it would cost £39,000. The scheme fell though, and the platform was never brought into regular use.[253]

At the eastern end all of the platforms merged into a single wide concourse, with

---

*   The bay platform was originally intended for Metropolitan line services extended from Baker Street. In the event these never happened.

a flight of stairs leading up to join a subway beneath the Euston Road. The south end of this subway connected to street level, and the north end led into the new Tube Ticket Hall. Beyond this concourse, where the running tunnels converged a bell-mouth tunnel was formed with a steel-reinforced concrete roof; the same type of construction was used at the extreme west end of the station.

Unfortunately the plans do not show the detailed phasing of the work, but they do indicate that the station was not fully complete on its opening date of 14 March 1941. A coloured plan shows that the bay platform and the cross-passages to it were closed, as were the westernmost thirds of the main platforms, as they were awaiting their surface coating of asphalt. Part of the eastern concourse was also closed, as was the southernmost third of the flight of steps and the connection to the south side of the Euston Road; it would seem that the subway had been completed and opened in June 1939, but the connection with the new stairs was cause for it to be temporarily closed.

The reason for the station opening in an uncompleted state was that the original Metropolitan station was damaged by bombs on the night of 9 March; prior to this the new platforms were planned to open on 6 April. The finishing works do not seem to have taken long to complete, as they are not mentioned in the Ministry of Transport Inspection Report, which was written following a visit to the station on 28 March 1941. The Inspection Report for the escalator works to the tube lines notes that the new Metropolitan station was due to open around September 1940; that the war only delayed the work by six months is a credit to those involved.

Moving Aldgate East
The extreme eastern end of the Inner Circle — today called the Circle line — presented an operational problem for the LPTB. A triangular junction had been formed in 1884, with Aldgate station forming the western side. To the north and south of Aldgate were, respectively, Aldgate Junction (sometimes called North Curve Junction) and Minories Junction. The apex to the east was called Aldgate East Junction, and immediately beyond it were the platforms of Aldgate East station. With increased passengers during the 1930s the LPTB had lengthened trains from six to eight cars. The problem was that the sides of the Aldgate triangle were only six cars long, so an eight-car train held at a red signal at one of the junctions would be blocking another of the junctions. The outer rail (clockwise) Circle line platform at Aldgate had the same problem, so an eight-car train in this platform would prevent any other traffic across Aldgate Junction.

Schemes involving flyunders, to get rid of the flat crossings were considered, but such works at the edge of the City of London would not be cheap, and would probably involve the closure of Aldgate East station which would not be beneficial to passengers. The decision was taken instead to build a replacement station further east. This would be quite close to the existing station of St Mary's, which as a consequence could be closed. Aldgate East Junction could be moved eastwards as well, increasing the length of both the north and south curves, and by moving Minories Junction slightly further south the platforms at Aldgate station could be lengthened. The plan met all of the requirements for traffic, but there was one more: the work had to be achieved without interrupting the train service, or closing Aldgate East until the new station was ready, or interfering with the trams running in the street overhead.

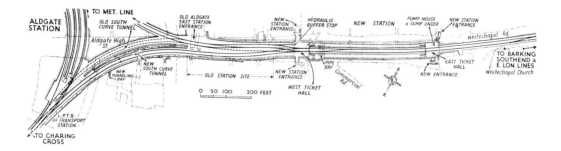

A plan of the Aldgate East reconstruction. The Aldgate triangle is at the far left; the north curve is mostly omitted, as is Aldgate Junction. Minories Junction is at bottom left, with the old and new south curve tunnels to its upper right. The site of the old station is marked, showing how this was widened to accommodate four tracks so that Aldgate East Junction could be moved to the east. The new station occupies the right-hand side of the plan up as far as the eastern entrance. The height of the track was adjusted as far as the crossover at the far right. *(Railway Gazette)*

The practicality of constructing a new station and tunnel with a live railway running through, and just beneath a busy street was a challenge.

In order to help visualize the work, two models were made, at a scale of ¼ inch to the foot, showing all of the services and tunnels below the streets. The first model was of the situation before the works started, and the second showed how things were to be after the works completed.

The basic premise by which the station resiting was to be done was straightforward enough. The new station was to be built around the tunnel east of the station. A new south curve tunnel would be formed to the south of the existing tunnel. The new station would be opened, and the old station closed. The old platforms would be demolished and the tracks could then be diverted into the space that the platforms had occupied and then continue westwards into the new south curve tunnel.

In order to fit four parallel tracks through the site of the old station the existing columns supporting the roof needed to be removed (they were in the way of the new tracks) and the tunnel had to be widened on the south side. The widening was done first by building a new south wall. This passed underneath buildings on the south side of Whitechapel High Street, and some of the work was carried out from the basements. The wall was needed to hold up one end of the 21 new girders, which would span the tracks and support the ceiling without the need for columns. They were specially shaped to span the existing tracks, and, being up to 68 ft long and weighing up to 30 tons, very difficult to manœuvre in the confined space of the tunnels. They each had to be installed in the six-hour period on Saturday nights when trains were not running, making the task even more difficult.

The solution was to make the girders in two pieces, and place each on a separate wagon with a turntable beneath. They were brought to the worksite on these wagons directly from the manufacturer, the Fairfield Shipbuilding Company in Chepstow. Each works train followed the last passenger train into the station, and the work then began to swivel the girder halves into position, and move them onto trucks running on temporary rails laid on the platforms. The two halves were then bolted together before being lifted into position.[254]

Further west the new south curve tunnel was made adjacent to the existing tunnel by mining a heading from the underground (and disused) WCs along the line of the new north wall. The south wall was more complicated to build as it passed directly beneath several buildings, and their foundations were considered to be weak. Pits were dug under short sections of the front walls of the buildings, where the party walls between buildings were located. Concrete foundations were cast in the pits, and girders were then inserted between them and the north wall. The weight of the buildings was transferred onto the girders, and then work on constructing the rest of the south wall could proceed. This was extended south to a point beyond Minories Junction so that the tunnel roof could be extended southwards as well. This allowed the air space above the junction (which had previously been in the open) to be covered over and used for a new bus station.

On the site of the new station there was a snag with the design. There was to be a sub-surface ticket hall at each end, placed on a mezzanine above the tracks. In order to gain sufficient headroom the tracks needed to be lowered by up to 7 ft, which meant that the tunnel inverts also needed to be lowered for some distance either side of the new station.

The work of building the new station was done in two halves, starting on the north side first; by doing one side at a time the flow of traffic on the Whitechapel High Street could be maintained. Fortunately the tram tracks were along the middle of the road, above the old tunnel. The work took place behind the existing tunnel walls, by excavating down from the surface, mostly at night. Temporary steel supports were placed across the excavations to keep the old tunnel arch from spreading as the earth was removed from behind the walls. Concrete foundations for steel stanchions were cast in lines along and below the length of the future platforms, and mass concrete retaining walls cast in trenches to form the outside walls of the station. A thick layer

One of the girders has been assembled across the platforms, with the special transporter wagons still in place below. The slot to take the girder has been made in the existing roof (top right), and the columns that will be removed later can be seen on both platforms. *(Railway Gazette)*

An unusual view looking beneath the suspended tracks after the wooden trestles had been removed. The ballast is ready to take the tracks. At the left side advertisements can be seen ready on the walls of the new station. *(LTM)*

of asphalt waterproofing was placed on the rear surface of the walls. Replacement sewers were built behind these walls, to replace those that were now between the old and new tunnel walls, in the space to be occupied by the platforms. Once they were brought into use the old sewers were broken out so that the steel stanchions could be installed. Longitudinal girders running the length of the station were bolted to the top of both lines of stanchions, and then the remainder of the material around the stanchions was removed, thus forming the space for the new platforms.

When the work on both sides of the old tunnel was ready, the old tunnel arch was demolished. To allow this to continue during traffic hours a curve metal 'shield', shaped to fit within the arch, was installed in the original tunnel and supported on brackets fixed to the tunnel walls. This protected the tracks and trains from any débris that might fall. As the shield moved along, large 'fish-belly' girders (i.e., girders with a trapezoid form, with the longest side uppermost) were lowered into the tunnel during the night and then raised up under the tram tracks and fixed to the longitudinal girders on either side of the railway. Rolled steel joists between these girders supported the tram tracks, and timber sheeting prevented any material falling into the railway tunnel. The proper tunnel roof could then be installed, using concrete beams between the girders. A layer of concrete, followed by asphalt water-proofing was then laid across these, and the road surface was reinstated above.

Beneath the tracks the existing tunnel invert was broken out during night-time possessions of the line. Each night a 60 ft length of new sleepers fixed to steel joists was brought into the station area on a flat-bed truck and suspended from eye-bolts in the roof. The wagon was removed, and the 60 ft length of track beneath the new

The eye-bolts remain in the ceiling of Aldgate East today, acting as a small reminder of the massive operation to resite the station in 1938. *(Author)*

sleepers was dismantled and some of the ballast was removed. Timber baulks that were to form the top of trestles were laid down every eight feet and the new sleepers lowered into position. The original running and conductor rails were then fixed to the new sleepers. Once all of the track had been completed through the length of the new station work began on breaking out the existing invert, excavating downwards, and constructing the new invert. As this progressed, wooden trestles were inserted beneath the trestle tops that had been laid under the rails. This process was continued on both sides of the new station, with the tunnel walls being underpinned down to the new invert. In this way 1,200 ft of double track was supported on trestles with an intensive service of trains operating over them for 20 hours per day.

The new station needed to be completed as far as possible. Walls and pillars were tiled, signs fixed to the walls, and even advertisements pasted to the platform walls. Stairways leading down from the street were constructed, and the mezzanine ticket halls were formed — in part. The centre portion of both ticket halls, above the tracks, could not be completed whilst the trains were running. Everything else was made ready for passenger use. Then, starting at 01.00 on Sunday 30 October 1938 the changeover began. Around 900 men descended on the station and the track was again suspended from the eye-bolts in the ceiling on block and tackle gear, having first been cut into sections 240 ft long. The sleepers were unbolted from the steel joists that had held them in place whilst on the timber trestles, and then the latter were dismantled and removed. The track was then lowered onto a new ballasted formation. Signalling and other equipment was reconnected and tested. Meanwhile, in the western ticket hall the steelwork to support the portion of the floor above the tracks was assembled and a temporary wooden floor was laid. The line reopened to traffic first thing on Monday 31 October, having been closed for just one day.[255]

The platforms and stairways of the old station were demolished on the same Sunday that the track was lowered. This made space for the new tracks leading into the new south curve tunnel. Over the course of the next four weeks these tracks were laid, and the necessary signals and other equipment were installed in the new tunnel. Finally, on Sunday 27 November, between 01.00 and 05.00 the new south curve was connected at both ends and the tracks leading through the site of the old station were moved to their final positions.[256]

Wartime works

Floodgates

The fear that a bomb dropped into the River Thames could lead to widespread flooding of the Underground tunnels led to the construction of floodgates in the tunnels either side of the river. For engineering reasons these were of several different types, and required careful installation.

Common engineering features included a break in the conductor rails where the gate closed, and the creation of a sill in the tunnel immediately below the tracks through which cables carried the current between the sections of conductor rail on either side. Rubber-coated metal blocks were placed across the sill prior to the gate closing to form a watertight seal. The cables that run along the side of all tube tunnels were diverted into new cable runs built behind the tunnel segments where the gate was located so that they would not impede the gate. Spare ducts were made at the same time in case additional cables were run through at a point in the future. These were sealed by tapered caps made of gunmetal screwed onto the duct; if a cable needed to be run through the duct then the cap was cut off at the point that matched the cable thickness, thus forming a good fit around the cable. It was then sealed fully by forming a wiped lead joint.

Special signalling was installed to ensure that the gates could not be closed if there was a train approaching, especially from the under-river tunnels, and a flood-gate control room could monitor and command the operation of all the gates from one location. A cabin was placed on each platform adjacent to the gate, from which the operation of the gate was actually controlled. Upon receiving the signal from the control centre the local gate operator would check the signal panel to ensure that no trains were in the under-river sections of tunnel and then trigger the gate closure.

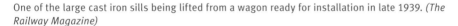

One of the large cast iron sills being lifted from a wagon ready for installation in late 1939. *(The Railway Magazine)*

Embankment station, in close proximity to the river, was one of the areas of greatest concern. Gates were fitted at the ends of all the platforms, including the District line. At the south ends of the Bakerloo line platforms the end walls were stripped of any decoration and the gates were installed flush against the walls and in a slot at the platform end, so that they could slide sideways across the tracks and into a cast iron frame. The sills were formed from special iron castings that were set into the tunnel inverts. This work required the enlargement of the tunnels around the gate location.

The gates were electrically operated, with closure taking just one minute, but like all such floodgates had the ability to be closed manually (in 4½ minutes) in case of electrical failure. A rack on the gate was driven by a pinion gear driven by the motor, via a chain drive and gearbox, or by a hand crank. The motor could be switched between the local electricity board supply, or the LPTB supply for greater redundancy.

The sill blocks had to be positioned across the railway tracks before the gate was closed, as they formed the track on which the rollers on the bottom of the gate would move. They fitted over the running rails, and had metal pins at each end which dropped into holes cast in the sills for this purpose. The mild steel gates were manufactured by Glenfield & Kennedy Ltd of Kilmarnock, and were each 13 inches thick, and weighed just under 6 tons. Once closed they could resist a force of 800 tons, with the help of a large reinforcing strut constructed vertically across the tunnel and a metal 'lip' fixed to the lintel above the tunnel mouth, behind which the top of the gate rested. This was estimated as being several times the actual force that would be exerted by the water from a damaged tunnel. There were rubber seals to make the joint between the gate and the tunnel watertight. An escape hatch was installed on the river side of the floodgates so that if anyone was in the tunnel when they gate closed they would have an egress route around the gate and into the platform area via an opening in the headwall.[257] The reinforcing column also held the switch that proved the position of the gate. This worked by engaging in a slot on the gate, which was horizontal across the majority of the gate, but curved up at one end and down at the other; as the gate closed the switch was moved in the slot to show the status changing from open, to intermediate, to closed.[258]

The Northern line tunnels at Embankment had a different type of gate fitted. It was not possible to enlarge the tunnels at the southern end of the platform as the waterlogged ground around them would have required compressed air working; impossible to achieve without suspending the train service for a period of time.[259] Instead, a series of protective doors were installed. A square metal frame was fitted at the north end of the platform, and a curved metal beam above allowed the two sections of the steel gate to be swung into position using an electric winch. These were then dropped into the slot between the end wall and the frame, blocking the tunnel portal. A manila rope was pressed into the joint between the gate sections and the frame to prevent water from coming through.

Being at the north end of the platforms, these gates would not prevent water from a damaged tunnel from entering the station via the stair and escalator shafts. These access points to the platforms were fitted with their own gates as protection, three on each platform. These gates were made of single pieces of armour plate steel, and curved to match the inside curvature of the tunnel. They fitted into rails on either side of each cross-passage and could be lowered into position by gravity. They were raised again by electric motors placed on girders above the platform and tracks; curved racks fitted to the gates engaged with sprockets on axles driven by the motors.

The District line was protected against flooding if the Victoria Embankment wall was breached by gates weighing 14 tons hinged from the tunnel roof fitted at both ends of Charing Cross station and a single gate at the east end of South Kensington. This latter gate dropped vertically, like a sluice gate, and was the width

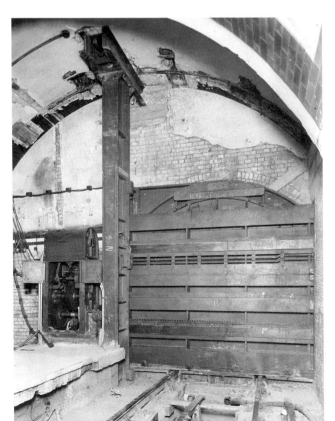

A sliding floodgate in position at Embankment station, on the Bakerloo line. The control equipment can be seen on the left. Above the gate is the lip on the tunnel frame. Much of the headwall decoration has been removed as part of the work to install the floodgate. *(LTM)*

A view south along the southbound platform at Embankment (then called Charing Cross), showing the gravity-operated gates that closed the access passageways. The motors above the tracks are prominent, and the racks which were used to raise the gates can be seen just to the right of the motors. *(LTM)*

of the double-track tunnel. A similar gate, but in two sections, was fitted north of Rotherhithe station on the East London line.

At Waterloo, the north ends of both the Bakerloo and Northern line platforms were fitted with more floodgates, of the same design as the Bakerloo gates at Embankment. Those on the Northern line were demonstrated to journalists on 5 October, who reported that the Bakerloo line gates on either side of the river were complete and that work was proceeding on the Northern line.[260] A decision was still awaited on gates for the City branch of the Northern line, which in the meantime was plugged with concrete on either side of the river. Work installing gates of the type used on the Bakerloo line at Embankment started in March 1940, and the train service resumed two months later.

At London Road depôt on the Bakerloo line, a single hand-operated floodgate sealed the tunnel mouth. This was installed to protect the tunnels from a burst sewer in the vicinity of the depôt.

Within some central stations there was a risk of flooding if a water main or sewer was damaged in a bombing raid. Large watertight doors were fitted in key passageways, at stations such as Trafalgar Square and King's Cross. At the latter station the risk of flooding was such that the Northern and Piccadilly line platforms were closed and the access passageways sealed with concrete plugs until the watertight doors could be fitted. When open they were designed to fit into recesses in the walls so as not to impede passengers.*

The factory tunnel

When war broke out, the tunnelling between Leytonstone and Newbury Park was practically complete, but there was no possibility of getting it ready for trains during the war. In autumn 1940 it was offered to the Ministry of Aircraft Production by LT, after the Ministry had sought help in finding protected facilities for manufacturing

---

* The doors at Leicester Square remained visible until around 2003 when they were tiled over as part of a refurbishment scheme. Others remain on show today, for example on the lower concourse at Maida Vale station.

OPERATING EQUIPMENT
AT FLOOD GATES
Numbers 2.3.5.10.12.20.21 and 22

A diagram issued to station staff about the operation of floodgates. *(LT Air Raid Precautions Appendix 3)*

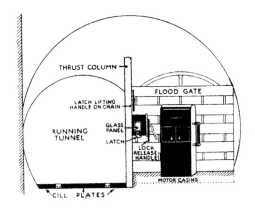

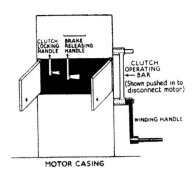

critical aircraft components. The nearby Plessey factory was thought to be vulnerable to German bombing, and alternative sites were needed.

The work to convert the tunnels into a factory took until March 1942. A concrete floor was installed along their length, which included narrow-gauge tracks along one side for a railway that carried material to the workers and removed completed products. The other side of the tunnel was for the various pieces of manufacturing equipment. Precast concrete blocks were fitted to the tunnel invert where the sleepers would eventually be fitted, and on these precast concrete slabs formed the floor. The two lines of blocks subdivided the area beneath the floor into three; the central duct was used to supply fresh air throughout the tunnels via metal ducts that were regularly spaced along the tunnel wall and fed the air in above head height. The side spaces beneath the floor were used as exhaust ducts, pulling in air at floor level. Alongside the railway, power and telephone cables for the factory were hung on the metal brackets installed for the railway cables. A power 'bus bar' run along the tunnel crown supplied the various machines used by the workers, and lighting was installed over the machines all along the tunnels. The tunnel linings were sprayed with white paint to maximize the effectiveness of the lighting. The height of the floor was set to maintain a minimum headroom along the centre of the tunnel of 9 ft 3 ins. The factory had a floor area of 300,000 ft^2 over the 8,500 yards of tunnel that it occupied.

All three of the future station sites allowed access for factory workers and materials. They also all housed air conditioning equipment pumping air into the under-floor ducts, fire stations, and electrical substations for the machinery (installed in part of the ticket hall area at Gants Hill).The latter supplied a ring main through the factory tunnels supplying three-phase 400 V AC. Redbridge station included an underground canteen for 600 people, and at Wanstead and Gants Hill mess rooms were provided. Further ventilation equipment was installed at the shafts at Whipps Cross, Nutter Lane, and Redbridge substation.

Four additional shafts were sunk in pairs at Cambridge Park (diameters of 15 ft and 5 ft) and Danehurst Gardens (diameters of 10 ft 6 ins and 7 ft); the latter involved demolishing the house at 252 Eastern Avenue and replacing it by a brick shafthead building which remains today. Lifts in these shafts allowed factory workers access to the tunnels, and reduced the longest walk for any worker through the tunnel to ¼ mile. Hoists were also provided for materials at both locations, as well as at all three stations. Additional tunnels at the base of these shafts provided space for mess rooms. Sewage from the toilets in the factory was forced to the level of the sewers using compressed air, via pipes installed in the shafts. Where these were too far from the toilets, additional 10-inch-diameter steel-lined pipes were sunk from the surface. These had 4-inch sewage ejector pipes installed within, and the remainder of the space was used as a ventilation extract.

A number of protective measures were taken for the safety of the workers in the factory. The air intakes supplying the ventilation equipment were placed in towers 30

Two cross-sections of the Plessey tunnel factory. (*LTM*)

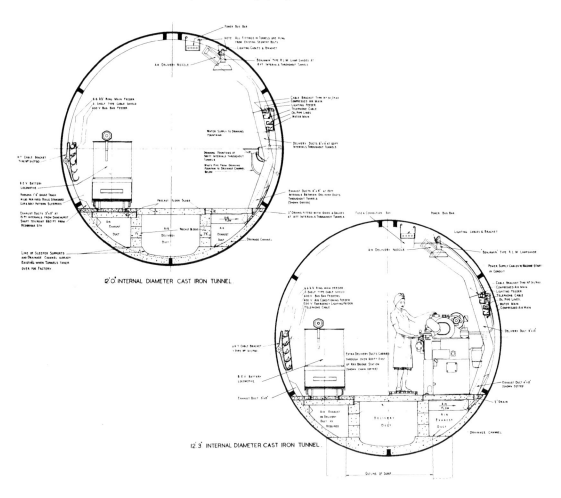

Workmen installing lighting and machinery on the platform at Redbridge ready for the Plessey factory. The tracks for the factory railway can be seen on the left-hand side of the tunnel. The white-painted pillars in the middle of the scene, behind the equipment, run along the centre of the platform. *(LTM)*

ft above the ground to reduce the risk of drawing in poison gas (which is heavier than air). Heavy floodgates were installed either side of the shallow section of tunnels beneath the River Roding. No equipment was placed between the gates, which could be quickly closed if a bomb were to rupture the tunnel at this point. Furthermore, the ground cover above the tunnels near to the river was increased by embanking soil excavated during the digging of the deep-level shelters in London (see next section) over them. [261]

Once operational, the factory remained in use until 1945, with around 2,000 workers per shift producing components for Halifax and Lancaster bombers as well as other military equipment. After the war the factory was closed, and between January and May 1946 Plessey removed their equipment. LT then took the rest of the year to break out the concrete floors and restore their tunnels so that fitting out as a railway could take place.

Demolition of the structures in the tunnels for the Plessey factory.

A design for a deep level shelter, shown in an LT workshop at Parson's Green. *(LTM)*

Shelters beneath stations

In late 1940 the Government consulted with LT about how best to provide deep-level bunkers under London. LT recommended that such bunkers should be built along the route of the Northern and Central lines so that they could be joined together after the war to form duplicate tunnels for express train services. By building the bunkers alongside existing stations joint access arrangements could be made. Ten sites were identified, on the Northern line at Belsize Park, Camden Town, Goodge Street, Oval, Stockwell, Clapham North, Clapham Common, and Clapham South, and on the Central line at Chancery Lane and St Paul's.

The work was undertaken by the LPTB on behalf of the Ministry for Home Security. No time was lost: designs for the shelters were being put together in November 1940, at LT's works at Parsons Green, and construction started on 27 November. Shafts were sunk for the bunkers on derelict sites or abandoned buildings where possible, and the 1,400 ft of 16 ft 6 ins internal diameter twin tunnels for each shelter was excavated by hand-mining without the use of Greathead shields, which would have taken too long to procure. The main shelter tunnels were divided into two levels by means of a concrete floor installed half-way up, and connections between the two levels were by stairs at the cross-passages. These passages linked the two tunnels together at both levels.

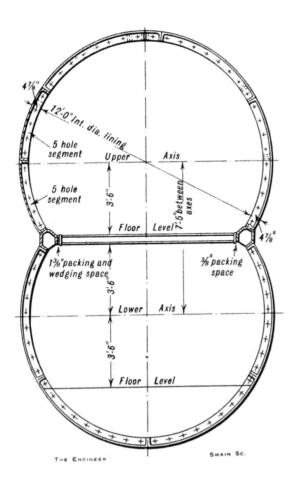

4⅞"

12'-0" Int. dia. lining

5 hole segment   Upper   Axis

5 hole segment

3'-6"

7'-6" between axes

Floor   Level

4⅞"

1⅜" packing and wedging space

3'-6"

⅜" packing space

Lower   Axis

3'-6"

Floor   Level

THE ENGINEER

SWAIN SC.

A cross-sectional drawing of the overlapping passageways. Each level used four segments, and the hexagonal wedges are noticeable where the tunnels meet. The floor/ceiling between the passages is a structural component. *(The Engineer)*

Each bunker had two shafts sunk 200 yds apart, and the tunnels were constructed so that the shafts were one-quarter and three-quarters of the way along. In this way eight tunnel faces could be operated at each site, speeding up the work. During construction work the shafts were the limiting factor on the work, due to the volumes of material that needed to be moved, and each shafthead crane was averaging one lift every 40 seconds. When the work was completed the shafts were fitted with metal spiral staircases. Two were fitted in each shaft, entwined like a DNA double-helix, each serving a different level of the shelter.

Work at St Paul's was never started owing to opposition from the Cathedral authorities who feared for the stability of the building if tunnels were made nearby. The shelter at Oval was never completed because of problems with water at the site. Although both shafts were sunk and a little tunnelling was completed, further work would have required the use of compressed air, and the increase in cost was not seen as being worthwhile. Instead, the remaining eight shelters (still under construction) had their main tunnels continued to a length of 1,400 ft from the originally planned 1,200 ft.[262]

The construction work was standard for most of the shelters. Once the shafts were down, cross-passages were made running at right-angles to the direction of the main shelter tunnels. At some shelters two passages were made one above the other, but some were made with the tunnels overlapping. These tunnels were made by excavating the lower tunnel slightly ahead of the upper (by two tunnel rings). The segments for the lower tunnel were erected, but not at the crown, where poling boards supported the clay. Once the upper tunnel had progressed the boards were replaced by steel joists that connected with the upper and lower segments via special hexagonal wedges.

From each of these cross-passages, the four headings for the main tunnels were made. The work of excavating these was slow, in part because of the lack of skilled labour, but also because the tunnels were large and no shields were used. Typical progress was the completion of two tunnel rings per shift. Kinnear, Moodie & Co., who were constructing the shelters at Clapham North and Stockwell, improvised some rudimentary shields and doubled their rate of construction. The shield was made by assembling four complete cast iron tunnel rings with packing to give a diameter of 16 ft 8 ins. A mild steel skin was attached around the rings, and the flanges of the rearmost rings were cut away to allow some second-hand hydraulic jacks to be connected. Additional structural support was made within the shield from

The improvised tunnelling shield at work. On the right is a conveyor belt for removing the spoil, and the vertical steel joist is prominent in the centre of the photograph. *(The Engineer)*

rolled steel joists and steel plates, and the front ring was filled with concrete to the depth of the flanges to reinforce the cutting edge. A timber platform 35 ft long was attached to the back of the shield, on which a conveyor belt was made to remove the spoil. Rollers and an electric winch assisted with erecting the tunnel segments behind the shield.

The wartime conditions made it difficult to obtain the large amount of cast iron tunnel segments, although over 6,000 were obtained from Middlesbrough. Two-thirds of the tunnelling was completed using concrete segments, following their successful use on the Central line extensions east of Liverpool Street. The shafts for the shelters built using concrete segments were 16 ft 6 ins diameter, whereas those where cast iron segments were used had a diameter of 16 ft.[263]

The concrete segments were made by three different companies. A specification was provided to them, but otherwise the type of concrete was left up to them. After some experimentation with timber and steel moulds, the best solution was found to be a mould with a concrete base (forming the inside surface of the tunnel) and timber sides. Each ring was made up from eight segments and a key. The segments were bolted together like those of cast iron, with creosoted wooden packing between the segments in a ring. A tarred hemp rope was used to form the seal between adjacent rings.

Each segment of the concrete lining was divided into five by flanges running from side to side. Adjacent rings were staggered to increase the strength of the tunnel. This view was taken in 1941 during construction work. *(Hulton Archive)*

The Victoria line

The planning for the first completely new underground line across London since 1907 started in earnest in the late 1940s. By the mid-1950s the route between Victoria and Walthamstow was fairly well defined. A major change in approach to tube railways was that the Parliamentary powers that authorized the line, the British Transport Commission Act 1955, authorized the taking of the subsoil rights for the line, with payment of compensation. This allowed the line to cut across the street pattern entirely, without the time-consuming and costly need to negotiate with a huge number of property owners to agree easements.[264]

In 1946 the Railway (London Plan) Committee recommended that Route 8 (the embryonic Victoria line) should have running tunnels that would allow the passage of main-line rolling stock (with a diameter of "not less than 17 ft"), as it would have connected with the L&NER near Hornsey and with the Southern Railway near Norbury. In the 1949 London Plan Working Party Report, the line had altered to have tunnels with a diameter of 12 ft, as this would allow cross-platform interchange with the Bakerloo line at Oxford Circus.[265] As the plans developed consideration was given to the intermediate diameter of 14 ft 6 ins, as this would allow more passengers to be carried but without incurring the substantially greater costs of tunnels 17 ft in diameter.

The problem was threading the line through the increasingly crowded sub-strata of London, and in particular arranging the cross-platform interchanges that were seen as highly desirable. In the discussion that followed a paper read to the Institution of Civil Engineers in 1959 noted that

> If the line was built for larger than normal size tube rolling stock it would follow that as well as greatly increasing the constructional costs for the larger diameter tunnel, the cross-platform interchange at Oxford Circus, Euston, Highbury, and Finsbury Park would have to be forfeited which would be out of the question. Furthermore since the railway would be deeper, in order to clear some of the existing tunnels, [...] the escalators would cost more to build and to maintain, and the journey time for passengers would be longer. It was considered, therefore, that the advantages of building a tube for larger rolling stock, with a 10% greater carrying capacity, were outweighed by the disadvantages given above.[266]

Early experimentation
The missing ingredient, as ever, was money. Although the Government refused to commit the £50 million estimated cost of the line, money was made available for the construction of a length of experimental tunnel designed to try out new forms of tunnel building. These were built along the route planned for the Victoria line, so that they could be used if the line was approved, and because the route already had

Parliamentary powers. Approval for the construction of the mile of twin tube tunnel was given in 1959, at a cost of around £1 million.

Two contractors were appointed for the work. Edmund Nuttall, Sons & Co started work first, in January 1960, sinking a 25 ft diameter shaft to a depth of 60 ft. A heading at the base of the tunnel crossed the line of both running tunnels, allowing shield construction chambers to be built by hand. Shortly afterwards Kinnear Moodie & Co sunk a shaft to the same depth, but only 15 ft in diameter, in Finsbury Park, near to the tennis courts. Another pair of shield construction chambers were built here. Both contractors then began tunnelling separate running tunnels towards each other until in March 1961 they reached Manor House, where a cross-passage was dug connecting them. This allowed the precision and tunnel alignment to be checked. Each contractor then returned to their original shaft and constructed their other section of running tunnel parallel to the first, and connecting with the first-bored tunnels at Manor House. The tunnels were completed in July 1961.

The first innovation that was tested in the making of the new tunnels was a new type of rotary excavator called a drum digger, invented by Arthur Foster Constructional Engineers Ltd and Kinnear Moodie.[267] Both contractors used this machine, which was the next major evolution of the Price rotary excavator.* The outer skin of the shield had the usual cutting edge around its circumference at the front. Within this was a second steel cylinder 7 ft 6 ins in diameter which was rotated at up to 4 r.p.m. by six hydraulic motors placed near the bottom of the machine. These drove the outer edge of the inner drum. Cutting teeth on radial arms extending between the two cylinders, and on an arm placed across the smaller drum excavated the soil. This was transferred through the central drum to conveyor belts which allowed it to be deposited into skip wagons for removal from the tunnel. The skip wagons could be loaded from either side of the belt, as the tracks diverged just behind the shield. A ramp further back linked the tracks on the conveyor platform with the main 2-ft gauge track in the tunnel. The skips were hauled back to the shafts: at Finsbury Park this was done using an electric winch, and at Netherton Road battery locomotives were used. At the shafts they were unloaded onto a conveyor belt that transported the clay to the shaft. A vertical bucket conveyor lifted it to the shaft-head, from where it could be loaded into lorries. The buckets were heated with hot air before being loaded at the bottom as it was found that this prevented the clay from sticking.

Fourteen hydraulic rams at the rear of the shield drove it forward in the conventional manner. Valves allowed the operator, standing at the back of the shield, to control the speed of the drum and the pressure applied to each ram so that the shield could be steered. The hydraulic pressure came from two separate systems, one for the rams and one for the motors, both located behind the shield under the conveyor belt trailer, and powered electrically. Electric hoists were used to raise the tunnel segments into position. All of this equipment was moved along the tunnel with the shield as it progressed, being mounted on an articulated platform. The oil used in the hydraulic motors for the rotating drum became very hot, and a heat-exchanger cooled it using water piped in a circuit back out of the tunnels to a cooler at the shaft head. As the shield progressed the water pipes had to be regularly extended.

---

*   It had been used to construct a 19 mile water tunnel between Hampton and Chingford.

A battery-powered works locomotive hauling spoil skips back to the Netherton Road shaft in one of the experimental tunnels lined with an expanded cast iron lining. The shallower segment flanges are noticeable. *(LTM)*

Right A section of the concrete tunnel lining in the northbound experimental tunnel, near to Finsbury Park. *(LTM)*

The two other innovations that were used were the tunnel linings, which avoided the need for grouting. The section of tunnels between Finsbury Park and Manor House were lined with unbolted cast iron rings 2 ft long and 1 inch thick. The internal diameter of the tunnels was 12 ft 8 ins, and the drum digger for these tunnels had an external diameter of 13 ft 1 in. Each ring comprised six segments with concave and convex joints at opposite ends. When the segments were placed together the two types of end formed a knuckle joint. To form a complete ring the two invert segments were laid first, followed by the side segments. Finally the two crown segments were lifted into position and supported on rods fitted to the back of the shield. Hydraulic jacks operated by a common hand pump then pressed the segments apart against the clay with a force of 12 tons so that the crown segments could be fitted into position. Special cast iron knuckle pieces and packing were placed into the joints between the invert and side segments. The new ring was thus pressing out on the clay behind, which was squeezing the segments together. Without the need for bolts the flanges could be made much shallower, saving on the amount of iron used. Lugs with holes were cast into the edges of the shallow flanges to help with handling the segments, and to provide points onto which equipment such as signals could be attached. Between adjacent rings wood packing was used to absorb the pressure from the rams; however, with the shallower flanges the pressure from the rams was concentrated on a smaller area, and some segments needed to be replaced after fracturing.[268] One key difference had to be made to the tunnelling shields when using these 'expanded' linings: there was no tail-skin in which the tunnel rings were assembled. When the rams forced the shield forward the clay was exposed all around the tunnel, and the segments were erected directly against it.

The other section of the tunnels built by Kinnear Moodie used concrete linings with an internal diameter of 12 ft 6 ins. Each ring comprised fourteen segments with

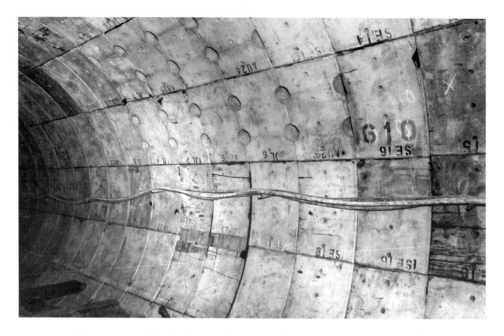

convex and concave ends similar to those on the cast iron segments. The segments were 6 inches thick (this having been determined by previous testing), and this required the drum digger to have an external diameter of 14 ft. Once assembled a pair of concrete wedges were forced by hydraulic rams into the remaining 7 inch gap in the tunnel crown. This completed the tunnel ring and held it in position. Holes cast into the segments were, like the lugs on the cast iron segments, for handling as well as attaching equipment. The rate of construction was impressive. The drum digger operated by the Edmund Nuttall team set a world record for clay tunnelling when they managed to drive 934 feet of tunnel in two weeks, an average of 3½ ft per working hour. An average of 60 ft per day (working three shifts of eight hours) was seen as achievable for sustained periods. The limiting factor on the rate of progress seemed to be the removal of spoil from the workings.[269]

Once complete, the new southbound tunnel was extended by 350 yards to meet the existing Northern City line (the name given to the GN&CR in 1934 by London Transport) at Finsbury Park. Track was laid for 1,600 ft through the tunnel and test trains operated from May 1962 so that data could be collected on noise and ventilation issues, using a Northern City line train.[270]

Tunnel stability

One concern facing LT's engineers was the effect of deep piled foundations passing near to tube tunnels. In the 1960s buildings began to be built higher and higher, and so their foundations had to go deeper and deeper. LT was not always consulted before this occurred. The experimental Victoria line tunnels were seen as the ideal opportunity to perform some practical tests. It was for this reason that for a reasonable length they passed beneath Finsbury Park, where no buildings would be affected by subsidence that might occur.

Two unlined 6 ft diameter shafts were sunk passing just 3 ft away from the tube tunnels, and measurements were taken in the tunnels. Some of the linings were also dismantled to check the effect of the stress release on the clay. Two further shafts were then sunk, and the tunnels monitored for six days. The tests showed very small alterations to the tunnels, but not significant enough to cause concern.[271]

Construction

Approval for the construction of the new line came on 20 August 1962. LT was ready for the decision, having spent years planning the details of the line and work soon started at Oxford Circus, where a new ticket hall was to be built below the road junction. The sub-surface utilities needed to be mapped before excavation could begin.

One of the most important powers that LT was granted for the Victoria line was that to compulsorily acquire easements under private property. This allowed the tunnels to be more direct, and meant an end to sharp curves where tunnels followed the street pattern above. Combined with the slightly larger running tunnels, this would allow trains to operate at higher speeds along the new line.

One of the Kinnear Moodie drum diggers (number KM4) being hauled through the completed southbound platform tunnel at Green Park. A track has been laid down to ease its passage through the tunnel. *(LTM)*

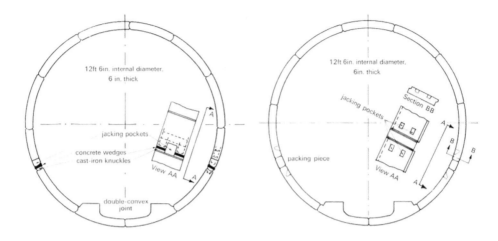

The two designs of concrete tunnel lining: (left) the MHA lining, and (right) the Halcrow lining. Within the two cross-sections are drawings of the pockets used by the jacks to expand the lining. *(Concrete Quarterly)*

Much of the tunnelling was performed using the new drum diggers. Four were supplied by Kinnear Moodie, two of which had been used for the experimental tunnels and subsequently reconditioned. They were mostly used on the tunnels constructed by John Mowlem & Co. (Victoria – Oxford Circus), and Kinnear Moodie themselves (Oxford Circus, and King's Cross – Finsbury Park). Sir Robert McAlpine & Sons supplied the other four, to their own design, for use on the tunnels contracted to Charles Brand & Son (Finsbury Park – Walthamstow).[272] These were driven from a central axle by motors nearer the middle of the machine, and had four radial arms. The spoil was again removed via the central part of the shield.

Nine conventional Greathead shields were also made for running tunnel excavation, as well as seven large Greathead shields for boring the platform tunnels along the line, manufactured by W. Lawrence & Son (London) Ltd. The shields for the line cost over £500,000.[273] Together with the drum diggers, they were all purchased directly by LT and provided to the contractors; this saved time during the tendering process.

Most of the metal tunnel segments were ordered from Stanton & Staveley of Nottingham in a £5 million contract. One-third of this order was then subcontracted to Head Wrightson Iron Foundries, who had made many of the segments for the early tubes. Some special high-strength steel segments were also ordered for work at Oxford Circus, where a heavy department store building was directly above the site of the new southbound platform tunnel, and King's Cross, where the platform tunnels were beneath the Metropolitan and Circle line tunnels which needed careful support. All of the other platform tunnels were constructed from cast iron segments, this comprising about one-quarter of the 130,000 tons of cast iron segments used for the line.[274]

Concrete segments worth £70,000 were manufactured by Kinnear Moodie for use on around 60% of the line. Two different designs of concrete lining were used: one from Sir William Halcrow & Partners, and the other by Mott, Hay & Anderson (MHA). These used eleven and twelve segments respectively to form each ring. In both types, the side segments above the level of the track were made with special jacking pockets. The hydraulic jacks were fitted into these to force the segments apart so that the final component for each ring could be inserted. In the Halcrow lining this was a short concrete packing piece, whereas MHA used a cast iron knuckle together with a concrete wedge.

The Kinnear Moodie drum digger proved to be less effective than McAlpine's alternative rotary digger. An improvement was developed, but ran into difficulties near Walthamstow, when the tunnel subsided below Forest Road on 21 May 1965. A cavity formed at the surface, some 15 ft deep, which had to be filled with concrete before the road could be reopened.[275] For a time the machine was left in position, and the tunnel closed up until the recovery work could be performed. The soil around the shield was stabilized through the use of chemical consolidation, but another collapse occurred when further tunnelling took place at this site. A similar incident occurred near Green Park, also in 1965.[276]

At Green Park station some ingenious spoil removal equipment was designed for John Mowlem & Co., the contractors at this site. It consisted of a pair of large skip wagons with integral conveyor belts, as well as a further conveyor that could reach between them. Spoil from the shield was deposited into the closest of the two skips, which could accommodate the entire amount removed to advance the shield by one tunnel ring – a mass of 15 tons. Once full, the integrated conveyors transferred the clay into the second skip. This would then propel itself at up to 14 m.p.h. (using battery-driven motors initially, but one set was converted to use a diesel engine) back along the narrow-gauge railway in the tunnel to the fixed conveyor leading to the shaft, where it would automatically discharge. The fixed conveyor would transfer the spoil to the vertical bucket conveyor in the shaft, and so to the surface for disposal.[277]

During 1964 the tunnelling work increased until the peak of simultaneous working was reached, with 40 separate worksites in use, accessed from 33 shafts along the length of the route. A new record was set when 470 ft of tunnel was bored in a single week. The mechanical erectors fitted to the shields allowed a complete ring of the precast concrete linings to be installed in as little as seven minutes.[278] By July 1965 half of the tunnelling work was complete.

On 20 September 1966 the running tunnels were completed when a drum digger from Highbury broke into a tunnel 100 yds north-east of King's Cross. Only three other short sections of platform tunnel remained for completion at this point, and this was done by the end of the year.

Working on the line
Many of the tunnellers and labourers who built the Victoria line were Irish (particularly from Counties Mayo and Donegal), and came from families with a long history of tunnelling and mining. The work in the Greathead shields was a lot more physically demanding than the use of the drum diggers. The shifts were longer too, there being two twelve-hour shifts each day. On the drum diggers there were three eight-hour shifts: 07.00 – 15.00, 15.00 – 23.00, and the 23.00 – 07.00 night shift. The tunnelling work ran continuously from Monday to Friday, with the weekends off.

Health and safety rules were a lot more lax than in modern times. There was no high-visibility clothing, for instance, and few wore hard hats. They preferred to wear caps as these kept the sweat from pouring into their eyes in the heat of the tunnel. Many of them smoked in the tunnels too. Although there were very few deaths during the building of the Victoria line, injuries were not uncommon. The 'tough' attitude that typified the Victorian navvies was still a part of their culture though. One noted that "The skips carrying the muck used to come off the tracks, and someone would break a leg or lose a finger. But I wouldn't call it really dangerous".[279]

Within the Greathead shields each mining 'gang' had a lead miner, two miners, and two labourers. The three miners would use pneumatic spades and picks to tear lumps of clay from the tunnel face, letting them fall onto wooden staging boards across the tunnel on which they stood. The labourers would clear this spoil from the boards and load it into the skips. At many sites locomotives would collect the skips and tow them back to the shafts for emptying, but at some the skips were moved by hand by the junior members of the team: the 'pony boys'.

At the shafts, banksmen in the tunnels guided the crane drivers, who were above the surface, by means of hand signals. Another role performed by the banksman was that of teaboy. One fondly recalled the way that other London workers carefully avoided him and his muddy clothes as he left the site to purchase the tea, and then the process of brewing up. This involved pouring quarter of a pound of tea into an enamel bucket, full of hot water heated by a small stove. One or two pints of milk would be tipped in, together with a large amount of sugar, and a new pickaxe handle would be used to stir the lot. An improvised spout would be fitted to the bucket for pouring out.[280]

A plan of Highbury & Islington station platforms, showing how the running tunnels were altered to allow cross-platform interchange between the Northern City and Victoria lines. (London Transport)

Tunnel diversions

The new line required many complex pieces of tunnelling, just in order to be threaded through the existing network of tunnels under London. One of the key objectives was to improve interchange, and where possible allow this to be cross-platform. This further complicated the work and meant additional tunnelling to bring new platforms alongside those of existing lines.

One of the first of these to be constructed was at Highbury & Islington, where cross-platform interchange with the Northern City line was planned. Although the Northern City was not heavily trafficked, it was planned for it to be transferred to British Rail, who would connect it with their main line at Finsbury Park (as had been the original intention at the turn of the century). Once this happened, passengers would prefer to make a short, cross-platform connection at Highbury rather than via stairs and passageways at Finsbury Park, and this would encourage them to use the Victoria line rather than the overcrowded Piccadilly line.[281] It was not convenient to make the new platforms flank those already there, as the Northern City line platforms would have needed switching sides in their tunnels (together with many other changes resulting from this). Instead, a new pair of northbound platforms was built, and the existing northbound platform became the new southbound Victoria line platform.

The diversion tunnel for the Northern City line being constructed at Highbury & Islington. The shield is just over 16 ft in diameter, and the hydraulic rams are just visible at the top of the picture. This tunnel was dug by hand. *(LTM)*

Victoria Line
FINSBURY PARK STATION

A plan of Finsbury Park station showing the complex rearrangement of tunnels to allow cross-platform interchange between the Piccadilly and Victoria lines. *(London Transport)*

This work was one of the first tunnelling contracts to be let. It was contracted to F.J.C. Lilley (Contractors) Ltd, who started work in early 1963. It required a large tunnelling shield to construct the replacement 16 ft diameter running tunnel, and a conventional Greathead shield was constructed by Joseph Westwood & Co. Ltd (it not being worth providing a drum digger for such a short length of tunnel). In total the diversion was about half a mile long, and included one station platform tunnel. At each end of the diversion step-plate junction tunnels were built around the existing tunnels to allow the diversion to be 'plumbed in'. This took place in August 1965, after which the original platform was comprehensively rebuilt for the Victoria line.

At the next station to the north, an even more complex diversion took place. Finsbury Park had two pairs of tube platforms: one for the Piccadilly line, and one for the Northern City line. These were all built side-by-side in 1902 under the main-line station. The Northern City line was truncated back at Drayton Park from 4 October 1964 so that its platforms at Finsbury Park could be reused as part of the Victoria line works, avoiding the need and cost of building two more platforms. However, it had been decided that rearrangement of the layout of the platforms would allow cross-platform interchange between the Piccadilly and Victoria lines both northbound and southbound. To do this, the southbound Piccadilly line needed diverting into the northbound Northern City line platform. Two new diversion tunnels were needed either side of the platform, together with step-plate junctions where these met the Piccadilly line.

The contract was let in January 1964 to A. Waddington & Son. They commenced by building the step-plate tunnels around the southbound Piccadilly line tunnel, which continued to have trains operating through it. As the clay was excavated from around the tunnel massive timbers were used to prop it safely, and the concrete invert also helped with this. Trains passing through the tunnels at these points were limited to 25 m.p.h.

The northern step-plate was excavated via the shaft at Finsbury Park tennis courts from which the experimental tunnels had been driven. A new heading gave access to the Piccadilly line above the point where the centre of the junction would be. A series of tunnel rings ranging from 18 ft 6 ins at the north end to 29 ft 6 ins at the south were constructed by hand mining, first the larger half, and then the smaller. A second heading was also driven to allow the diversion tunnel to be constructed between the step-plate tunnel and the ex-Northern City line platform. This tunnel joined the existing 16 ft diameter overrun tunnel at an angle.

Similar work took place to the south of the station, three months after the work started to the north. A new shaft was needed as none already existed here; this was sunk at Isleden Road, with a heading leading below both existing Piccadilly line tunnels to a point half-way along the new diversion tunnel, which had to dip down to cross below the Victoria line. The diversion tunnel was then dug southwards to the north end of the step-plate junction tunnel. A smaller 7 ft diameter pilot tunnel was then driven alongside the Piccadilly line tunnel to the mid-point of the junction tunnel. The problem here was that the diversion tunnel entered the step-plate tunnel 5 ft lower than the original tunnel, because of the dip. This made the tunnelling of the junction particularly difficult because the old tunnel lining needed to be supported from underneath whilst the new tunnel was constructed. Steel trestles were installed at 5 ft intervals, with wooden saddles on top supporting the outside of the old tunnel lining.

Once both the step-plate junction tunnels were completed, in March 1965, the high voltage cables running along the old tunnel walls were diverted into the new junction tunnel. This was arranged by installing a new cable along the junction tunnel wall and connecting it into the old cable at each end via holes made by removing three segments at each end. The old tunnel linings through each of the junctions could then be carefully dismantled above rail level during night-time engineering work. In parallel with this work temporary signal cables and compressed air mains (to operate points and signalling equipment) were installed. Concrete from the old track bed was also broken out between every other sleeper, and the speed limit through the tunnels was reduced further, to 10 m.p.h.

Work to dismantle the old tunnel invert then began. The invert segments were removed in pairs (two segments forming the base of the tunnel), with six pairs being removed each night. In the north step-plate the track was placed on the new concrete invert. In the south tunnel it was placed onto new wooden timber way-beams that rested on the steel trestles in place of the wooden saddles.

The platform tunnel had already been reconstructed with an anti-suicide pit to confirm to standard LT practice. To the south of the platform tunnel lay a crossover tunnel, which was being retained. Beyond this the tunnel was filled with weak concrete into which the north part of the diversion tunnel was bored. Temporary points were installed in the north step-plate junction tunnel, allowing works trains to run into the new tunnel throughout July, August, and September 1965. These laid track and cables all the way through to the south junction tunnel.

The operation to switch the southbound Piccadilly line into the new tunnel was planned with military precision. Two runway beams had been installed in the step-plate tunnel: one over the old tracks was 150 ft long, and the other, over the diversion line, was 50 ft long. At 00.03 on 3 October 1965 the work began. An engineering train split into three, with one section parking south of the step-plate junction, and one each in the two tunnels at the north end. That on the old line stopped on the old supported track and a large team of men began to dismantle the track behind

The change-over work in the step-plate tunnel constructed on the Piccadilly line. This is the step-plate on the left hand side of the previous diagram. A battery locomotive is coming along the original tracks, which are supported on trestles. The tunnel visible on the right is the new tunnel leading to the old Northern City line crossover tunnel. *(LTM)*

it (to the south). The rails were thrown to one side, and the heavy timbers and steel trestles were hooked onto chains supported from the runway beams and slid along to the works train wagons. As the tracks were dismantled the train moved slowly northwards with all the old track materials and supports being loaded on. Once the first wagon was loaded it was shunted via a crossover onto the eastbound Piccadilly line, and the train returned with a second empty wagon. The process was repeated until this wagon was loaded; the train then returned into the tunnels and collected the first wagon.

The train on the new line at the step-plate junction then collected the remaining parts of the old track and its supports and withdrew northwards. Meanwhile, the first part of the train which had been to the south of the tunnel brought the necessary track materials along so that the workmen could start to slew the southernmost part of the old track onto the new alignment, and then construct 92 ft of new track to connect with that in the diversion tunnel. Conductor rails were installed, and finally a team of signal engineers were given time to reconnect all of the necessary signalling equipment. Passenger traffic resumed at 14.00, leaving only the final concreting of the track bed to wait until engineering hours.

With the completion of the work, the northbound Victoria line tunnelling could proceed, connecting into the now-disused Piccadilly line platform. North of this, a short length of tunnel cut through the old Piccadilly line tunnel to connect with the end of the northbound experimental tunnel of 1961. The southbound Victoria line tunnel north of the station had already been constructed as far as Netherton Road as part of the experimental tunnels.

Unusual station works

The ground conditions along the northern part of the line were poor, with many of the tunnels encountering wet, gravelly soil. The escalator shaft at Tottenham Hale needed to be bored through these conditions and so the soil was frozen to enable it to be safely excavated. A series of 4-inch metal tubes was sunk into the ground at 5 ft intervals, so that they were just above the top of where the escalator shaft was needed – 6 ft to 35 ft below the surface. These had smaller metal tubes within them, down which liquid nitrogen at -196°C was pumped. It rose back to the surface in the space between the two tubes, whereupon it was then pumped down an adjacent tube. It was found that the nitrogen could be passed down five tubes before its freezing effect had worn off, and it was then discharged as a gas at -10°C. Temperature probes placed between the tubes monitored the progress of freezing. Once the ground was frozen solid down to the base of the escalator shaft the nitrogen was replaced with brine at -18°C, which kept the 500 yd³ of ground frozen while the tunnel was mined. This work took place during the hottest weeks of summer 1966.

The umbrella bridge at Oxford Circus under construction on 4 August 1963. Two of the cranes can be seen, and at the bottom of the photograph a lorry waits with another panel section for the bridge. *(LTM)*

The Oxford Circus umbrella was one of the most visible signs of the Victoria line works to the public outside the Underground. In order to build a new ticket hall directly beneath the busy road junction, a large steel bridge was constructed 3 ft 6 ins above the road surface. Four ramps gave access to traffic from Oxford Street and Regent Street, and whilst this drove over the bridge men were hard at work beneath removing the soil.

The work started with a detailed survey of the utilities that would need to be moved. This also determined locations for 25 concrete piles that would support the umbrella, which were sunk during night time closures of small areas of the road. The umbrella bridge was manufactured by Rubery Owen from 245 steel components, comprising support girders, ramp girders, and surface sections. Over the course of 65 hours during August bank holiday weekend in 1963, starting at 13.30 on the Saturday, Oxford Circus was closed to all traffic. A team of 200 men with cranes and lorries carried out a carefully planned routine, bringing each carefully labelled component to the right place and at the right time so that it could be craned into position. The 600-ton umbrella bridge was completed by Monday lunchtime, and then work concluded by making tarmac joins onto the ramps, and reinstating kerbstones, road signs, markings, and traffic lights. Traffic flowed over the bridge from 06.30 on Tuesday morning.

At King's Cross, the only place for the platforms to go was beneath the Metropolitan and Circle lines, and above the Piccadilly line. The main Metropolitan line tunnel was built without inverts, so great care had to be taken to avoid any ground movement below. Strengthening the tunnels from within, or constructing a raft structure beneath them was infeasible whilst trains were operating. This meant that constructing three large parallel tunnels (for the two platforms with a 18 ft 5 in diameter passenger concourse between) was a challenge.

An especially strong station shield was used here, with 33 hydraulic rams at the rear to ensure that the clay at the tunnel face was well-supported. As it moved forward the tunnel rings for the northbound platform and concourse were assembled from unbolted high-strength steel segments, and fitted into place using hydraulic jacks that could exert a force of 100 tons.[282] The design of the segments ensured that as they were pressed into position, the stresses through the clay were directed towards the footings of the tunnel walls above, thus maintaining the support for the 100-year-old brickwork.

North of Victoria the running tunnels cut beneath the site of the old Stag brewery,* which had been constructed with piled foundations. The tunnellers were unaware of these, and only discovered the piles when they encountered them. One hand-mined access tunnel used hydraulic bursters to break through them. Others were encountered by one of the drum diggers, which was fitted with specially hardened cutting teeth and then chewed its way through the concrete, although this placed a heavy load on its power supply.[283]

To the south of the platform tunnels at Victoria, four sidings were created. A pair of step-plate junctions and a crossover tunnel were made to connect them together.

---

* The Stag Brewery, owned by Watney's, closed in 1959, and was replaced by the Stag Place office development in the early 1960s. The site has been redeveloped again and is now occupied by the Cardinal Place shopping and office complex.

The outside pair of tunnels were never used as sidings, but were instead extended to form the northernmost part of the extension of the line to Brixton, the work for which followed on from the construction of the line north of Victoria, and which is described in Chapter 21. Of the two inner sidings, one was built with a conventional diameter of 12 ft, but the other was made with a diameter of 14 ft so that an inspection pit could be included; this would allow checking of trains, and even minor repairs to be carried out, away from the depot at the north end of the line.

Ventilation

The Victoria line was constructed with rather better ventilation systems than the earlier tube railways (see p 147). Several construction shafts were sunk between the station sites, and these were retained and fitted out with fans to ventilate the tunnels. Eleven fans were provided in these inter-station shafts.

Local residents were not keen on having industrial-looking shafthead buildings in their area where the shafts emerged at the surface. LT disguised a number of the structures to better fit in:

- At Gibson Square, in Islington, a Georgian-style structure was built in the square, after the residents complained about the originally proposed 60 ft tower. It was designed by Raymond Erith, and is known as the Temple of the Winds. It has been suggested that this is "the only interesting piece of architecture generated by the Victoria Line."[284]
- In Moreton Terrace, Pimlico, a house had been demolished to create the site for the shaft. After the railway was completed the shaft was incorporated into a building that blended with the adjacent houses (although, unlike the fake façade at Leinster Gardens, the building does not make any pretence at being a house).
- The shaft in St George's Square, also in Pimlico, has a small brick shafthead building. The metal mesh roof shows this to be a ventilation shaft.

The Temple of the Winds ventilation shaft for the Victoria line at Gibson Square, between King's Cross and Highbury & Islington. (*Author*)

Cut and cover revisited

The Barbican realignment

The northern part of the City of London was badly damaged by bombing in WWII. Many of the buildings in the area between Aldersgate & Barbican (renamed Barbican in 1968) and Moorgate stations were damaged beyond repair and after the war plans were drawn up for a major development scheme. Work began in the mid-1960s on what was named the Barbican Estate, which remains one of the City's main housing areas.

Two pairs of tracks, one for the Metropolitan and Circle lines and the other for the City Widened Lines, ran in a curve across the development site, and an opportunity was seen to realign the tracks to facilitate the redevelopment scheme.[285] Several large buildings requiring deep piled foundations were planned, and the original 1865 track alignment was in the way of these. In 1962 it was announced that the realigned tracks would be in a new covered way built using cut-and-cover beneath the planned buildings. The contract was let in August 1963, work started the following month, and the £1.2 million costs were met by the City of London Corporation but the work was planned and supervised by LT. The contractors were Higgs and Hill Ltd.

The Metropolitan and Circle lines, looking west from Moorgate, with the City Widened lines on their left. The white dashed lines show the new alignment for the tracks, through an area almost completely destroyed by wartime bombing. *(The Railway Magazine)*

A view looking east from Barbican, half-way through the diversion work. The City Widened lines have been diverted from the arched tunnel (second from left) into the rectangular tunnel on the right. The Metropolitan and Circle lines are still using their original tracks through the arched tunnel on the left, and will eventually use the new rectangular tunnel (second from right). *(LTM)*

The term 'cut-and-cover' suggests the original construction style of the MR, with a trench being dug and a covered way constructed within, completely below ground level. The process was somewhat different for this diversion of around 500 yards of railway, as the site across which it was to be built was what would be termed 'brownfield' today. In order to avoid disrupting train services for any longer than the bare minimum, the work was planned in three stages.[286]

Firstly, the new covered ways in the central section of the new alignment were built. This was a pair of parallel structures constructed from reinforced concrete, about 300 yards long. The surface of much of the area had been lowered as part of the preliminary works for the Barbican Estate, and so the new covered ways were assembled at this level, rather than in a trench. There was no interference with property (as the site was clear) and only a small impact on roads.

The bridge carrying Barbican (a road that no longer exists, but which ran along the rough alignment of Beech Street east from Aldersgate Street) was demolished, to allow the existing railway tunnels beneath to be broken out. The road was placed onto a temporary diverted alignment. Two 26 ft long prefabricated metal shields were used, one in each tunnel, to protect the two adjacent pairs of tracks whilst the brick arches of the old tunnels were demolished around them each week-night. Each Saturday night the shields were moved along by 20 ft in readiness for the next week of demolition, until 390 ft of tunnel had been removed. Two other road bridges at Milton Street and Jacobs Well were also removed. Track was laid in the new tunnel for the Widened Lines, and the final part of this stage involved connecting these tracks at each end to the existing lines at Aldersgate & Barbican and Moorgate, and altering the platforms at the latter station. This took place on the weekend of 19/20 June 1965.

The second stage involved the removal of the old Widened Line tracks and the extension of the new covered way for the Metropolitan and Circle lines at each end, over the old Widened Lines formation. Moor Lane bridge at the west end of Moorgate station was reconstructed for the new alignment, as its original piers would obstruct the new tracks, and the Underground platforms at Moorgate were replaced by temporary structures that could quickly be realigned with the new covered way. The bridges at Jacobs Well and Milton Street were not replaced, as the Barbican Estate obliterated the former, and the southern half of the latter.

Stage three connected the Metropolitan and Circle lines into the new covered way, which was carried out during a line closure on 5 December 1965. At each end of the new covered way the tracks were in the open air where the connections had been made. In order that the Barbican Estate could be constructed above, the new covered ways were then extended across these areas, allowing Barbican (the street) to be returned to its original alignment. The platforms at Moorgate were completed, as was Moor Lane overbridge. The old tracks were removed from the original Metropolitan and Circle line alignment.

The new covered ways were constructed on a series of 426 bored piles, with the walls and roof made from reinforced concrete. The central section built in stage one had these all cast *in situ*, whereas the roof over the end sections built in stages 2 and 3 by necessity had to be of pre-cast concrete sections as they were assembled above the railway tracks. The covered ways were designed to carry the weight of parts of the new Barbican Estate above them, which included a large portion of the central rectangular lake. Unsurprisingly a lot of attention was given to the waterproofing, and a sandwich of materials was used between the lake and the roofs of the covered ways to ensure that the water remained in the lake, and that if it did not it would be channelled away from the covered ways into a cavity which could be inspected regularly. A layer of corrugated asbestos sheeting formed the channels, laid above a layer of asphalt $1^{1}/_{8}$ inches thick, which was on top of the concrete roof. The tracks were laid on a concrete deck supported on rubber bearings to reduce noise and vibration, rather important given that the Barbican concert hall was located above the covered ways.

Piccadilly to Heathrow
In 1977 London became the first city to have a metro running to its main airport, when the Piccadilly line extension between Hounslow West and Heathrow Central opened. The extension had been planned since the 1960s, and was authorized in 1970.

The cut and cover construction work taking place alongside the Great West Road. The side walls for the tunnel have been cast, and earth is being excavated in readiness for the roof slab installation. *(LTM)*

Construction work began the following year. The extension was 3·15 miles long, and included an intermediate station at Hatton Cross, and new platforms at Hounslow West.

The first part of the extension between Hounslow West and Hatton Cross was built using cut and cover techniques below the grass verges of the Bath Road and then the Great South West Road. Because of the need to avoid unduly disturbing the householders along these roads, the 'top down' construction approach was used. Once the necessary utility diversion work was completed, 6,123 interlocking concrete secant piles 2 ft 11 ins in diameter were driven along the route to form the walls of the new covered way, 24 ft to 31 ft apart. The surface was removed between these and a capping beam was cast along the top of the piles. The roof slab was then constructed spanning between the two capping beams from pre-cast pre-stressed reinforced concrete beams, with some beams temporarily omitted to form openings. A layer of concrete the filled the spaces between the beams, and the upper surface was waterproofed with bitumen. A further layer of concrete was laid to protect the waterproofing.[287] The concrete used was supplied from a central batching plant, and brought using a fleet of cement mixer lorries.[288]

Secant piles

A watertight wall can be constructed by driving piles into the ground so that they overlap. The first part of the process is the sinking of alternate piles for the wall; these are termed the 'female' piles. In the second phase the intermediate 'male' piles are driven, which overlap with and remove some of the concrete from the female piles. In this way a solid wall of concrete is formed to the depth required.

The piles on the Heathrow extension were formed by driving a steel casing (like a tube) into the ground using equipment called a piling rig, whilst simultaneously twisting it. A grab bucket removes the soil from within the tube to slightly less depth than the casing. Once the casing reaches the correct depth, concrete is poured in and the casing is slowly withdrawn, again whilst being twisted.

The work to excavate the core of the covered way then took place from within the structure, which attenuated the construction noise. Spoil was transported to the openings left in the roof using a double-layered conveyor belt; in the other direction the conveyor took concrete back to the worksite to form the floor of the covered way. Pre-cast concrete trays mounted on rubber bearings were installed to hold the track, again to reduce noise and vibration in the eastern section where the roads were residential. The rest of the fitting out could then proceed. The roof openings were closed and sealed, and the surface reinstated over the roof panels to a depth of between 2 ft 6 ins and 3 ft 6 ins.

Concerns were raised about the covered way forming an underground dam. There was a flow of water through the gravel above the clay that tended in a north to south direction, and therefore the covered way could result in water being dammed on the north side and causing problems. Several siphons were constructed beneath the covered way to allow the water to pass beneath, with the intention of avoiding such problems. Monitoring of the water after the completion of the covered way was inconclusive, possibly because the extremely hot summer had lowered the water table.[289]

Beyond the road junction between the Great South West Road and The Parkway the line entered an open cutting (the residential area having been left behind) and rose to ground level. This allowed it to cross the River Crane on a bridge, a cheaper solution than building a tunnel beneath the river. To the west the line descended back into a covered way built using cut and cover as far at Hatton Cross, at the eastern edge of the airport. After a gas explosion occurred in this section which injured three men on 24 February 1972, the remainder of the work west of the River Crane was undertaken in an open trench.

Hounslow West and Hatton Cross stations were also built using cut and cover to form the station box, in the same way that the covered ways just described were made. At Hatton Cross the station platform was an island at shallow depth, and staircases were provided for access. West of the station the concrete box continued for 750 ft, but descending in level, to the point where the next construction contract would begin. Construction of this was different to the rest of the cut and cover work because it was within the Heathrow perimeter and near to the end of one of the runways. The use of any equipment to a height greater than 3 m required specific authorization from the airport operator, BAA. However, the width of the working was not constrained, and so a wide site was excavated to the water table, at a depth of 10 ft. Within this hole, larger equipment could now be used, and so pile drivers placed a series of sheet piles down to the level of the clay around the edge of the area in which the tunnel was to be made. The gravel layers were removed above the clay and large piles were sunk every 6 ft along the line of the tunnel box. Excavation between these allowed concrete slabs to be formed between them, making the box walls. Concrete inverted T-beams were placed across the box, and used to support a roof formed from concrete slabs. The clay within was then taken out, leaving the concrete box complete. Before backfilling the site the sheet piles were also extracted from the ground around the box.

Beyond Hatton Cross, the work started in early 1972, with the contract having been let to John Mowlem & Co. the previous December. The tracks descended to between 22 ft and 45 ft below the surface. It was impossible to excavate in a working airport, so standard Greathead shields were used to construct tube tunnels of 12 ft 6 ins diameter almost as far as the next station. It was not thought economic to provide drum diggers for these short tunnel lengths, so instead different excavation equipment was used through the aperture in the shields, allowing the tunnel face to be attacked by the miners and excavated more quickly. The westbound tunnel used a Westfalia scraper chain boom cutter, and the eastbound a road header made by Anderson Mavor.[290] Both of these were established pieces of equipment used in underground mining, especially for coal, but this was the first time that they had been used to make tunnels on the London Underground. The road header was mounted on a carriage that moved along the tunnel with the shield, whereas the boom cutter had its own 'sledge' that could move independently from the shield.[291] They had different ways of handling the spoil as well. The teeth on the Westfalia machine rotated upwards, delivering the spoil onto an integrated conveyor belt, whereas the Anderson Mavor machine just deposited the spoil in the tunnel invert where separate equipment was needed for its removal. On conclusion of the tunnelling the agent for the tunnelling contractor noted that whilst both machines were good, the Anderson Mavor road header was a "superb machine" that was better suited for the clay tunnelling. One of the problems had been claystones, which caused the Westfalia boom cutter to stall, whereas the road header just chopped through them.[292]

Mowlem reused the idea of the self-propelled skip wagons that they had pioneered at Green Park during the Victoria line works. These shuttled back and forth between the tunnel face and the access shaft, taking spoil away and returning with concrete tunnel segments. About the first 1,000 segments were of the Victoria line MHA-designed lining, with 12 segments and a key piece forming the rings.[293] Thereafter, each tunnel ring was formed of 20 segments plus two wedge keys which expanded the ring into position as they were pressed into place. Power winches and hydraulic jacks helped assemble each tunnel ring as work progressed. The cast concrete tunnel segments were manufactured in a facility next to the airport and were produced at the rate of one every minute with the concrete being pressed into the moulds hydraulically. This was another experiment, although one that was not deemed to be a success due to the high rate of wear on the steel moulds in use.[294]

A crossover was needed before the station platforms, and to house this a large tunnel with a diameter of 31 ft 2 ins was constructed just below the upper level of the clay, with sand and gravel just above. Compressed air was used for this piece of construction work, which was assembled using cast iron segments. The alignment of the tunnels was checked not by plumb-lines but using the latest technology: laser beams.

The station box at Heathrow airport was built under a separate contract by Taylor Woodrow Construction Ltd, starting on 31 October 1972. Located in the middle of the airport 'central area', it was another piece of cut and cover construction. Concrete diaphragm walls 3·3 ft thick were cast to form a box 400 ft long, 80 ft wide, and 60 ft deep. These were made using the Soletanche process (described below). In this way the walls around the entire station box were safely cast.

Diaphragm walls

The creation of large underground spaces with concrete walls is much simpler if the walls can be formed before the soil occupying the interior space is removed. If the soil were to be excavated first there is a risk that the sides will collapse, particularly for deep excavations or where ground conditions are poor. The problem is cutting deep, narrow trenches in which the walls can be formed without these collapsing in on themselves.

The French company Soletanche developed and patented a process in the 1950s and 1960s in which the trenches were dug from ground level in short sections which were immediately filled with bentonite. This is a type of liquid clay thick enough to hold the side of the trench in position without collapsing. Bentonite is a thixotropic fluid, which means that it becomes more fluid when moved (e.g., being poured into the trench), but sets to a jelly-like state when it is still, and thus provides support. Metal reinforcement cages were lowered into the trenches and concrete was then pumped in from the bottom up. As this happened, the bentonite was pumped from the top of the trench to prevent overflow, and so that it could be reused after impurities from the soil were filtered out.

The earth core within the concrete box was then excavated, and large temporary struts built across the open space as this went on. Once complete, each level was built in turn, from the platforms at the bottom, via the mezzanine floor and ticket hall, through to the roof. This was 2 m thick, to allow for construction of a six-storey building above.* At platform level two short platform tunnel extensions were driven to the west of the station box, as it was not quite long enough to accommodate the platforms. Beyond these, both tunnels continued for 600 ft as overrun and siding tunnels.

In May 1974 the first running tunnel shield broke into the Heathrow station box. The concrete wall had been prepared for the arrival, holes having been burned through the concrete with a thermic lance. In January 1975 the running tunnels between Hatton Cross and Heathrow were completed.

---

* In the event no building was ever constructed and the surface is occupied by the station building and a bus station.

The tunnelling shield for the eastbound tunnel breaks through into the station box at Heathrow Central on 6 May 1974. The Anderson Mavor roadheader is in the centre of the shield, in front of the tunneller. *(LTM)*

Tracklaying and other activities to fit out the tunnels and stations proceeded from east to west, via a single-track connection with the eastbound line at Hounslow West. Hatton Cross station was ready to open in July 1975, and following a weekend closure to reroute the track just east of Hounslow West into the new platforms, trains began running (empty) through the tunnels on 14 July. Five days later they began to carry passengers, and Hatton Cross was open. The station at Heathrow, requiring more fit out work with escalators and subway connections into the airport terminals, opened on 16 December 1977.

The subways connecting the new station ticket hall with each of the three terminals at Heathrow were the responsibility of the BAA. They were built at shallow depth using secant piles to form the walls, with a width of 8·5 m so that two passenger conveyors could be installed, with a central walkway. The piled construction had the advantage of avoiding any prolonged road closures in the congested central area. However, there were over 250 utility and service pipes and cables crossing the routes of the subways, and only some of these could be conveniently diverted. For those that could not, the secant piles were formed either side of the service, and the ground was chemically consolidated beneath. Then, when the tunnel was excavated between the piles and beneath the service the concrete wall would be cast *in situ*. The roof was formed from either precast concrete panels or from poured concrete, depending on the location.

At Terminal 1, the end of the subway passed beneath the main car park. Secant and bored piles were created from within the lowest level of the car park without the need to close the facility. To ensure that the structure was not affected by any subsidence, the ground was consolidated along the route of the subway where it passed beneath.[295]

Tube tunnels of the 1970s and 1980s

The Brixton extension

It was always intended that the Victoria line would continue beyond Victoria station, with different alignments being considered at various times. The decision was made to extend to Brixton in the mid-1960s, with Parliamentary authority being granted in 1966. The timing allowed the tunnelling teams working north of Victoria to continue, rather than risking them being dispersed and struggling to recruit a new team. Had this occurred, it was estimated that the cost of the extension would have risen by £1 million.[296] As it was, the continuation was a close-run thing, with only 30 miners still employed on the original section of the line when the extension work started, but who were able to form the nucleus of the tunnelling team of 200 required for the Brixton extension.

Some preparatory work was authorized before the Government approved the full cost of the extension. Boreholes were sunk along the line of the route to determine the geology through which the tunnels would pass, and a seismographic survey of the river bed was conducted from a barge. Orders were placed for tunnel segments worth £1·5 million, as this allowed some continuity for the manufacturers.

Work started properly in May 1967 with a 75-ft-deep shaft being sunk at Bessborough Gardens in Pimlico by Balfour Beatty & Co. Ltd. From its base the running tunnels were excavated northwards to join up with the outer two of the four sidings constructed south of Victoria station. Six fossil nautiloids were found during this work, which are now in the Natural History Museum. The tunnels southwards were driven as far as Vauxhall station. Mitchell Bros. Sons & Co. Ltd excavated the tunnels from this point to Stockwell, and the contract for the final sections to Brixton was awarded to A. Waddington & Son Ltd. The tunnels advanced around 150 ft each week, working for 24 hours a day five days per week.

All of the tunnelling on the extension used Greathead shields with the tunnel face excavated using pneumatic spades, as the ground conditions were not conducive to the use of rotary excavators or drum diggers. Some of the shields were reused from the construction north of Victoria. Compressed air was used for the section beneath the Thames, where a minimum of 24 ft was kept between the tunnels and the river bed. Cast iron segments were used for these tunnels. South of the river the ground conditions worsened, particularly beneath Vauxhall Park and in the vicinity of Stockwell station, and again, cast iron segments were used for these sections. Elsewhere, when the tunnels passed through London clay, concrete tunnel rings were installed. The tunnel lining for the sidings which continued for 1,200 ft south of Brixton station were made from ductile cast iron segments as an experiment.

Ground freezing had to be employed at Vauxhall for the sinking of the escalator shaft, where there was a layer of waterlogged gravel above the clay, as well as the underground River Effra passing close by in a culvert. The ticket hall was

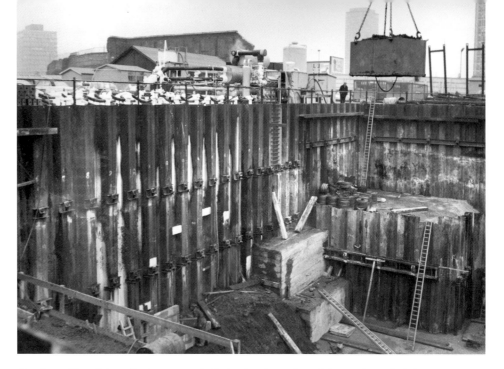

The sheet piling of the cofferdam at Vauxhall showing the outline of the escalator shaft (in white rectangles) in February 1969. Above the top of the piles the white pipes are being used to freeze the ground prior to the shaft being excavated. *(LTM)*

constructed within a cofferdam* made of steel sheet piling to keep the water out. There was a significant amount of work in diverting utilities at the station site, and so the work was split into three stages. When the first stage was completed, Wandsworth Road was diverted over the completed works so that utility diversion work could take place below its old route, and the remainder of the ticket hall could be constructed. When this had been done the third stage could commence, with the sinking of the escalator shaft.

At Stockwell the tunnels diverged to pass either side of the Northern line station, allowing cross-platform interchange to be obtained between the northbound platforms, and between the southbound platforms. The maze of tunnels that had been built at Stockwell by the C&SLR for depot access and train stabling, and then in WWII for the deep-level shelter beneath the station, caused further problems. Some of the tunnels were in the way, and the new Victoria line tunnels had to cut through them. This was a problem if the old tunnels were in use as cable ducts, as alternative routes for the cables then had to be made. The poor tunnelling conditions, noted earlier, led to a suspension of Northern line services between Clapham Common and Kennington on 14 and 15 August 1968 after a fall of gravel occurred in the adjacent Victoria line workings.

The terminus, at Brixton, was constructed with a crossover to the north of the platforms in a tunnel with a diameter of 31 ft 6 ins and lined with cast iron tunnel rings. Other than this, the work at Brixton was relatively straightforward.

Pimlico station, which was authorized after the rest of the extension, was another

---

*   A cofferdam is a temporary enclosure made in water or water-bearing ground, within which the water is removed to allow construction work.

waterlogged site, caused in part by the Tachbrook or King's Scholars' Pond Sewer which bordered the station site. A 15 ft diameter shaft was sunk as part of the initial works for the station. A high water table hindered the work, and five 6 inch boreholes were then sunk around the site in the hope that the water level could be lowered sufficiently to let the work proceed. The clay was at a depth of 40 ft here though, and the boreholes were unsuccessful. At the nearby St George's Square site the 18 ft diameter shaft also suffered from water ingress at its lower level, and a 15 ft diameter shaft was assembled within this. Jacks were then used to force the smaller shaft down into the clay in an attempt to create a water-free shaft. The gravel from within the shaft was removed using a grab from surface level.

Ultimately more ground freezing was required at the Pimlico station site. Brine was pumped through a series of pipes sunk into the ground, and cooled by refrigeration equipment that used ammonia, typically to around -18°C. This enabled solidification of the ground so that the escalator shaft could be sunk down to platform level.

Work on constructing and fitting out the tunnels for the extension finished in 1971, with battery-powered works trains using the line from early that year. On 23 July 1971 the extension was formally opened by HRH Princess Alexandra.

The ground-freezing equipment at Pimlico. The equipment behind the white tubes supplies the ammonia-cooled brine. *(LTM)*

The Jubilee line

The most notable new work on the Underground in the 1970s was the opening of the Jubilee line, right at the end of the decade. Like the Victoria line, the planning had been going on for some time before work began but disagreements on the funding delayed being able to start.

The creation of the Stanmore branch of the Bakerloo line in 1939 (see p 223) had relieved the congestion on the Metropolitan line between Baker Street and Finchley Road. The drawback was that as traffic levels grew on the Underground the converging routes led to Bakerloo line congestion, particularly as the two-platform terminus at Elephant & Castle restricted the number of trains that could be reversed and sent back to the north. The plan was to transfer the Stanmore branch to a new line that would form a new route across central London and follow the line of Fleet Street towards the City. This routing led to it being named the Fleet line, although the GLC renamed it the Jubilee line in 1977 to mark the Silver Jubilee of the Queen.

Powers to build the Fleet line were gained in stages. The first stage was from Baker Street to Charing Cross; stage two would extend east to Fenchurch Street, and stage three was tentatively planned to continue south-east to Lewisham. Funding was only made available for stage one, and contracts for the tunnelling were soon let.

At Baker Street, a new northbound platform was required, together with a step-plate junction some way north of the station to connect it with the tunnel to Stanmore. On the southbound line, which had had a new platform constructed in the 1930s for the trains from Stanmore, a new step-plate junction was required immediately to the south of the platform. All these works were entrusted to John Mowlem & Co. As usual, the step-plate junctions were hand-excavated around the existing tunnels whilst trains continued to run, and were constructed using cast iron

A view of the northbound step-plate junction under construction just west of Baker Street. The Bakerloo line running tunnel is still intact in the middle of the scene, with the lining propped using the temporary vertical girders. The photographer is standing in the portal of the new tunnel, looking towards the narrow end of the junction chamber. *(LTM)*

segments. Timber props supported the existing tunnels from both sides, for whilst most of the enlargement took place on one side (the side from which the new tunnel was to join), in order to construct the new tunnel rings a small gap was needed on the far side, of about 46 cm. This was a rather cramped working position for the miners. Once the step-plate tunnel was completed the cabling along the inside of the old tunnel was diverted into the new junction, with the exception of the tunnel lighting and tunnel telephone, which might still be required. These were only removed once the old tunnel was dismantled.

Mowlem used a shield to drive their sections of the running tunnels, and encountered problems with the clay around Baker Street. In some places layers of sand caused the crown of the tunnel to collapse before the lining could be erected. In other places the clay swelled more than had been predicted as soon as the shield move forward. With an expanded concrete lining the segments were installed without the protection of a tail-skin, and the swelling made this difficult. The solution was to fit the shield with tailboards, i.e., wooden boards that extended beyond the shield to act like a rudimentary tail-skin. A further problem was the lack of experienced miners. Although Mowlem had intended to hand-mine all of the tunnels on their contract, when a Westfalia boom cutter became available from another contract they brought it in and continued with just twelve miners.[297]

The running tunnels south of Baker Street were constructed under three separate contracts, to get the line completed as quickly as possible. As with the tunnels on the Heathrow extension, Greathead shields were used for both running and platform tunnels, and some sections used boom cutters or road headers to perform the excavation. At others the miners used pneumatic shovels to excavate the clay, four to a shield. From Baker Street, Charles Brand & Son Ltd bored the tunnels to Bond Street, A. Waddington & Son Ltd continued south through Green Park (including the platform tunnels) to a point near Admiralty Arch (on the west side of Trafalgar Square), and Kinnear Moodie constructed the final section through Charing Cross and its platforms to the end of the overrun tunnels, at Wellington Street. A large crossover tunnel was built to the west of Charing Cross to allow trains to depart westwards from either platform whilst the station served as a terminus. Narrow gauge railways were used in the tunnels to remove the spoil and bring tunnel ring segments back to the shields. Some of the spoil removed from the tunnels was transported to west London to form earthworks on the M4 motorway.

Both concrete and cast iron rings were used for the running tunnel construction, with the tunnels having internal diameters of 12 ft 6 ins or 12 ft 8 ins respectively. All of the platforms used cast iron for their tunnels, which had diameters of 21 ft 10 ins.* The cast iron segments came from the Nottinghamshire foundry of Stanton & Staveley, who were a regular supplier to the Underground throughout the 20th century. The £3 million order for 197,000 segments kept 300 men busy for over a year, finishing in 1973.[298] Around two years later the final bolt (having been painted gold to mark the occasion) was tightened to mark the completion of the tunnelling in July 1975.

---

*   The new platform tunnel at Baker Street was an exception. It was made the same
        diameter as the other tube platforms at the station, namely 21 ft 2½ ins.

Between Baker Street and Bond Street a new ventilation shaft was constructed in 1972 which emerged into the south-west corner of Park Square, across the Marylebone Road from Regent's Park station. This was designed as an ornamental octagonal pavilion with a seating around the outside and a decorative trellised roof. (On the opposite side of the road, in Park Crescent, are two more pavilions that disguise ventilation shafts for the Bakerloo line, although they are different in style to that for the Jubilee line).

The work to enlarge the ticket hall at Bond Street was conducted from beneath a large steel 'umbrella' bridge built in Oxford Street, similar to that used the previous decade at Oxford Circus for the Victoria line work. It weighed around 600 tons, and comprised 300 separate parts, all manufactured by Markham & Co.[299] This enabled traffic to continue to flow whilst a large ticket hall and associated utility diversion work was carried on just below street level. The most significant of the utility diversions was the reconstruction of the Northern Outfall Sewer, one of the largest sewers in London. From the new ticket hall two new escalator shafts were sunk. Balfour Beatty was awarded the £2.5 million contract for this work, which included all sub-surface work apart from the platform tunnels, and started in early 1972. Over the Easter weekend the road was closed so that the concrete supporting piles necessary to support the umbrella could be sunk; the umbrella was installed over the August bank holiday period and remained in place until Easter 1975.

At Charing Cross, the new Fleet line platform tunnels were constructed with escalators at each end connecting to the Bakerloo line station of Trafalgar Square to the west, and Strand station on the Northern line to the east. The entire complex was named Charing Cross from 1 May 1979.

The £3 million works to form the new combined station were complex because there were few potential locations on the surface nearby which could be used as worksites, and at Strand station the lifts that had served the platforms since 1907 needed to be replaced by escalators. The small ticket hall beneath the main-line station forecourt needed considerable enlargement, which was made trickier by the heavy stone Queen Eleanor memorial cross (actually dating from the Victorian period), which was too fragile to be moved. During 1974 seven steel beams 41 ft long and 3 ft deep were installed beneath it, and its foundations were wrapped with more steelwork, in order to underpin it and keep it from moving.

The first visible change at the station was the closure of the Villiers Street entrance, in January 1973. In the same month piling work took place in the main-line station forecourt in readiness for the installation of another steel umbrella bridge, similar to that used at Bond Street. This was constructed over the Easter weekend

Shoppers walking over the umbrella bridge at the junction of Oxford Street and Davies Street in June 1972 were probably unaware of the scale of the hole beneath their feet. The underside of the bridge is the black area at the top of the photograph. Utility pipes and wires are suspended across the worksite, with planks either side to protect them, and large metal props spanning the excavation. *(LTM)*

SOUTH MOLTON STREET
DAVIES STREET
OXFORD STREET
N
STRATFORD PLACE
TICKET OFFICE
WESTBOUND CENTRAL LINE
EASTBOUND CENTRAL LINE
SOUTHBOUND FLEET LINE
NORTHBOUND FLEET LINE
LONDON'S GROWING UNDERGROUND
2 THE NEW BOND STREET STN.
This impression, by artist E. Barker, shows how Bond Street Underground Station will look when its reconstruction is completed in 1976.
The station is being enlarged to handle the eight million extra passengers a year expected to use it when the first stage of the new Fleet Line serves Bond Street in 1977. The ticket hall is being trebled in size, with two extra street entrances. One will give access for the first time from the north side of busy Oxford Street. There will be five new escalators. The work is being financed by the Government and the Greater London Council.

LT published posters featuring isometric drawings of the new Jubilee line stations, showing passengers how the stations were being transformed. The five new escalators being installed are the trio descending to the Jubilee line platforms, and a new pair between the enlarged ticket hall and the Central line level, at the back of the drawing in the poster. *(LTM)*

in 1973, with both Strand Underground station and Charing Cross main-line station closed for the duration of the work. Five months later Strand station was closed again for almost six years to allow the escalator shafts to be excavated. The only suitable location for them cut through the existing lift shafts, and so it was impossible for the station to remain in operation. The new escalator shaft cut through the lift shafts at different levels, reaching its lower concourse on the south-eastern side of them. Side passages from this concourse then connected back into both the lower lift landings, allowing the existing access passageways to be reused. Grilles in the sides of these passages now mark the location of the disused lift shafts. One of the now-disused lift shafts was made even deeper, and a new electrical substation was installed in it. This provided power for the new line.

The extension for the ticket hall was excavated out beneath the forecourt (as the original ticket hall had been in 1905), making the final space substantially larger. The Eleanor cross remained *in situ* throughout the work, and now rests on the ticket hall roof. The umbrella over the forecourt was removed in October 1975 once the structural work was complete and the forecourt surface had been reinstated. Fitting out of the new ticket hall then started, using brightly coloured plastic panels (as a contrast to the grey that characterized the Victoria line). The work was originally scheduled to allow the reopening of Strand in 1976, with escalators, but industrial relations problems at Otis, the escalator manufacturer, caused considerable delay.[300]

A working site was made by Kinnear Moodie Ltd at Whitcomb Street, where the Sainsbury Wing of the National Gallery now stands. Two shafts were sunk to a depth of 120 ft. From these access tunnels were excavated beneath Trafalgar Square (and diverging to avoid passing below Nelson's Column) to enable the construction of both the lower levels of the station and the running tunnels. One of these tunnels split in two at the station, with branches heading in opposite directions to the existing Northern and Bakerloo line lower escalator concourses. Although originally intended to be a temporary working tunnel, it was realized during construction that it would be more convenient if it was fitted out for passenger use to enable passengers to access the Northern line from the Trafalgar Square ticket hall without having to descend to the level of the new platforms and then up again (and vice versa). The tunnel remains in place behind a locked door, mostly used for storage but occasionally bringing the Underground some income from filming use.

The loop to Heathrow Terminal 4

In the late 1970s it was anticipated that Heathrow airport would require additional capacity by the mid-1980s, and planning started for a fourth terminal. This was to be placed towards the southern perimeter of the airport, and LT considered how best to connect this with their existing Piccadilly line tunnels. The decision was made to form a 6-kilometre-long single-track loop, branching off at Hatton Cross and connecting with the overrun tunnels beyond Heathrow Central station via a single platform station at the new terminal.[301] Time was of the essence after delays in agreeing funding. After a hurried tendering process, a consortium of Thyssen (GB) Ltd and Taylor Woodrow Construction Ltd was appointed to build the new extension, with the tunnelling work costing £10·6 million. Work started on 9 February 1983.

There were two key areas of the construction work. At Hatton Cross a new junction had to be made immediately west of the station. This site was within the airport boundary, and first needed to be re-fenced so that it was technically landside, thus avoiding security issues. The work was started by constructing a new concrete wall to form the southern edge of the enlarged concrete box, so that the box could accommodate the new track formation branching off. The roof beams in the affected section were replaced by longer pre-cast concrete beams to span the widened structure. Once these changes had been completed the original southern wall of the existing concrete box was demolished. Beyond the box an open trench was dug, surrounded by a sheet-piled wall to hold back water from the gravelly soil. The first 230 m of tunnel was constructed in this trench using 403 cast iron tunnel rings of 3·85 m diameter bought for the abortive Jubilee line beyond Charing Cross, on towards Fenchurch Street.* A concrete bed was laid along the trench and the tunnel was supported by this around its entire lower half. The upper part of the tunnel was built by lowering in pairs of half-rings, bolted together, using a crane. Once completed the outside of the upper half of the tunnel was waterproofed. At the west end of the trench a 6·5 m diameter shield chamber was built, connected with the tunnel, and supported by further sheet piles. A temporary shaft was made for access to the tunnelling equipment, as well as a drift tunnel (inclined shaft) at an angle of 18° from which the spoil was removed. The trench was then backfilled to cover over the tunnel, using material removed originally, and the sheet piles were removed The shield chamber was subsequently used as a pump room for tunnel drainage.

The main work was the driving of the new running tunnel. This started at the foot of a 7·5 m diameter shaft sunk at Wessex Road,** where two tunnel faces were started in opposite directions from a 5·0 m diameter shield chamber. The tunnelling used four Greathead shields (manufactured by Grosvenor Steel Fabrications) and Dosco TM 1800 boom cutters, similar to the machinery used for the original Heathrow extension in the 1970s, to bore tunnels with an internal diameter of 3·81 m (the external shield diameter was 4·115 m). Mechanical segment erectors facilitated the installation of the tunnel lining behind the shields. One shield tunnelled around 2,900 m south and then eastwards to the station site at Terminal 4, whilst the other curved round to a step-plate junction constructed at the end of the existing overrun tunnels, forming a tunnel 1,150 m long. A third shield (a second-hand and refurbished machine made by Priestley) and Dosco boom cutter started work from the shield chamber built at the end of the cast iron tunnel at Hatton Cross, and bored about 1,350 m westwards to Terminal 4. Once the tunnelling crews had gained experience on the project the tunnelling rate increased to a peak of 139 m per week (185 rings), working for 20 hours per day in two shifts for five days per week.

The step-plate junction was built from another shaft of 3·85 m diameter sunk just west of Terminal 3 from an aircraft parking stand. The shaft descended through 6 m of gravels and then a further 11 m of clay. From its base an identically sized access tunnel was hand-mined to a point between the end of the existing eastbound overrun tunnel and the location for the junction. One tunnel face excavated the 270 m long tunnel east to join the existing tunnel, whilst in the other direction it formed a pilot tunnel for the larger end of the step-plate tunnel. Both of these tunnel faces were excavated by hand and the tunnels were lined with cast iron segments. The 9·0 m diameter section of the step-plate junction was then excavated, by enlarging part of the pilot tunnel. When the shield arrived from the Wessex Road shaft it met the end of the hand-mined tunnel, which was then enlarged to a diameter of 8·25 m in front of the shield (adjacent to the section previously enlarged to 9·0 m diameter). The shield was then jacked onto a cradle and pulled through the larger section of the step-plate junction to its headwall, where it was used to excavate the final section of running tunnel that connected with the existing westbound overrun tunnel; this final section was lined with concrete segments. Meanwhile the remainder of the

---

* Some of the ventilation shafts, shield chambers, and parts of the step-plate junction also made use of these surplus segments.

★★ Wessex Road no longer exists, having been removed when Terminal 5 was constructed.

step-plate junction was enlarged by hand from the pilot tunnels, using 160 cast iron rings.[302] Internal supports were fitted to the lining of the pilot tunnel whilst this was completed.

The electrically-operated boom cutters removed all of the soil at their tunnel faces except for a 10 cm layer around the outer circumference of the tunnel. This was easily removed by the cutting edge of the shields when their 12 hydraulic rams forced them forwards with a thrust of 600 tons. Spoil was removed back into the tunnels on conveyor belts. All of these sections of tunnel were lined with self-supporting pre-cast concrete segments manufactured by Taylor Woodrow locally at Southall, in a new plant established for the project and adjacent to their existing offices. The internal diameter was 3·81 m, and each ring was longer than usual, at 75 cm, to increase the speed with which the tunnel was completed. A higher-than-usual degree of accuracy was required in manufacturing the segments, as the tunnel needed to withstand the force exerted on the ground above it by the undercarriage of a Boeing 747 landing. Part of the tunnel near Hatton Cross passed at shallow depth beneath the emergency overrun for Runway 5, where this occurrence was a possibility.[303]

Another 18° drift tunnel with a diameter of 1·52 m was also sunk at Wessex Road, and was initially used to establish a base-line and location details for the tunnel underground, as described in Chapter 6. A conveyor system was then installed to remove the spoil from the tunnels. This was brought to the conveyor in side-tipping spoil trucks pulled by five 37 h.p. battery locomotives running on a 60 cm gauge railway laid in the tunnels by the contractors. Behind the shields the trucks were loaded from the shield conveyor belts, each truck accommodating the spoil removed from advancing the shield by one tunnel ring.[304] A further shaft was sunk at Bedfont Road (which was subsequently renamed Sanctuary Road). This provided services to the tunnellers, and was converted into a permanent ventilation and escape shaft for the loop.

The two shields advancing on the new station platform had to stop on either side for dismantling as the station itself was nearing completion. This had been constructed by the airport owner, BAA, as a cut and cover concrete box. Work started on the station box before the tunnelling had even begun as BAA needed to build a new car park for the terminal above the station site.

Provision was made for another station on the loop at a proposed Terminal 5. The section of tunnel just south of the Wessex Road shaft was given a straight alignment (curved platforms are heavily frowned upon in modern times) and about 15 m of the tunnel was constructed with a diameter of 8·25 m to help start the process of enlargement when the station was to be built. However, when the plans for Terminal 5 were finalized it was placed over 1 km away from the loop tunnel, and so the straight section was destined to remain just a part of the running tunnel.[305]

The tunnelling was completed in June 1984, and track laying and fitting out with railway equipment then began. The track used flat-bottomed rails secured to pre-stressed concrete sleepers using Pandrol clips, which was a first for the Underground. To reduce vibration the sleepers were mounted in neoprene 'boots' fixed to the tunnel floor.

Stations and experiments

THINGS TO COME
AT SOUTH KENSINGTON

This artist's impression shows the general layout of South Kensington Underground Station as it will be when the present extensive improvements scheme is completed.

South Kensington is used by 20 million Underground passengers a year. Under the scheme, costing well over £1m., the old lifts serving the deep-level Piccadilly Line will be replaced by escalators, and stairs from an intermediate landing will give a direct link with the sub-surface District and Circle Line platforms, greatly improving interchange. A single ticket hall will serve all three lines.

The lifts will be taken out of service and the new lower flight of escalators brought into use in the near future, and the whole scheme should be completed late this year.

The Government and the GLC are contributing towards the cost of the work.

July, 1973

There were many other interesting engineering works on the Underground in the post-War period. A selection of those with particularly unusual or interesting features are presented in this chapter.

Lengthening platforms on the District line

The platforms along the District line between Gloucester Road and Tower Hill were all too short for the trains that served them following electrification in 1905. Very narrow catwalks had been installed in the tunnels beyond the platform ends to allow passengers to carefully alight. Whilst these allowed the operation of longer trains and therefore the line capacity was augmented, the increased dwell time at stations reduced the benefit somewhat. In 1957 the Ministry of Transport recommended that the catwalks should be replaced by proper platforms. LT had been reaching the same view and work was planned for proper platform lengthening.

Over the period of a year until March 1962, the platforms at Blackfriars were lengthened in a £140,000 project. The extension ran westward for 74 ft, as the eastern end was beneath the main-line station. Before new walls for a wider tunnel could be built, a large number of telephone cables and other utilities needed rerouting. Then trenches 30 ft deep and 8 ft wide were created along the lines of the new walls. The infill of the Embankment was poor, and to ensure that the walls had sufficient support bored piles were created descending to 90 ft below the surface and into the

The section of extended platform at Blackfriars is very distinctive, with this series of angular arches spanning the tracks. *(LTM)*

underlying clay. These supported reinforced concrete bases, each of which supported nine 7-ton precast concrete columns. Wall slabs were fitted into slots on the columns to create the rear platform wall, and then concrete was poured into the space behind the slabs. On the north side of the line the wall had to be constructed next to an existing pipe subway, which caused the most westerly column to be out of line with the others.

Constructing the tunnel roof had to be done at night, as it was not possible to close the busy road overhead during the day. Each night a small section of the road was opened up and a 19 ton precast concrete beam would be lowered by two cranes into position spanning two of the columns. The road surface was then temporarily reinstated. Between the columns a new roof was built from above using 12-inch-thick reinforced concrete slabs, which also had to support the roadway.

Great care also had to be taken as the extension sat above the Fleet sewer, which had already been rebuilt at this point by the railway (see p 40-1). The concrete bases for the columns spanned the two channels of the sewer, and a new wall had to be constructed to close off the upper end of the original brick sewer before the channels were reached.[306]

Following work at Monument and Blackfriars, the lengthening of Westminster's platforms took place at their eastern ends. This section of the tunnel passed beneath the New Scotland Yard building (dating from 1891) and the Victoria Embankment. The work involved constructing new walls behind those of the tunnel to provide space for the platform extensions, but was complicated on the eastbound side by the presence of the building, which was partly supported on a girder across the tracks.

The wall on the westbound side was relatively straightforward to construct. A trench was dug across the pavement and part of the roadway, and was supported with bentonite using the Soletanche process (described on p 275). To prevent the bentonite from leaking away in the loose soil that filled the Embankment, grout was injected from the tunnel through the existing tunnel wall, to help consolidate the ground. Reinforcement cages were lowered into the trench, and concrete was pumped in as the bentonite was removed, leaving a reinforced concrete wall 65 ft deep.

The eastbound side wall was largely under a single-storey annex building of New Scotland Yard. This was carefully dismantled so that the area could be used as a work site. The bentonite process could not be used beside the building, and so the wall was built in eight sections to provide protection. Those alongside the building were supported on twelve bored piles sunk to a depth of 100 ft. The Joosten process was used to consolidate the ground in lines either side of the line of piles prior to the work, and a milder consolidation was made between these lines where the piles were sunk. The wall was then constructed to a height of 6 ft above the future station roof. The section of wall away from the building, and partly beneath Derby Gate, was constructed using bentonite in a similar manner to the westbound wall.

The New Scotland Yard building was then underpinned using eight temporary girders, and jacked up very gently to remove its weight from the girder that spanned the District line tracks, which was 45 ft long, 8 ft deep, and had a mass of almost 30 tons. Over two nights the pressure in the jacks was increased with very careful measurements being taken to ensure the stability of the building. The old girder was then cut away with cutting torches.

New permanent girders were then installed, spanning the tracks between the new side walls, forming the first section of the new tunnel roof. Six of these were fixed in position at first, 43 ft long and 3 ft 6 in deep. Once in place the weight of the building was transferred onto them from the temporary girders, which were removed and reused to form the final section of new roof over the widened tunnel. Precast concrete slabs 3½ inches deep were supported on the flanges of the new girders to form the tunnel ceiling, and a further 6½ inches of reinforced concrete was poured above them. This layer was waterproofed by a layer of bitumen 1⅛ inches thick, and a final covering of 2 inches of concrete was laid to protect the bitumen. The site was then backfilled with about 5 ft of soil, and the single storey building annex was reconstructed.

Demolition of the old tunnel arch started concurrently with the construction of the new roof. A temporary steel arch was constructed within the old tunnel whilst the old brickwork was removed from around it. The side walls were demolished to platform level, and then used to support precast platform sections made from reinforced concrete.[307]

During the work, two plane trees that were in the way were lopped and carefully removed. They were looked after at LT's own nursery so that they would remain alive and were replanted in the autumn of 1964.

Other stations had their platforms lengthened. Work at Cannon Street started in 1968, and Victoria had its platforms extended as part of the Victoria line construction work. The work at South Kensington was done in 1971–3 in conjunction with a project to install escalators. Charing Cross (now Embankment) was one of the easier stations at which the platforms were lengthened, as a short locomotive siding had been provided on each side of the line at opposite ends of the platforms. These had not been needed since the MDR was electrified in 1905, and the tracks had been removed. The platforms were extended into the spaces that they had used, which explains why the platforms are slightly staggered.

Protecting the Bakerloo line

The Bakerloo line tunnels beneath the Thames are close to the river bed. Fears during the First World War that a bomb dropped by a Zeppelin airship might breach one or both tunnels and flood the Underground led to the installation of an armoured steel lining in 1919, fitted against the flanges of the tunnel segments. The track was replaced by shallower bridge rails on longitudinal timbers (rather than transverse sleepers) because of the new lining across the tunnel invert. Special conductor rails were made so that they would not be too close to the new plate lining. Above track level, grouting was inserted between the armour plate and the original tunnel lining. The internal lining was built in panels about 4 ft long (130 panels in the southbound tunnel, and 115 in the northbound), and as a result of these the effective internal diameter of the tunnel was reduced to 11 ft 6½ ins.[308] This gave a very tight clearance for the rolling stock.

During the Second World War engineers found the lining to be in a poor condition. The grouting had disintegrated because of water leaking into the tunnel, and the armour plate lining was moving as a result. The line was closed south of Piccadilly Circus for twelve days in August 1944, and the floodgates closed to seal off the work

Workers breaking out the damaged concrete invert of the under-river Bakerloo line tunnels. The armoured lining inside the tunnel can be seen, giving the inside of the tunnel a smoother appearance than normal.

site. Holes had to be cut through the plates using oxy-acetylene equipment and brackets installed to fix the plates to the cast iron lining. Meanwhile the track was broken out, the plating underneath was removed, and then conventional track was installed set into a new concrete invert.

In 1996 LU announced plans to re-strengthen the under-river tunnels of both the Bakerloo and Northern lines between Embankment and Waterloo, at a cost of around £30 million. The Bakerloo was seen as being the greater priority as it had barely 3 m of clay above the tunnels at some points, and passed through gravel on the south side of the river. Tidal scour since the tunnels were built had removed some of the cover that had existed. Although the fear of bombs being dropped from airships and planes had passed, concerns about terrorist attacks or even a boat sinking and striking the tunnels meant that greater protection was required. It was decided that the best approach was to build a protective box around the outside of the tunnels.

There was always a risk that work around the tunnels might cause the flooding that it sought to avoid, and so it was necessary to close the line south of Piccadilly Circus and the floodgates once more – but this time for eight months between 10 November 1996 until 14 July 1997. One of the first tasks was the refurbishment of the floodgates, which had fallen into disuse.[309] The contractors for the piling work were Christiani & Neilson, who worked from two piers in the river that were specially built for the work. The first part of the work was to create a sheet-piled box around the location of the tunnel protection, 160 m long by 25 m wide. This allowed the river bed within the box to be levelled off before the permanent concrete piles were built. A combination of 144 steel tubes 1·4 m in diameter and sheet piles were sunk about 6 m into the clay either side of the tunnels to form walls. Noise from the work to hammer these into place caused anger at the nearby Royal Festival Hall on the Southbank, as it disturbed concerts and led to concert-goers walking out during intervals.[310]

London Underground published a detailed leaflet explaining the works and alternative bus services for passengers who would be inconvenienced by the tunnel closure. *(LUL)*

Going to work on the Tube

The soil inside the tubes was excavated using an auger, which removed the soil 10 m deeper than the tubes. They were filled with concrete and divers cut off the tops to make them the same height as the piles forming the walls. Finally, 24 pre-cast concrete slabs 22 m long, 6 m wide, and 2·5 m deep with a mass of 450 tons were brought by barge from the Royal Docks, where they were manufactured. The barges were designed to be able to sink; at low tide they were coupled onto fixed gantries and sunk to lower the slabs into position on top of the piled walls, and the joint where they met was sealed to make it watertight.[311]

The temporary works, such as the piers, were removed from the river after the train service was restored. A ceremony to reopen the floodgates was held, with local MPs present.

Acid at Old Street

An unusual problem occurred with the tunnel linings of the Northern line south of Old Street station. A little water ingress had been noticed in 1945, but this was in itself not strange. Thirteen years later a tunnel inspector noted a "mushroom-like yellow deposit" on the tunnel wall. No action seems to have been taken until

September 1962, when the crust on the tunnel rings was analysed and found to be acidic. A closer examination of the tunnel found 29 cracked segments in the southbound tunnel, and 5 in the northbound tunnel. Water containing sulphuric acid was leaking into the tunnels in this area. When the tunnels had been enlarged in the 1920s sand had been encountered here in discontinuous patches, but it had been mostly dry. During this work "considerable anxiety" was caused because the sand was felt to increase the risk of subsidence to the GN&CR tunnels above.[312] The area of concern lay beneath the City Road in between the junctions with Oliver's Yard and Epworth Street.

A ¼-inch hole was drilled through one of the tunnel segments and a steel plug was inserted. This had dissolved to a large extent 48 hours later, indicating that the water was strongly acidic. Work was carried out to see if the acid could be neutralized, by injecting over 2,500 gallons of sodium hydroxide solution into the ground from the tunnel.[313] The original grout holes in the tunnel segments were unsealed and 100 holes were drilled into the soil behind the segments to determine the condition of the ground. More checks were made from the tunnels of the Northern City line, which was directly above the Northern line with about 6 m of clay in between. Nothing untoward was found from these latter test borings.

Steel straps were installed on 70 tunnel segments in the southbound tunnel. These fitted into the segments between the flanges to provide support and strengthen the lining. Also, the bolts joining adjacent rings were replaced in this section of tunnel by high-tensile steel bolts. A large amount of alkaline grout was forced into the ground behind the tunnel segments in March 1963. It was hoped that this would resolve the problem, but the tunnel was kept under close scrutiny.[314]

The running tunnel south of Old Street in the 1960s, with the steel strapping in place on both sides. Damage from the incursion of acid can be seen below the strapping in the left foreground. *(Transport for London)*

By the late 1980s further investigation was needed, and LUL commissioned a geological survey. The geology of the area is relevant to the problem. The tunnels are at a depth of 80 ft, and cut through a bed of wet sand that lies between the London clay (above) and Woolwich bed clay (below). It was known that the lowest levels of the London clay were often sandier than the layers above, and the survey made in 1987 discovered a high level of iron pyrite in the sand at Old Street. Pyrite is iron sulphide (FeS_2), and in water it oxidizes to produce sulphuric acid. Oxygen is also required, and this was present because of the tunnel; every time a train passed along, the pressure forced some air through the lining. The water table in this part of London had risen considerably during the twentieth century as a result of the closure of industries that had extracted lots of water from the ground, such as breweries.

Boreholes were sunk either side of the running tunnels, and found that there was more water to the east of the tunnels. The level suggested that it would have spread throughout the sand to a common level, but was being held back by the southbound tunnel, which was acting like an underground dam. A similar body of water was retained between the two running tunnels, and was corroding the eastern side of the northbound tunnel. Water ingress to the southbound was estimated at 20 litres per year. Analysis of the water showed that it also contained two types of bacteria that would catalyze the oxidation reaction and enable the sulphuric acid to form faster.[315]

The cracking of the tunnel segments was due to another chemical reaction taking place. The sulphuric acid reacted with the cement grout behind the segments (and possibly with calcite-bearing sand) to form crystals of gypsum and other minerals. These take up a greater volume than the original reactants, and exert pressure as they form. This pressure was sufficient to deform the tunnel. The acidic attack on the iron segments only occurred where the water and acid in the sand could penetrate the grout. Even the steel straps were being corroded by the acid, and it was clear that further work was required in the northbound tunnel. Between 12 November 1990 and 15 February 1991 some repairs were undertaken to this tunnel, which was closed between Moorgate and Angel in the evenings to allow more time for the work, in which some tunnel segments were replaced. The contractors, Morgan Est, found that each of the 1,800 straps installed (two per segment) needed to be shaped for its location, and so plywood templates were created for each strap to record the unique profile required.[316]

A more extensive programme of work to fully replace the tunnel linings began in April 1994, at a cost of £15·3 million. Considerable thought had gone into the choice of material for the new lining. Cement was not inert, a coating on iron segments could be damaged during handling or construction, and glass-reinforced plastic was unproven for long periods. The new tunnel needed a design life of 400 years, and so despite the cost, stainless steel was chosen. This was the largest ever single order for stainless steel in the world at that time, with a mass of 750 tonnes and costing £4·5 million, and the 3,500 segments were cast by Weir Materials Ltd. The segments were cast in sand moulds and then heated in ovens to 1,100°C for several hours before being quenched in cold water. Only then could they be machined so that they would fit together to the required tolerances.[317]

★   The steel was a 25% chromium duplex steel (50/50 austenitic-ferritic) alloy.

Amec Civil Engineering were appointed as contractors, and as they were not permitted access via Old Street station they sank a shaft 32 m deep from the car park of a nearby school to a level below the Northern line tunnels. A heading was constructed by hand below the southbound tunnel to a point between the running tunnels. Two 2·44 m diameter shafts were then built upwards until it broke into a disused reversing siding tunnel. From this location, north of the problem area, all of the tunnel lining replacement work was carried out for a length of 80 m in each tunnel.

The work was similar to the tunnel enlargement of the 1920s. A large Greathead shield weighing 54 tonnes was manufactured by Markham of Chesterfield, with an aperture large enough for trains to pass through, allowing the tunnel to be supported during the day when work was not taking place. A track bridge fitted into the shield, which supported the track passing through the shield to allow trains to run during the day, but also allowed the track to slide through unimpeded as the shield was driven forward at night. Shield chambers 5·75 m in diameter were built in the running tunnels (just north of Oliver's Yard), and were lined with conventional SGI segments as the chambers were to the north of the affected area. The chambers were connected with the disused siding tunnel, the shield was erected, and once on the move each night a few more rings were reconstructed. Because of the need to allow trains through the shield it had a diameter 1 metre larger than the tunnel, so the 4·68 m internal diameter of the new lining was rather larger than the old, which itself had been enlarged from the original 10 ft 6 ins tunnels. The work was carried out in each tunnel in turn; whilst the northbound tunnel was relined all of the cables it carried were diverted into the southbound tunnel via cross-passages, and vice-versa.

Two shield skins were supplied by Markham, one for each tunnel, with the shield equipment, including the track bridge, being transferred between the skins but the skins left in position behind the new lining. Work to break out the concrete track bed proceeded up to 15 m in advance of the shield, with trains proceeding at reduced speed through the area. Two of the tunnelling shield skins used for the 1920s tunnel enlargement work were also discovered, still in place where the work had stopped.* Where the renewed sections of lining ended, brick was used for the headwalls from which the smaller, unaffected tunnels continued.[318]

By the time the work was completed, 263 tunnel rings each 60 cm long had been replaced by new rings. During the work, which took 48,000 man-hours to complete,[319] different approaches were taken to the train service. The northbound tunnel was relined first, without significant interruption to the train service. For the southbound tunnel, the work was arranged to be at the same time as the diversion of the southbound tunnel at London Bridge (see next chapter). No services ran southbound between Moorgate and Kennington after 22.30 on weekdays, or at all at weekends, from 1 July until 20 October 1996. When finished, the access shaft, heading, and disused tunnel were backfilled with foamed concrete.

More acid — now on the Jubilee line

A similar problem occurred in the southbound running tunnel of the Jubilee line between Baker Street and Bond Street. In around 2003, spalling of the expanded concrete lining was noticed in a section of tunnel 215 m long. The damage slowly worsened, and investigation showed that it was due in part to the lining having been poorly aligned when it had been installed in the 1970s. The tunnel is very deep here, and it lies in the Lambeth beds beneath the London clay. These contain layers of clay, sand, and gravel, together with water. The lining would have been installed tightly against the subsoil when it was expanded into position, but the warmth from the tunnel had slowly dried the ground out behind the lining, causing it to shrink away from the concrete and crack. Air entered from the tunnel, and reacted with the water and pyrite in the ground. This allowed acidic ground water to form and gain access to the lining.[320]

The most visible effect in the tunnel was discolouration of the lining, and the build up of mineral deposits, probably being leached from the concrete. Tests showed the water entering to have a pH of around 2, giving it a similar strength to lemon juice. Staff working in the tunnel were advised to wear rubber gloves beneath their work gloves, and eye protection.[321]

Unlike the lining at Old Street, which could be unbolted and replaced, the concrete lining had been expanded into position and adjacent rings interlocked. There was also no convenient location for getting site access, other than the tunnel itself. A different approach was called for, and so in 2012 LU, together with Harmill Systems Ltd, developed special segment handling plant (SHP) with equipment for removing and replacing the lining. This was tested in the running tunnels near Charing Cross station, disused since 1999 when the Jubilee line was extended to Stratford (see next chapter). This enabled the staff to develop the right techniques and practice

---

*   These were cut up in order for the new lining to be installed.

without affecting the tunnels used by passenger trains. Two of the new SHPs were manufactured and mounted on flat-bed wagons, which were both brought to the site and then worked on different sections of the lining to enable it to be replaced more quickly. There were 359 concrete tunnel rings to be dismantled, comprising 6,103 segments, and they were replaced by SGI rings using 1795 new segments.[322] Much of the reconstruction work was done overnight, with late opening of the Jubilee line between Finchley Road and Waterloo on Sunday mornings extending the available time. The work was finished ahead of schedule in June 2015.[323]

The replacement lining is made of spheroidal graphitic iron (SGI), and a gel grout is being used to create an airtight seal between adjacent tunnel segments and rings, and to form a watertight barrier around the tunnel. The use of this has avoided the need to procure expensive stainless steel segments.

Spheroidal Graphite Iron (SGI)

The cast iron used for lining tunnels since the Tower Subway was built is known as grey cast iron. It has been manufactured since the Industrial Revolution, and contains a higher proportion of carbon (2½–4%) than is found in steel. The carbon exists throughout the structure of the iron as microscopic flakes of graphite. This has the disadvantage that cracks can form at the ends of the flakes due to stress concentrating there, making grey cast iron brittle. It was discovered in 1943 that the addition of magnesium causes the iron to form microscopic sphere-like nodules. This reduces the brittleness and makes the iron more ductile.

Tunnel lining segments made from SGI are stronger than those of grey cast iron, but cheaper than steel. They were first used on the Underground for the construction of two pilot tunnels for the Brixton crossover.[324] They were subsequently dismantled when the crossover tunnel was enlarged to its full

At the time of writing the replacement work is continuing, having started in mid-2013. Weekend possessions of the Jubilee line allow the work to continue; some of these have been full weekends, and others have just been Sundays. Longer closures during holiday periods have allowed bigger chunks of the work to be undertaken. After an initial set of unfavourable headlines from the London free newspapers about the closures, the media has seemingly forgotten about the work and is just letting LU get on with it.

The New Cross bentonite experiment

In 1971 LT decided to run an experiment. The sands and gravels of the Woolwich and Reading Beds were shallower south of the Thames, and any tube tunnel construction tended to encounter them. Consolidation of the ground in places was an option, but for constructing long running tunnels it was not feasible. Compressed air working has a number of disadvantages which have been described previously.

Mott, Hay & Anderson had been consulting engineers to the Underground since the earliest days of tube railways in London. One of their engineers, John Bartlett, conceived the idea of a tunnelling shield with an enclosed cutting face and which supported the tunnel face using bentonite. Pressure could thus be maintained on the tunnel face, avoiding subsidence, as the shield drive forward.

Bartlett developed the idea with the support of his employers, and the idea was discussed with LT. Their Chief Engineer was enthusiastic, and plans were soon being drawn up for a trial. The National Research Development Corporation funded 56% of the c.£500,000 cost of constructing the tunnel, in exchange for the patent rights,[325] with LT covering the remaining 44%.[326] The question was now where to run the trial? The Fleet line was being planned to take over the Stanmore branch of the Bakerloo line, and then run in new tunnels to Charing Cross and east to Fenchurch Street and the Docklands area (although this was two decades before the transformation of Docklands into a financial hub). Of the various routes being planned east of Fenchurch Street, one envisaged taking over the southern part of the East London line and extending south from New Cross to Lewisham. As the line was only single track to New Cross, and there was no space at ground level to double it, the additional track would have to be in tunnel.[327] The geology of the area was the type of sand and gravel layers that the bentonite shield was intended to work in, and so the decision was made. A short length of experimental tunnel would be made along the planned route, with the intention of being incorporated into the Fleet line at a later date.* As the Parliamentary powers for the route as far as New Cross had been obtained in 1971 there was no impediment to the trial.

---

*   The Fleet line, renamed the Jubilee line in 1977, never made it to New Cross. After remaining at Charing Cross from 1979 until 1999, it was finally extended to Stratford in 1999.

Mott Hay & Anderson were, unsurprisingly, the engineers for the tunnel, and after a tendering competition (based on technical merit, not cost) Edmund Nuttall were appointed as contractors, with Robert Priestley Ltd manufacturing the tunnelling machine. This was not based on a drum digger, because of the difficulty in sealing off the cutting face with the large set of rotating components. Instead an existing tunnelling machine that was made by Priestley was adapted through the installation of a fixed bulkhead at the front diaphragm of the machine.

This provided a sealed chamber at the front of the shield which contained the rotating cutting head. The chamber was pumped full of bentonite, which was stirred around by the rotating action. As the cutter bored through the ground, the spoil mixed into the bentonite. A system of pumps removed the contaminated bentonite from the cutting face and replenished it with clean bentonite. It was pumped up to a cleaning system on the surface which filtered the gravel and sand from the slurry, so that it could be reused. An additional advantage that this brought was the reduction in equipment in the tunnel behind the shield; only the pipe-work was necessary.

At the rear of the shield, a pneumatic ring fitted around the inside edge of the tailskin provided a seal against the newly erected tunnel lining. Sledge trailers 27 m long were towed behind the shield. These contained pumps, grouting equipment, electrical transformers and switchgear, and the pressure control panel, as well as telescopic piping to accommodate the forward movement of the shield and transport the bentonite to and from the shield.

The bentonite cleaning plant was a major focus of the work, as the economics of the use of this type of shield depended in part on how much bentonite could be recycled. The plant at New Cross used a vibrating screen to remove gravel, and then two series of hydro-cyclones to remove sand and other particles. These functioned in a similar way to the cyclonic vacuum cleaners available in the home today; the incoming material is spun around very fast and the unwanted components are separated out through centrifugal action. One of the problems at New Cross was that it only filtered out particles down to 75 μm, which was not sufficient to prevent the smaller particles from contaminating the bentonite and reducing its effectiveness. This would particularly have reduced its usefulness had clay been encountered.[328]

The particularly complex part of the design was the outlet from the cutting face. This was required to allow the bentonite and spoil to be removed, but had to allow the pressure to be maintained on the tunnel face. The solution was a helical feed-wheel, which prevented a direct path from ever occurring between the two sides of the bulkhead. Screens prevented large lumps of stone from jamming the feed-wheel.[329] Shortly after tunnel boring started, the feedwheel mechanism needed to be completely redesigned as it was being frequently jammed by the finer grains of excavated spoil.

Work started on the tunnel on 24 February 1972, following construction of an hexagonal shaft 19·6 m deep near Milton Court Road. Outside the shaft, a 12 m length of ground was chemically consolidated. The shield without its sledge trailer or hydraulic power pack was lowered into the shaft, and hoses run to the ground-level hydraulic supply (this was due to limited space in the shaft). The shield was then used to conventionally excavate the first part of the tunnel from the shaft into the consolidated ground, i.e., without the use of bentonite. When only 95 cm

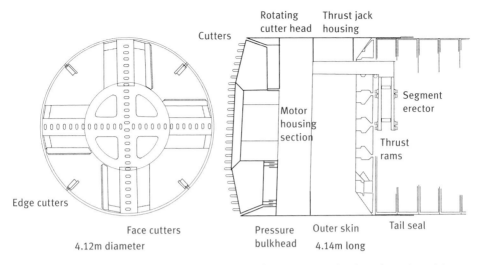

Diagrams of the experimental tunnelling machine used at New Cross, showing a front view of the cutting face, and a longitudinal section.

of consolidated ground remained, the sledge trailer and hydraulic power pack were installed behind the shield. An air lock was also constructed in the tunnel as a precaution. A further 50 cm of tunnel was bored under compressed air conditions, and then, with only a thin skin of consolidated ground remaining, the shield was converted to use bentonite. The air lock remained in place so that the tunnel face could be inspected occasionally.

A 144-metre length of tunnel was bored at New Cross, through layers of sandy gravel. The external diameter was 13 ft 6 ins, and it was lined with cast iron segments forming rings 50 cm long.[330] The rate of progress was around 2·5 m per 10 hour shift, with a maximum of 4 m in a shift.

The experiment was deemed a great success, although Britain did not get much of the financial benefits that accrued from the development of the bentonite shield. This was in part because after the conventional tunnelling in clay for the first stage of the Jubilee line (from Baker Street to Charing Cross) there was no construction work on the Underground south of the Thames until the Jubilee line extension started in the 1990s.* However, bentonite shields were used extensively elsewhere in the world, with 35 of them at work in Japan by 1979.[331]

A better Angel
During the 1980s the number of passengers using Angel station rose considerably, in part through the general increase in passengers on the Underground, but also because of nearby shopping and office development. The narrow island platform in its single tunnel, served by four lifts (two still dating from the C&SLR reconstruction

---

*   Some tunnelling using a bentonite tunnelling machine was performed in the UK, for example, a sewer tunnel was constructed by Edmund Nuttall in Warrington, using the same machine that had been used at New Cross.

work in 1924) was a cause of congestion and some concern for passengers, who disliked standing in the narrow space between two moving trains. There was a need to replace both the lifts and the platform arrangement, so early thoughts of just installing more lifts were not viable, despite Parliamentary powers having been obtained for this.[332]

Unless two banks doubling back were used, a new surface site was required, as escalators travel diagonally rather than vertically. This was advantageous, as the existing ticket hall in Torrens Street was around the corner from the main traffic centre of Islington High Street, and so the new station entrance would be in a better location. Two different schemes were considered for the platform improvements. First was a diversion of the northbound line to form a loop around the back of the existing platform. A new platform would be formed on the loop, and the trackbed for the existing platform would be filled in, to create a very wide southbound platform. The alternative was to enlarge the southbound tunnel to the west of the station site to form a new southbound platform, and construct a wall along the edge of the existing southbound platform to protect passengers from trains and allow it to become a dedicated northbound platform.[333]

During 1988 the options were compared, and the diversion of the northbound tunnel was chosen. The option for creating a new southbound platform did not have escalators descending to the level of the northbound (existing) platform, and so it would have been less convenient for passengers. Government authority for the £56 million scheme was given in August 1988, and Taylor Woodrow were awarded the main contract the following year. Balfour Beatty started the work, however, as they were to construct a new office development called Angel Square on the site of the new ticket hall. This was to be within the ground floor of the new building, for which piling had already taken place. Balfour Beatty excavated the pilot tunnel for the new escalator shaft from the site of the new ticket hall. Great care had to be taken

The step-plate tunnel to the east of the station, with a train of 1959 Tube Stock disappearing into the northbound tunnel. The diversionary tunnel will be on the left, behind the metal gates in the background. *(LUL)*

with digging the escalator shaft, as it passed just 1·6 m away from the piles at the closest point.

The 400 m of new running tunnel was excavated from the base of a shaft sunk near the existing station on a site between City Road and Goswell Road. This descended to a point south of the existing platform tunnel, and north of the new platform. A heading was driven from the base of the tunnel to the new tunnel, from where work commenced. The tunnels were in the Woolwich beds, which fortunately consisted of clay at this location, and for this short length of tunnel hand-mining was used. Between the old and new platform tunnels at the west end of the station a short concourse was tunnelled, with cross-passages onto the new platform. By September 1990 the platform tunnel was complete and work was progressing on the running tunnels. At each end of these a step-plate junction was formed around the existing running tunnel, which was supported by large metal struts whilst trains continued to run through. Once complete, the original tunnels were unbolted and dismantled during the night-time engineering hours. All of the new tunnel segments were made from SGI, and this was the first time that this material had been used for any substantial work on the Underground.

In October 1991 points were installed in the junction to the east of the station to allow engineering trains access so that the installation of track and other equipment could begin. Once this was completed and the new platform was ready, northbound trains were diverted into the new platform following a weekend possession of the station on 8 and 9 August 1992, and closure of the northbound line to all trains between Moorgate and Camden Town. The station reopened on the Sunday evening, but with only northbound trains stopping at the new platform.

The southbound platform remained closed until January 1993 for reconstruction. This consisted of filling in the trackbed for the old northbound platform, completing the access passages to the new concourse, and redecorating the platform and tunnel to match the new works. Whilst passengers used the new escalators, the workmen had access to the surface via the newer two of the passenger lifts to the old ticket hall, which were used to transfer materials and equipment. The shaft that had been constructed prior to the new northbound diversion tunnel was equipped as an emergency exit, and a small shaft-head building constructed at the top.

Cooling the Tube
Ventilation has continued to be a problem for the Underground. The confined tunnels make it difficult for heat to escape, and almost all of the electricity consumed by the trains whilst in the tunnels is released as heat, either from the motors or the brakes. Further heat is contributed by the passengers and staff. Over the years various experiments have been made. In 1938 a 'weather maker' was installed at Tottenham Court Road, on the southbound Northern line platforms. This blew air across pipes in which water at just above freezing point was circulated. The effect was said to be the equivalent of piling 50 tons of ice on the platform each day. Around the same time, equipment to blow water vapour over the tunnel mouth on the Bakerloo line at Trafalgar Square was introduced.[334]

In recent years the problem has become more acute. The clay around the tunnels has warmed up, and is no longer able to absorb as much heat as it did previously.

More trains are being run, and even though they are more energy efficient than their predecessors, they are still net producers of heat. Regenerative braking (where the motors are used as dynamos to slow the train and deliver electricity back to the current rails for use by other trains) is one of the key technologies that has helped here.

The problem was recognized by the 1990s, and the Jubilee Line extension was constructed with significantly greater ventilation capacity than previous lines. In total, its ventilation capacity is equivalent to that of the Bakerloo, Central, Piccadilly, Northern, and Victoria lines combined.[335]

The first, and most obvious, place to start was by upgrading and in many cases re-enabling the fan shafts at and between stations. Many of these had fallen into disuse over the years. The work to upgrade them configured the inter-station fans to run as exhaust fans, pushing hot air out of the tunnels. Cooler air would then be brought into the tunnels at stations, where it would be of most benefit to passengers. The fans on the Victoria line were some of the first to be upgraded, since the impending line upgrade had the potential to increase the temperature of the line otherwise. Its fans were doubled in capacity by this work, to handle approximately 75 m³/s of air.

The first innovative cooling scheme was developed for Victoria station, in conjunction with South Bank University. Groundwater entering the District and Circle line tunnels was drained into a sump from where it could be pumped into a sewer. In August 2006 this cool water, in part from the nearby underground Tyburn river, started to be pumped via water filters into heat exchangers hung from the ceilings of the Victoria line platform tunnels. These used the water entering at 12°C to produce cool air on the platforms, and in total provided almost 100 KW of cooling power. The energy consumption was very low: all that was needed were pumps for the water and fans for the air. After leaving the heat exchangers the water was disposed of in the sewers. In 2007 this project won the Innovation Award from the Carbon Trust.

One stop north on the Victoria line a similar experimental cooling system was deployed. Green Park had no shallow tunnels from which to extract cool water though, and instead boreholes were driven. These descended 130 m to the aquifer in the chalk beneath the clay. A pair was sunk 10 m apart for the extraction of cool water using an auger rig within Green Park, near to the station. These had a diameter of 0·7 m at the surface, but narrowed in stages to 0·45 m at the bottom. After filtration the water was piped to heat exchanger units in the station, which worked in a similar way to those used at Victoria. However, rather than requiring a complex framework to support them they were redesigned with a frame that attaches directly to the cast iron tunnel segments. The water leaving the heat exchangers was returned to the aquifer via a pair of boreholes 200 m away; this prevented the problem of the warmer water just being recirculated and the cooling effect diminishing. The boreholes have been carefully located with regard to the natural flow of the groundwater to ensure that the warmer water is discharged downstream of the extraction boreholes.

The Jubilee line extension

A different approach

On 8 December 1993 a ceremony was held at Canary Wharf to mark the official start of the Jubilee Line Extension (JLE) project when the Prime Minister, John Major, pressed a button to drive the first pile for the new station. After years of indecision about how the Jubilee line was to be extended, the massive redevelopment of the Docklands area of London had required greater public transport capacity than could be provided on the Docklands Light Railway (DLR). The main developer of the site, Olympia & York, forced the Government's hand by starting planning work for their own underground railway between Waterloo and Canary Wharf, and then on to Westcombe Park near Greenwich, where the depôt would be located. London Transport (LT) preferred an underground line that would provide wider benefits to London, and after many months of negotiation an extension of the Jubilee line was seen as the best option.[336]

The need to serve Waterloo station (as it was otherwise poorly connected with the Docklands area) meant that it would not be possible to keep the station at Charing Cross; the curves would be too great. Instead, the JLE branched off just south of the platforms at Green Park and bored its way to Westminster and then under the Thames to Waterloo. The tunnels would run east via London Bridge and the Rotherhithe peninsula and then cross back under the river to Canary Wharf, before curving northwards to Stratford.

The JLE was designed to be very different from the tube railways that had come before it. The penny-pinching approach taken to the Victoria line was a world away from the wide platforms and lavish provision of escalators on the JLE. The Docklands sites allowed the stations to be built using cut and cover techniques, making for more spacious stations and the admission of daylight into some of the depths.

Archæology was to take a greater role than before. In previous tube railway construction work old artefacts were uncovered and presented to museums, but this occurred by chance. On the JLE, archæological teams from the Museum of London were invited to the worksites once the ground had been cleared, and time was made in the project plans for some careful excavation work. A series of relics found at the London Bridge site were put on display in glass cases in the new ticket hall.

New techniques for tunnelling

The JLE heralded a major change for tunnelling on the Underground. For the first time, Tunnel Boring Machines (TBMs) were being used to construct the running tunnels. These were the next evolution of the tunnelling shield, and arguably LT had helped drive their creation when they part-funded the experimental tunnel at New Cross (see p299). In the twenty years since the technology had progressed considerably, with a number of specialist manufacturers of TBMs around the world.

The running tunnels for the JLE were larger than the rest of the Underground, having an internal diameter of 4·4 m so that a continuous walkway was provided

A view along the eastbound JLE running tunnel, between Westminster and Waterloo. The emergency walkway is to the right of the tracks, with the fire-fighting water main against the tunnel wall. One of the valves can be seen on the main. The tunnel telephone wires, which can be used in an emergency to discharge the traction current, are further up the wall, and a tunnel light is in the top right corner of the photograph. On the left-hand tunnel wall is a sign showing the distance to the nearest access points. *(Simon Lewis)*

for emergency purposes. This meant a 28% increase in the amount of spoil to be removed. Between London Bridge and North Greenwich the tunnelling was not through London clay either; the tunnels were in the Woolwich and Reading Beds, and even dip into the Thanet Sands below. Thames Water had constructed a large ring main beneath London in the late 1980s and early 1990s, and had gained valuable experience that was used by the JLE team.

The TBMs used for the JLE were of a type known as an Earth Pressure Balance Machine (EPBM). These can be operated as an open-fronted TBM to cut through clay, but when waterlogged or unstable soils are encountered the cutting chamber can be sealed off and filled with a slurry such as bentonite to support the face by maintaining pressure on it. The variable geology of London south of the Thames made this type of machine a sensible choice. Small compression chambers at the front of the machines allow engineers to use small drilling rods to probe the ground ahead to check the conditions that they will encounter.

As the patron saint of tunnelling and mining is St Barbara,* it has become traditional to bestow female names on tunnelling machines. At least five of the TBMs for the JLE were given names.

---

* St Barbara is also the patron saint of military engineers, artillerymen, armourers, gunsmiths, and other professions that work with explosives.

Contract	Tunnel	TBM type	Distance	Names
105	London Bridge (east) – Canada Water (west)	Kawasaki / Decon	5·6 km	*St James the Mole* *The Bermondsey Burrower* *Giant Muncher*
107	Canada Water (east) – Canary Wharf (west)	Herrenknecht Mixshield	2·1 km	Unknown
110	Canary Wharf (east) – Canning Town portal	Lovat MP202SE	2·5 km	*Sharon* (westbound) *Tracey* (eastbound)

Details of the TBMs used for the Jubilee line extension

Work by the contractors, a joint venture of McAlpine, Wayss & Freytag, and Bachy, started from the site of the station box at North Greenwich in August 1994. The box had not been completed, and the 5·3 m diameter Canadian-manufactured TBMs had to be lowered down a small shaft made on part of the site. Both of the TBMs departed eastbound, and the tunnels to the portal at Canning Town were completed in December. All of the work had been done in 'open' mode, without recourse to the use of slurry.[337] The machines were then brought back to North Greenwich, with the shield heads being transported by lorry (since they could no longer fit through the tunnels once the lining was installed) and the rest being reversed along the tunnels.

The first JLE TBM (called *Sharon*) being assembled in part of the station box at North Greenwich. *(LTM)*

The two TBMs then set off in the opposite direction, only to run into trouble in May 1995 when the lubricating greases of the main bearings became contaminated with fine particles from the clay after seals failed. After some tense meetings where expensive proposals for digging down to the machines to extricate them were considered, it was decided to attempt the repairs *in situ*. The manufacturer, Lovat, sent engineers to help with the task. One shield was operating again in four weeks; the other took twenty weeks and included the removal of the machine's main bearing. After tunnelling resumed they set the speed record for the extension when one bored 253 m of tunnel in a week on its way to Canary Wharf.[338] The machines met a sad end though. Having reached the edge of the station box at Canary Wharf there had been hopes that they would be removed once the holes for the tunnel connections were made. Delays at the station site thwarted this idea though, and instead the TBMs were cut up with gas cutting equipment where they had halted and were removed for scrap. The 2·5 km of twin tunnels made by these TBMs were lined with reinforced concrete segments manufactured by Charcon Tunnels who worked with the project team and contractors to meet the exacting requirements for the JLE. The segments were stronger than usual to resist the high pressures of the EPBM as it moved forward, and six were used to form each 1·2 m long ring. Neoprene gaskets were fitted between adjacent segments; these were squeezed together by the connecting bolts, forming a watertight joint.

The next tunnel contract to the west, between Canary Wharf and Canada Water, was also contracted to McAlpine-Wayss & Freytag-Bachy JV, and was bored by a pair of Herrenknecht Mixshields. These German-made machines had an external diameter of 5·13 m and were designed to operate with a closed, pressurized tunnel face at all times. Bentonite was used in the cutting chamber with compressed air helping to maintain the pressure on the face. The TBMs were launched from a 30 m deep shaft at Durand's Wharf, on the eastern side of the Rotherhithe peninsula. The shaft was formed as a caisson (similar to the construction of a bridge pier in a river) 14·5 m wide and 24 m long, with walls 1 m thick and weighing approximately 5,000 tonnes. It encountered problems as it sank into the water-bearing ground. The bottom 10 m had to be sunk under compressed air to hold back the water, causing delays to this part of the tunnelling. Further delays occurred because of problems in the separation plant. This was based on the surface beside the shaft, and processed the bentonite returned from the cutting face. Its job was to remove the soil and return the clean bentonite to the shield, but it required modification to cope with the material from the Thanet Sands, which tended to clog the filtration system.

The first drives started in February and March 1995, and bored westwards to the station box at Canada Water. The TBMs were driven into the box in September and October 1995, saving the need to dismantle them. Lorries removed them from the site, and returned them to Durand's Wharf so that the tunnels to Canary Wharf could be bored. This work began in November 1995 and soon accelerated to 100 m of tunnel per week, using concrete lining segments made by C.V. Buchan of Stockton-on-Tees. The TBMs arrived at Canary Wharf in February and March 1996.

The tunnels from Canada Water to London Bridge were contracted to Aoki:Soletanche JV, who used four TBMs (these were also EPBMs) designed by Kawasaki of Japan to bore the two 2·8 km tunnels. The first TBM was made in

Japan, with the other three being made under licence by FCB in Lille. The backup sets (equipment trailers behind the cutting shields) were made in the UK by Decon. Temporary access shafts were sunk at Old Jamaica Road and used for installing the TBMs. The first drive started in December 1994 and was to make the 450 m tunnels to Bermondsey station box. This demonstrated the geological difficulties that defined this contract. The Woolwich and Reading Beds in this area contained clay, which gummed up the cutting head chamber and blocked the plenum chamber (the pressurized area at the front of the TBM) and screw conveyor through which the bentonite and spoil mix should have been extruded. It was found that the clay was balling into large lumps that refused to break up once formed. The contractors tried different types of bentonite, and then specialist (and expensive) polymers used for drilling oil-wells, but very little improvement was seen. Next they tried adding foam, and this was effective at coating the clay as it was cut away from the face and preventing lumps from sticking together.

The TBMs were then modified to mix the foam into the bentonite on a permanent basis. The foaming agent was brought in to the tunnels in barrels and added to the water being fed to the face. Compressed air made the agent foam as it was injected into the cutting face. The new system had to be manually operated as it could not be integrated into the existing TBM systems. Additional benefits were found from the foam. It reduced the torque on the cutting head and the screw conveyor, and made the spoil handling much cleaner. All these factors justified the expense of the foaming agent, which was even more expensive than the polymers, and was used at the rate of 50 – 100 litres of mixed solution for each cubic metre of ground that was excavated.

Bermondsey station box was reached in June 1995, behind schedule following the clay problems. The box would contain only part of the station, with the remainder of the 7 m diameter platform tunnels extending westwards. These were built by enlarging the running tunnels made by the TBM, and then relining with SGI segments. One TBM continued through on its way to Canada Water whilst the other waited for the station enlargement work to be completed. Meanwhile a second pair of Kawasaki TBMs started work from the Old Jamaica Road shaft but heading west to London Bridge. The power of their motors had been increased by 25% to reduce the risk of delays if the clay proved troublesome. They operated in closed-face mode for all but the last 800 m of the 1,400 m of twin tunnel, by which point they had entered solid London clay. The final tunnel on this contract was the remaining bore between Bermondsey and Canada Water, which was completed in August 1996.

All of the tunnels between London Bridge and Green Park were constructed using more conventional tunnelling shields and excavation equipment. Aoki:Soletanche JV were also responsible for the London Bridge to Waterloo section, which they subcontracted to Costain Taylor Woodrow. A single Dosco road header boom shield was used for all of the tunnelling, similar to that used on the Heathrow extension of the Piccadilly line. This cut away the clay at the tunnel face using a small cutting head with six spokes which could be positioned by the operator to clear the face. Conveyors took the spoil back to muck wagons which were removed to the main shaft at Redcross Way by Schöma diesel locomotives. The tunnelling started at Redcross Way in April 1995 and reached Waterloo in September, averaging 87 m per week.

Behind the shield the tunnel lining was built using steel-fibre reinforced expanded concrete segments made by Charcon Tunnels. These were designed to resist the 1,300-tonne force exerted by the 13 hydraulic rams on the back of the shield. Instead of having the usual steel reinforcement bars embedded into the concrete at the time of moulding, they had 30 kg of steel fibres mixed into each cubic metre of wet concrete. The fibres were dispensed into the mix using specialist equipment to ensure that they were evenly distributed. As the shield passed through the site for the platforms at Southwark station temporary bolted segments were used.

After reaching Waterloo the shield was dismantled and returned to the site at Redcross Way. It then started on the second tunnel to Waterloo in November 1995. The process was then repeated twice for the short tunnels to London Bridge, with tunnelling work completing in June 1996. The station platform tunnels at Southwark were made by removing the 4·4 m diameter temporary lining, and using a refurbished shield from the Newcastle Metro to enlarge the tunnels and erect a 7·0 m diameter lining using fibre-reinforced concrete segments.

The final pair of tunnels from Waterloo to Green Park Junction were contracted to Balfour Beatty Amec JV, which used a pair of backhoe shields from Wirth Howden of Renfrewshire. The main worksite was at Jubilee Gardens on the south bank of the Thames, from where the first shield was launched in December 1994. By May 1995 it had reached the junction site at Green Park, from where the step-plate junction was dug by hand with an SGI lining constructed around the existing tunnel. Because the tunnels were stacked one above the other at Westminster, the lower tunnel was completed before work began on the upper. The latter was excavated between September 1995 and February 1996. Both tunnels were lined with concrete segments manufactured by C.V.Buchan, which were dismantled subsequently at Westminster to form the station platform tunnels. These were expanded from west to east using the original backhoe shield equipment fitted into 7·3 m diameter carcasses, also made by Wirth Howden. These left tunnels that were lined with SGI segments brought in from a shaft at Storey's Gate (towards Green Park) so that there was no conflict with the spoil, which headed out under the Thames to Jubilee Gardens. Expanding these tunnels in the opposite direction meant that the shield equipment needed rearranging so that the spoil was removed from the front of the shields.

All of the spoil from the tunnels between Green Park and Waterloo was removed via the 32 m deep shaft at Jubilee Gardens. Conveyor belts transferred it across the riverside walkway and into barges moored alongside. Each barge took 1,100 tonnes of clay; pairs of filled barges were then towed down the Thames to East Tilbury, where the contents were unloaded into lorries and dumped on land.[339]

The SGI segments for the JLE were manufactured by three companies. The majority came from C.V. Buchan, in a contract worth around £12 million. The redesign of the tunnel works at London Bridge (see below) required further segments, and these were supplied by Biwater Pipes. Finally, around 700 rings of SGI segments together with specialist castings such as cross-passage openings came by lorry from Rotas Rotava in the Czech Republic.[340] The SGI segments were about twice as expensive as the concrete segments, and so their use was limited to areas where the increased cost was justified, usually because of the size or complexity of the tunnel.

The New Austrian Tunnelling Method

Another new tunnel-building technique that was used on the JLE was a variant of the New Austrian Tunnelling Method (NATM). It had been developed in Austria, and involved mining out the ground to form the tunnels and providing initial support through wire mesh, rock-bolts, lattice girders, and by spraying on shotcrete and allowing the ground to accommodate the new void. A further lining is often installed subsequently, using reinforced concrete. A critical part of the process is observation; the tunnel needs careful monitoring to determine exactly how the support needs to be formed at any given point. NATM allows engineers and tunnellers to get away from their work being made from cuboid boxes excavated from the surface and cylindrical tunnels bored through the ground. For the JLE the technique used was sprayed concrete lining, rather than true NATM which is used through rock rather than clay.[341]

Deep beneath Waterloo station a workman sprays shotcrete onto the tunnel wall to form an instant tunnel lining on the metal mesh that can be seen in the ceiling and wall. *(LTM)*

NATM was suggested for the stations at Waterloo and London Bridge by the contractors, who demonstrated that it would deliver cost savings of around 10%. A trial in 1992 had proven it to work in London clay, and it was to be used on the tunnels for the Heathrow Express airport rail link in west London. Specialist advice was sought from Austrian geotechnical consultancies, and the work was approved. For many of the larger tunnels pilot tunnels were dug and shotcreted first, and then enlarged subsequently with the pilot tunnel lining being broken out at this time. For example, the lower concourse at Waterloo was first made with a 6·2 m internal diameter pilot, which was enlarged to 11·2 m.

The NATM tunnelling followed a careful sequence. The top heading, at the crown of the tunnel, and occupying about the top 40% of the tunnel, was made in advance of the lower parts of the tunnel. Work progressed by digging 1 m sections of this, and then 1 m sections of the 'bench', which is the next 40% of the tunnel's height. After each section was dug the bare earth was sprayed with shotcrete to seal and hold the exposed surface. After the top heading and bench had advanced by 2 m, the invert (lowest 20% of the tunnel) was excavated for 2 m and then shotcreted. The sequence would then start again.[342] At Waterloo the excavation was made using Westfalia road headers for the larger tunnels, and a backhoe excavator for smaller adits and junctions.

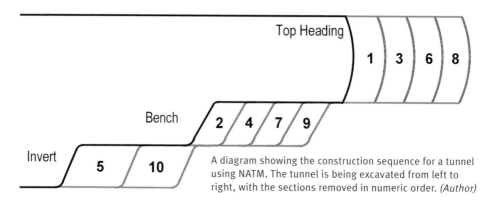

A diagram showing the construction sequence for a tunnel using NATM. The tunnel is being excavated from left to right, with the sections removed in numeric order. *(Author)*

Both Costain Taylor Woodrow JV at London Bridge, and Balfour Beatty Amec JV at Waterloo made good progress with NATM at their respective stations. The concrete used for the lining was pumped down from the surface sites into the tunnels to the spraying units, where an accelerant was added as it was sprayed. This caused it to harden quickly once it was in place. All was going well, when railway tunnels being constructed using NATM at Heathrow Airport (for the Heathrow Express) collapsed on 21 October 1994. The investigation subsequently found that the collapse was due to "a catalogue of design and management errors, poor workmanship and quality control", and cost the project £150 million.[343] The observation had been abandoned in pursuit of hitting targets. It cost the JLE project even more though, as all NATM work was immediately suspended. No problems had occurred with the technique on the JLE, but no one was prepared to take any chances, particularly when the work was beneath two of London's busiest railway termini.

The NATM work resumed after a 14-week delay, but by that time some of the work had been redesigned to use conventional tunnel linings. One partially completed NATM tunnel had been backfilled, as it was unsafe to leave it incomplete. The running tunnels were the first NATM work after the hiatus as they had the smallest diameter, and the Health & Safety Executive raised no objections to them restarting in January 1995. This process took longer for the larger concourse and platform tunnels, and when they were approved there were changes to the linings and tunnel shapes. The Jubilee line platforms at London Bridge were excavated and shotcreted in accordance with NATM, but the final lining was with tunnel segments. Other tunnels were given twice the thickness of the primary shotcrete lining (100 mm instead of 50 mm).

The 133 m tunnel at Waterloo that was to link the Jubilee line part of the station with the existing Bakerloo and Northern line areas was to have used NATM, but to save time a Wirth Howden tunnelling shield with a diameter of 7·5 m was purchased and the tunnel was hand-mined and lined with SGI segments. This tunnel now contains two passenger conveyors. The other new tunnels at the same level as this — the concourses above the platforms and connecting the two flights of escalators and the passenger conveyors — were also hand-mined and conventionally lined. The crowns of these tunnels had limited clay cover, and water-bearing Thames gravels were known to be above. The risk of using NATM was not seen as being worth taking. A new shaft had to be sunk for this purpose, and ironically the access adits from the shaft to the tunnels were made using NATM. Being of small diameter the risk was rather less.

Since 1996, the term 'sprayed concrete lining' (SCL) has been used in preference to NATM for this technique when used in soft ground. It was introduced by the Institution of Civil Engineers, and has been widely adopted.[344]

Station boxes
Probably the most impressive of the stations are those made in cut and cover boxes, especially Canary Wharf and North Greenwich. At the former location, the old Middle Dock was used as it was already a large hole in the ground (albeit full of water). It was one of the piles for the cofferdam constructed around the site that had been inserted at the ceremony to start the JLE. A double wall of the piles was installed in the dock surrounding the site of the station and allowing the water to be drained. Within this, a concrete box 280 m long and 32 m wide was formed, long enough for the platforms and a scissors crossover at the west end.

At the bottom of the box the dock was excavated downwards until much of the site was 24 m deep. Water was pumped from nearby boreholes to keep the site dry, and beneath the floor of the box 163 piles were sunk to keep it in the ground. Once completed, the groundwater around the box would exert a lifting force (hydrostatic uplift) calculated at 200,000 tonnes, and the piles were necessary to resist this — the massive weight of the station and its concrete box were not sufficient by themselves. Barges removed the spoil from the site, continuing a long tradition on the Underground.

The walls of the box were made thicker than had been originally planned. As work continued on the large office buildings nearby it was feared that the shifting forces in the ground could affect the station box otherwise. A large hole in the ground to the north, intended for new offices but unlikely to see any development until the precarious finances of the Canary Wharf developers were sorted out, added to concerns about uneven loading of the station box. Bearings were installed on support columns and escalators allowing the structure to tolerate some movement as well.

The island platform was built in the bottom of the box. Above this, a thick concrete slab forms the floor of the ticket hall level, which is wider than the platform and track area to allow for equipment rooms. Holes in the slab accommodate nine escalators rising from the platform to the ticket hall; a further ten escalators connect with the street level at each end of the station box. Elliptical concrete columns rose from the centre line of the platform and through the ticket hall, reaching a stunning ceiling formed of 'gull-wing' concrete panels.

A new park has been created above the station where the water of the dock used to be. Early plans for the station had water above it, with the entrance structures standing above this. Deliberately placing water above an underground station justifiably caused safety concerns, and the plans were dropped. The isolated section of dock left to the west of the station was connected with the dock to the south by a new length of canal cut between the two, over which a new bascule bridge was provided.

Looking east along the ticket hall box from the western escalators emphasizes the volume of the station. *(Author)*

A new station on an old line

The JLE crossed the East London line between Rotherhithe and Surrey Quays stations. Although the distance between them was not great, it was not practical to connect either with the Jubilee line, and so a new station had to be constructed on the East London line (ELL) at Canada Water. The site for the station made the work awkward, as it was constrained by tower blocks to the west (the construction records for which could not be found) and a former dock to the south-east. The ELL tunnel, which was a brick arch built using cut and cover, ran across the site.

A secant-piled wall was constructed around the perimeter of the station box and wells were sunk to lower the water table. The ELL closed on 25 March 1995 for refurbishment of the Thames Tunnel, and during the closure the new station platforms were made. Piles were sunk behind the existing tunnel and a capping beam cast running along them to ensure the stability of the arch as the soil was removed from around it.[345]

The station has the new Jubilee line platforms in an east-west box beneath those of the ELL, which run north-south. Four large piles were sunk at the corners of the crossing point, and once the ELL tunnel had been demolished two 100 tonne beams each 20 m long were placed across these to form the bridge on which the ELL tracks and platforms would rest. Smaller beams were placed across these main beams, and either side, to form the track base in place of the previous tunnel invert. The track was then reinstated and a plywood shield was to have been constructed around it. This would have protected the trains as they passed through the station shell prior to opening. But the original five-month closure extended further and further as the sudden listing of the Thames Tunnel started a long debate about how best it should be refurbished. The ELL remained closed, and the contractors took advantage of this to complete the permanent station structure.

The excavation of the station box down to the level of the Jubilee line started at the western end of the site when the ELL closed. A concrete base slab was installed at a depth of 22 m once excavation was completed in November 1995. Some of the fitting-out work then had to wait until the delayed arrival of the tunnelling machines from Canary Wharf. The station was then constructed in a conventional bottom-up approach, with escalators leading from the Jubilee line to the ELL platforms, and then up to the ticket hall. Much of the box was roofed-over upon completion, but a glazed cylindrical drum above the ticket hall allows daylight to filter down to platform level.

Protecting Parliament

One of the riskiest parts of the JLE was at Westminster. The station was placed in a box beneath the planned new parliamentary building, with the station platform tunnels to the south beneath Bridge Street. This placed them just metres away from the 92 m high Clock Tower,* housing the world-famous Big Ben bell, and which had shallow foundations down into the loose Terrace Gravels above the clay. Adding to the complexity was the need to lower the tracks and platforms of the District and Circle lines to keep the floor slab of the parliamentary building at street level.

---

* The Clock Tower was named Elizabeth Tower in 2012 to mark the Queen's Diamond Jubilee. It has sometimes been referred to as St Stephen's Tower.

A view across
the station box
at Westminster,
showing the
massive steel
shores, exposed
diaphragm walls
(background),
and escalators.
(Author)

The first part of the work was to excavate below the existing station to lower the District and Circle lines. This work was performed at night, with the station being progressively propped as the work continued. A new support slab was cast beneath the tracks, and once the undermining was completed the tracks were lowered and new platforms provided. The work to excavate the main station box beneath the slab then started. The box, with a depth of 39 m, was the deepest ever made in London. Temporary protection was provided around the existing platforms so that the station buildings could be demolished. The diaphragm walls around the site were made by excavating trenches, filling them with bentonite for temporary support, and then making the final wall from reinforced concrete poured *in situ*. Nine large 3 m diameter piles were driven into the clay, with two supporting a girder holding up the station slab, two as part of the building foundations, and the remaining five running along the centre line of the station box. The diaphragm walls have been left on display rather than being hidden behind any form of cladding, and 660 mm diameter solid steel shores brace the walls against the central pillars, making this arguably the most spectacular station on the extension.

To protect the parliamentary clock tower from possible subsidence, an arch of steel pipes filled with concrete was installed above the platform tunnels. These were bored from a chamber excavated above the upper platform tunnel. A microtunnelling machine with a diameter of 1 m was used to make five tunnels in each direction over the line of the platform tunnel, which then had steel pipes inserted into them. Concrete filled the pipes to form a rigid structure. Specialist grouting equipment was also operated from down shafts sunk around the station and its neighbourhood. Steel pipes with internal diameters of 70 mm, and with holes at 1 m intervals were inserted horizontally into the ground from the shafts, at a depth that placed them 5·5 m below the base of the Clock Tower foundations.[346] Ground monitoring equipment detected the first signs of movement and a special mortar paste was injected from horizontal pipes into the ground above the tunnels to counteract the movement.[347] Electronic 'plumb-lines' were fitted in the tower 55 m above the ground to measure how much the tower was leaning, and to detect any changes. The grouting was effective at minimizing movement of the tower and preventing damage from occuring.

Designers and contractors
Unlike many previous extensions of the Underground, the design for each station was awarded to a different architectural practice. The construction of the tunnels was also divided into a number of smaller contracts.

Contract	Station	Contractor	Designer
102	Westminster	Balfour Beatty Amec JV	Michael Hopkins & Partners
102	Waterloo	Balfour Beatty Amec	LUL
103	Southwark	Aoki:Soletanche JV	McCormac Jamieson Pritchard
104	London Bridge	Costain Taylor Woodrow JV	Weston Williamson
105	Bermondsey	Aoki:Soletanche JV	Ian Ritchie Architects
106	Canada Water	Wimpey Construction / Tarmac[1]	LUL
108	Canary Wharf	Tarmac-Bachy JV	Foster & Partners
110	North Greenwich	McAlpine Wayss & Freytag – Bachy JV	Alsop, Lyle and Störmer
111	Canning Town	John Mowlem Construction	WSP / McAslan & Partners
111	West Ham	John Mowlem Construction	Van Heyningen and Haward
-	Stratford	Kvaerner Construction	Chris Wilkinson Architects

Contract	Tunnel	Contractor
102	Green Park Junction – Waterloo (east end)	Balfour Beatty Amec JV
103	Waterloo (east) – London Bridge (east)	Aoki:Soletanche JV
105	London Bridge (east) – Canada Water (west)	Aoki:Soletanche JV
107	Canada Water (east) – Canary Wharf (west)	McAlpine Wayss & Freytag – Bachy JV
110	Canary Wharf (east) – Canning Town portal	McAlpine Wayss & Freytag – Bachy JV

The London Bridge diversion

The Northern line station at London Bridge had not been altered since the escalators were installed in 1967. The platform layout was two adjacent platforms with short cross-passages and access from one end only. Passengers tended not to walk down the platforms, and so blocked the access passages. It was congested in the rush hours and without significant work the interchange traffic with the new Jubilee line station would overwhelm it. The LUL (Safety Measures) Act 1991 gave London Underground the powers to reconstruct and enlarge the station, together with several others, to alleviate the crowding.

It was decided to integrate the work at London Bridge with the Jubilee line extension work. The contract for the Jubilee line works at London Bridge therefore included the construction of a new southbound platform on the Northern line.[348] This would allow the existing platform tunnel to be converted into a concourse, providing easier circulation and also additional access. New running tunnels either side of the new platform were also needed to connect it back with the existing tracks. In early 1994 the £76·2 million Contract 104 for all the station works was let to a Costain-Taylor Woodrow joint venture.

The work was managed from a surface site at Redcross Way, west of the station and on the south side of Southwark Street. In early 1994 the contractors sank a shaft 11·35 m in diameter to a depth of 33 m. The top 10 m of the shaft was sunk through water-bearing Thames Gravel beds as a caisson. Below this depth the NATM was used to take the shaft to its full depth. This shaft is just 4 m away from a parallel, 7·62 m diameter tunnel that had been sunk to a depth of 15 m in 1992 to allow compensation grouting and a NATM trial to take place. This was later sunk to full depth so that it could be used for spoil removal.

At the peak of construction work, some 3000 m^3 per week of waste material was lifted from the muck bunker at the foot of the shaft to the surface, where it was stockpiled prior to being removed by lorries. Two large 30-tonne gantry cranes were erected on site to service the shafts.

From the lower end of the main shaft a trial tunnel was constructed parallel to the route of the JLE. A 45-m-long tunnel 11·3 m in diameter was created to the west (which acted as a muck bunker), and 50 m of 5·35 m diameter tunnel was dug to the east. This latter tunnel was then continued as a 130 m long inclined adit to the level of the Northern Line, some 4 m above the JLE. Rubber-tyred vehicles were used to transport soil, waste, and construction materials via the 32·5% gradient in this tunnel.

From the end of the adit the step-plate junction surrounding the existing running tunnel to the south of the station was dug first, by hand excavation and then erection of SGI tunnel rings bolted together. Unusually the junction tunnels had an elliptical cross-section to ensure that they did not get too close to the top level of the clay layer. This tunnel was followed by the new southbound running tunnel, and then the 115 m long platform tunnel with a diameter of 6·5 m. The platform tunnel was being constructed from south to north using NATM when a tunnel being constructed at Heathrow Airport for the new Heathrow Express railway collapsed on 21 October 1994. This was also being built using NATM, and London Underground immediately insisted on all NATM work ceasing whilst the Health & Safety Executive (HSE) investigated. In order to keep on track the contractors switched to traditional tunnelling techniques for the remaining 75% of the Northern Line platform that was to be completed. Some of the grouting for the work was carried out from the original C&SLR tunnels, which still exist directly above the Northern Line at London Bridge.

To the north it was decided that a step-plate junction would be too risky, as it would be just below the bed of the Thames on the site of the old London Bridge. This bridge was renowned for the rapid flow of water between its many piers, and it was feared that the consequent scour could have removed much of the clay in the river bed. The piers had been constructed from wooden piles which would have penetrated the clay layer. Also, the enlargement of the C&SLR tunnels in the 1920s had been "bodged up with concrete" where the tunnel rings did not line up properly.[349] For a time an elliptical step-plate junction was considered, built in compressed air, but the lack of good clay cover meant that there was a high risk of the air causing a blowout through the river bed. Placing a blanket of new clay on the river bed above the work would not guarantee a good seal, and ground consolidation (chemical or freezing) would be unreliable and cause a partial closure of the river to boats during the process.[350] A barge was used to sample the riverbed conditions, but when it failed to locate solid ground just upstream of the junction site it was quickly realized that the step-plate ideas would have to be scrapped.[351]

The final choice was to close the tunnel at the junction point, and drive the new tunnel in through the side of it. Originally the old tunnel was to have been filled with foam concrete for stability during the tunnelling, but this was decided to be unnecessary. Compressed air tunnelling, together with bulkheads to protect the rest of the tunnels in the event of a river breach were sufficient, and so the southbound Northern Line services were suspended from 1 July until 20 October 1996 whilst the work was completed. When the service resumed it was through the new platform and running tunnels. The original southbound tunnel north of the step-plate junction was left disused, along with a long-abandoned siding tunnel alongside.

Foam concrete

Often used for temporary infilling of spaces, foam concrete is made by mixing a cement slurry with a foam resulting in a final product with between 10% and 50% air. This is therefore lighter than normal concrete, typically having a density similar to water, and is a lot easier to remove if it is used for temporary stabilization of tunnels. It is also used to permanently fill voids such as disused drains, tunnels, and cellars as part of redevelopment work to mitigate the risk of collapse. It is easy to pump, allowing it to be manufactured away from cramped underground sites and brought in using hoses.

Another Heathrow extension

Heathrow Airport continued to grow towards the end of the twentieth century, and a fifth terminal was on the drawing board shortly after Terminal 4 opened. The planning process for the new terminal was one of the longest in the UK, with the public inquiry lasting four years. The new terminal was constructed west of the main airport site, between the two runways, on the location of Perry Oaks sewage farm. This precluded the provision of a station on the single-track Piccadilly line Heathrow loop opened in 1986.

A double-track extension of the Piccadilly line from Heathrow Terminals 1,2,3 to Terminal 5 was designed (known as PiccEx). The £30 million cost was financed by the airport owner, BAA, and constructed as part of a number of new tunnels at the airport by Morgan Vinci Joint Venture (formed by Morgan Est and Vinci Construction Grands Projets). Beneath the terminal building a new station box was constructed, 250 m long and 90 m wide.[352] This contained six platforms: two for the Piccadilly line, two for the Heathrow Express main-line service to Paddington, and two spare for a future service to the terminal from the west. The station box was built as part of the new terminal building (unlike the two previous Piccadilly line stations at Heathrow). West of the box a pair of reversing sidings and a crossover were provided for the Piccadilly line. The sidings, station box, and a short length of tunnel to the east were all constructed using cut and cover techniques.

Two running tunnels 1·65 km long were bored eastwards from the station towards the step-plate junction that had been made to the west of the station at Terminals 1,2 and 3 as part of the Heathrow loop (see p 286). These have an internal diameter of 4·5 m, and were created using a Dosco tunnelling shield (named *Bea*) with an integral boom cutter (similar to the equipment used to make the Heathrow loop). The shield was 4·57 m long and had an external diameter of 4·81 m. At the rear of the shield 16 hydraulic rams provided the thrust. Further equipment for the tunnel construction was towed behind the shield, making the overall machine 56·5 m long. The shield progressed at up to 26·9 m per day.[353] Behind it the tunnels were lined with expanded concrete segments in rings 1·0 m long and 150 mm thick; the concrete contained 30 kg of steel fibres per cubic metre as reinforcement.

The real complexity lay in the connection with the existing tunnels. The eastbound tunnel for the PiccEx was to connect in with the north side of the step-plate junction. The westbound tunnel passed beneath the Heathrow loop to reach a point on the south side. The problem was that the water-bearing ground made the excavation of two new step-plate junctions risky, and "would threaten significant structural failure of the existing tunnel and disturb the ground stability".[354] With some of the Terminal 3 buildings almost directly above the box this was not an option. The solution was to form a new box around the site, enclosing the existing tunnels, in which the new junctions could be made. Two aircraft parking stands were temporarily closed to enable this work.

Bachy Soletanche was brought in as a subcontractor to create the necessary

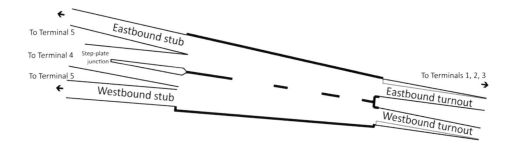

The new junction box (bold lines) was formed around the existing running tunnels about 16 m away from the eastern wall of the existing step-plate junction. New stub tunnels were formed either side of the step-plate junction (left) to connect with the tunnels to Terminal 5. The existing tunnels to the east of the box (right) were enlarged (grey lines) so that the junction points could be accommodated. *(Author, redrawn from Chapman, Metje, and Stärk)*

diaphragm walls for the work, which created a watertight cofferdam. The junction box was 25 m × 40 m, and 25 m deep, and allowed the work to proceed safely. A 20-month closure of the Heathrow loop commenced on 10 January 2005 for this to take place (during which a shuttle bus service operated between Hatton Cross station and Heathrow Terminal 4). The 1·2-m-thick walls were sunk around the site, mostly to a depth below that of the tunnels, except above the existing tunnels where they stopped short.[355] A horizontal slab with a large central opening was cast about half-way up the box, forming a gallery over the tunnel level. The central opening allowed all of the equipment needed for the construction to be lowered into the box by a crawler crane. Two central concrete pillars up the centre of the box gave additional support. The clay within the box was excavated out from around the two tunnels, which were then dismantled, allowing the end walls to be completed.

The TBMs working on the new running tunnels stopped 40 m from the wall of the junction box. Excavation finished on the westbound tunnel in January 2004, and the eastbound tunnel was completed eight months later. In order to connect the tunnels with the junction box the final lengths of tunnel were made by excavating out from the box; this was a safer way of completing the tunnels.[356] These short lengths of tunnel (the eastbound and westbound 'stubs') were constructed using excavators and given sprayed concrete linings, as the lengths were insufficient for using a shield. Before the eastbound stub was constructed the first 8m length of the adjacent, pre-existing eastbound tunnel was filled with foam concrete to give additional stability. This tunnel was carefully monitored during the work to measure the distortion, and it was seen to flatten very slightly (i.e., the tunnel became wider and shorter by up to 5 mm). This was not a cause for concern, as it had a cast iron lining, but the adjacent westbound tunnel had a lining of expanded concrete segments. These appeared to have moved at some time prior to the Terminal 5 works, with steps of up to 6 cm between adjacent rings.* Distortion of this tunnel would be more serious, and so the

---

*   No explanation has been found for why the lining had deformed.

entire length between the junction box and the step-plate junction was filled with foam concrete. These foam concrete plugs were removed after each stub tunnel was completed.

The excavation of the stub tunnels used a new technique called LaserShell, developed by Beton- und Monierbau and MorganEst. This was an evolution of NATM, and avoided the need for tunnellers to work under unsupported tunnel faces and crowns to install the steel mesh and frameworks onto which concrete was sprayed. The UK health and safety regulations had forbidden this, and so LaserShell was developed. An inclined tunnel face with a domed profile was excavated, monitored by a laser theodolite coupled with a laptop. This allowed very careful control of the tunnel shape without any vertical or overhanging faces, and the layers of concrete that were sprayed on resulted in fewer joints between adjacent sections.

On the eastern side of the junction box the existing Piccadilly line running tunnels needed to be enlarged to accommodate the points (or turnouts) for the junction: these were called the turnout tunnels. Foam concrete was used again to fill the tunnels, this time for a distance of about 26 m from the box wall, whilst the tunnels were enlarged. These tunnels were also given a sprayed concrete lining after enlargement.[357]

Once the work in the box was finished it was capped with a double layer of concrete slabs, and the area above was back-filled (with the exception of an emergency escape staircase that was constructed as part of the box). Track had begun to be laid in the tunnel in mid 2005, heading eastwards towards the junction. Fitting out of the station began in June 2006, and three months later when the tracks and signalling at the new junction were complete and tested, the train service around the Heathrow loop restarted. In July 2007 the extension was handed over to London Underground. Testing then started by running empty trains, and passenger services began when Terminal 5 opened on 27 March 2008.

Crossrail

Although technically not part of London Underground, as a new passenger railway being built beneath London its omission from these pages would seem strange, especially since it will come under the auspices of Transport for London (TfL). The line has been planned since the 1974 London Rail Study, although it was only in the 1990s that detailed planning really started. It might have been built then too, had it not been for the recession in the early 1990s cutting Government spending, and the diversion of planning interest to the Jubilee Line Extension.

The London Rail Study suggested a route that would be in tunnel between Paddington and Liverpool Street, with intermediate stations at Marble Arch, Bond Street / Oxford Circus, Leicester Square / Covent Garden, and Holborn / Ludgate. By the time that serious planning was about to start, the Central London Rail Study of 1989 had refined the route to that being built today (with the exception of the south-eastern branch to Abbey Wood), bringing it further north between Bond Street and Liverpool Street to serve stations at Tottenham Court Road and Farringdon. In order to protect the alignment, the Government issued a safeguarding order for the route. This provided legal protection for the route, preventing any developer from constructing anything that would conflict with Crossrail, even though there were no legal powers to build the railway yet.

The dramatic increase in the number of tall buildings with deep, piled foundations meant that it was increasingly difficult to route tunnels under London on alignments conducive to railways, i.e., with straight or gently curved routes at depths that could be reached from street level without excessive journey time through stations. In 2000 it was noted that to connect the Central London termini requires a tunnel for which there are relatively few feasible alignments due to the presence of building foundations, existing underground tunnels and obstructions.[358]

It is noticeable on the plans for Crossrail that the running tunnels splay apart immediately east of the station at Tottenham Court Road, and this is because there is no route wide enough for both tunnels to pass at a reasonable level here.

Parliamentary authorization for Crossrail was provided in the Crossrail Act 2008, and once the funding was arranged (in a complex deal between the Government, Transport for London, and the private sector) work finally started in 2009.

A main-line tube railway
Crossrail is not the first tube railway in London built to accommodate main-line rolling stock. That accolade goes to the GN&CR, opened in 1904, but only connected to a main line in 1976. In concept Crossrail bears far more in common with the Réseau Express Régional (RER) in Paris, or the S-Bahn systems in Berlin and other major German cities. These provide main-line links across the city centres in tunnel, joining existing suburban railways on either side. Operationally, they blur the boundaries between the services of the main-line railways and the metro operators; for example, different parts of the RER are operated by the SNCF main-line operator

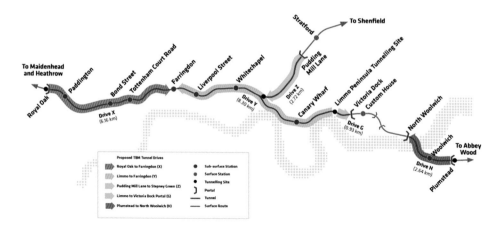

A map of the five tunnelling drives that are being used to create Crossrail. *(Crossrail)*

and the Parisian transport authority (RATP). So Crossrail will be branded as part of the Transport for London family of services, but will operate in a similar matter to franchised main-line services to the east and west of London. These will extend westwards to Reading (on the Great Western main-line), and in the east to Shenfield (on the Great Eastern main-line) and Abbey Wood (on the North Kent line).

The core of Crossrail is the tunnelled section from the portal at Royal Oak in the west through to a pair of portals at Pudding Mill Lane and Victoria Dock in the east. A subterranean junction has been excavated at Stepney Green, east of Whitechapel. There are two further tunnels on the south-eastern branch, the first taking the line below the Royal Docks, and the second between portals at North Woolwich and Plumstead crossing under the Thames. Eight TBMs were used for the work, which was accomplished in ten tunnelling drives. All of the TBMs were given names, which were chosen following a public competition.

At the Royal Oak, Pudding Mill Lane, and Plumstead portals the TBMs were launched directly into the tunnels, as the gently graded portal slopes allowed the machines to be assembled in line before advancing to the tunnel eyes (the points in the portal structure through which the tunnels pass). Space did not permit this approach at the Victoria Dock portal, which was a smaller site squeezed between the DLR and a road, and instead a large worksite was created on the Limmo peninsula, south of Canning Town.* The TBMs were lowered into the shaft in pieces and assembled below.

Two types of TBM were used. Six Earth Pressure Balance Machines (EPBMs) drove the main tunnels through central London, linking the portals at Royal Oak, Pudding Mill Lane, and Victoria Dock. These machines used the cut spoil to support the tunnel face by mixing it into a paste and keeping this at a pressure which balances that of the face. A screw conveyor removed the soil paste from the excavation chamber behind the cutting head, and the speed of this effectively controlled the pressure. The cutting head revolved at between 1 and 3 r.p.m.

---

*   The Limmo was also used as a worksite for the Jubilee Line Extension project.

Drive	Tunnel	TBM type	Distance	Direction	Name	Started	Completed	Tunnel rings installed
X	Royal Oak portal – Farringdon	Herrenknecht EPB	6·4 km	Eastbound	*Ada*	21 August 2012	24 January 2014	4,658
				Westbound	*Phyllis*	4 May 2012	8 October 2013	4,675
Y	Limmo shaft – Farringdon	Herrenknecht EPB	8·3 km	Eastbound	*Elizabeth*	29 November 2012		
				Westbound	*Victoria*	12 December 2012		
Z	Pudding Mill Lane portal – Stepney Green Jn	Herrenknecht EPB	2·7 km	Eastbound	*Jessica*	15 August 2013	3 February 2014	1,699
				Westbound	*Ellie*	25 February 2014	9 June 2014	1,728
H	Plumstead portal – North Woolwich portal	Herrenknecht Mixshield	2·6 km	Eastbound	*Mary*	19 May 2013	13 May 2014	1,700
				Westbound	*Sophia*	9 January 2013	29 January 2014	1,707
G	Limmo shaft – Victoria Dock portal	Herrenknecht EPB	0·9 km	Eastbound	*Ellie*	11 September 2014	18 October 2014	519
				Westbound	*Jessica*	2 June 2014	9 August 2014	523

Details of the tunnelling drives for Crossrail.

The first of the massive EPB TBMs before it started work beneath London. The cutting head can be seen on the left, and the hydraulic rams can be seen fully extended in the middle of the photograph. Behind the rams the rest of the TBM equipment continues for over 100m. *(Crossrail)*

For the tunnel between Plumstead and North Woolwich, known as the Thames Tunnel, a pair of slurry TBMs were used. Unlike the EPBMs, these were designed to work in the wet chalk which predominates on this tunnel, and had a permanently pressurized cutting face. Bentonite was pumped into the chamber at the front of the shield, and mixed with the spoil; the bentonite/chalk mix was then piped back to the surface to be cleaned and the bentonite reused. The excavation chamber was divided into two by a vertical wall running across the width of the machine; in front, the cutting head excavated the soil, which passed through an opening at the bottom of the wall into the pressure chamber. An air cushion at the top of this chamber was carefully controlled to maintain the pressure at the tunnel face. At the bottom, crushing equipment broke lumps in the spoil into a consistent size so that the spoil and bentonite mix could be pumped away for cleaning.

All of the tunnelling machines for Crossrail were manufactured by the German firm of Herrenknecht, and are their EPB Shield and Mixshield products. They were custom-built at a cost of about £10 million each, with external diameters of 7·08 m. It is not just in diameter that tunnelling machines have grown since the use of Price's rotary excavator: the mass of the EPBMs was 980 tons and they were 148 m long. The slurry TBMs had a similar mass, but were just 110 m in length. As well as the cutting equipment at the front, and the tunnel erectors behind, they contained a series of trailers, which were responsible for most of the length. These housed a number of essential systems for the TBM:

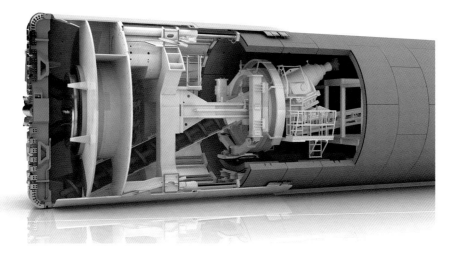

A cutaway diagram of a Herrenknecht EPB TBM. The sealed front chamber is behind the green cutting head, and the red Archimedean screw conveyor removes the spoil back to the main spoil conveyor (in blue). The screw conveyor passes through the middle of the segment erector, which removes concrete segments from a 'magazine', and uses vacuum manipulators to fit them around the tunnel to form rings within the tail-skin. Wire brushes around the inside edge of the tail-skin seal the gap between the completed tunnel lining and the shield. Grout is continuously injected behind the tunnel rings as the TBM moves forward. *(Herrenknecht AG)*

- conveyor belts that passed the spoil back to trains that removed it from the tunnels;
- the segment delivery system, which passed the segments forward to the erectors;
- electrical transformers and switchgear, which received electricity at 11 KV and converted this to supplies of 415 V and 110 V for all the various on-board systems;
- a generator, which maintained power to the TBM when the main supply cable was disconnected for extension;
- the control cabin, from which all the systems were monitored, and the direction of the shield was controlled; and
- welfare facilities for the team working on the TBM, including toilets and a kitchen.

The TBMs were operated by a team of 20, twelve of whom worked on the TBM itself, with the other eight providing support between the TBM and the surface teams.

Herrenknecht AG

Founded by Martin Herrenknecht in 1975 to make specialist equipment for pipe-jacking (pushing pipes through soil), the company has grown rapidly and diversified into other tunnel-building technologies, especially TBMs. Research and development has created a range capable of making tunnels through different ground conditions, as demonstrated by the types of machine used by Crossrail.

TBMs made by Herrenknecht have been used on a variety of tunnelling projects around the world. The 57 km long St Gotthard base tunnel has been bored by four Gripper TBMs, which are designed to work through rock. The Orlovski Tunnel, in St Petersburg, has been built using the largest diameter TBM ever made: 19·25 m.

The company is based at a large site in Schwanau, Germany, but has offices around the world. It has grown considerably in its 35-year history, and has supplied TBMs to build underground railways in Berlin, Moscow, Rio de Janeiro, Beijing, Istanbul, and New York, to name but a few.

A cutaway diagram of a Herrenknecht Mixshield TBM. The excavation chamber with its vertical partition is behind the green cutting head, and the air pocket is shown in the second part (at the top), with the crushing equipment at the bottom. The pipes shown in blue form the circuit for the slurry, bringing fresh bentonite back to the excavation chamber and removing the bentonite/chalk mix back for reprocessing. The erector and tail-skin equipment is the same as for the Herrenknecht EPB TBM shown previously. *(Herrenknecht AG)*

The western tunnels

The Royal Oak portal was the site of Crossrail's first TBM launch, in May 2012. It is a narrow site 21 m wide, bounded to the north by the elevated A40 Westway, and to the south by the Great Western main line railway out of Paddington. Once it had been cleared, a concrete ramp structure 285 m long was built, finishing at a pair of tunnel eyes in an otherwise blank concrete wall. The walls of the ramp were made by sinking diaphragm walls into the ground, placing temporary props between them, and then excavating the soil out. Once this was removed to the level of the ramp the concrete base slab was formed and permanent beams of reinforced concrete were installed above where the trains will eventually run.

Phyllis was the first TBM to start work. The machine was assembled at the western end of the site, where it made its first appearance in a photo-call with the Mayor of

London, Boris Johnson, and the Secretary of State for Transport, Justine Greening. Once the media paraphernalia was dismantled the shield section was lifted onto a self-propelled mobile platform and slowly driven to the top of the portal ramp. Temporary track laid behind the platform allowed the trailer sections to follow along behind. The footbridge across the site was temporarily closed and jacked up to allow *Phyllis* to pass beneath.

Once onto the ramp, the TBM was transferred from the self-propelled mobile platform onto skids, to provide sufficient clearance for it to pass beneath the concrete props spanning the ramp between the side walls. It was slid on these Teflon-coated skids towards its final position, 600 mm at a time.[359] After final testing the TBM proceeded down the ramp until the cutting head was against the tunnel eye. A large metal 'thrust ring' was then constructed behind the shield section to give the ten hydraulic rams something to push against so that the TBM could be driven into the ground. Once the first few rings of the tunnel were complete this was dismantled.

As with any new piece of equipment, the tunnellers had to test the TBM and its systems thoroughly, and so the tunnel boring work proceeded slowly at first. It took three weeks before the rear end of the machine disappeared through the portal. Work then began with the assembly of *Ada*, there not having been sufficient room to build the two alongside each other, together with the need to keep the two TBMs working some distance apart to reduce the risk of settlement. *Ada* was launched in August 2012.

The completed ramp at Royal Oak, with the tunnel eyes ready to receive their TBMs. The concrete props above the ramp in the foreground are permanent; the rust-coloured props near the eyes are temporary. *(Crossrail)*

The TBMs worked 24 hours per day, 7 days a week. Once up to full speed they were each boring around 100 m of tunnel each week. By keeping them moving there was a reduced likelihood of ground settlement occurring. Down-time for maintenance was carefully planned; one location for this was at Bond Street, where a shaft and a chamber were prepared so that the TBMs would break into them. This allowed maintenance work on their cutting heads before they continued east to Farringdon.[360]

A century of progress

Conditions for the tunnellers working within the TBMs have been very different in many ways from their predecessors, labouring within the Greathead shields on the C&SLR, W&CR, CLR, and the Yerkes tubes. However, there are also a number of similarities. Despite the larger size of the tunnels for Crossrail, space on board the TBMs was limited and the air in the tunnels was quite warm, due to the mechanical and electrical equipment on board. The lighting has moved on a long way from the guttering candles of the 1860s, used by the men who dug the Tower Subway, but great care still had to be taken by the tunnellers, who were effectively working within a large and powerful machine. Of course, all staff on the TBM wear full safety equipment including ear defenders, as the machinery is noisy – especially during the cutting phase. The team on board is highly trained, which is one of the best defences against accidents.

As with the Greathead shields, the rhythm of the work is governed by the length of a tunnel ring. Excavation proceeds with the slowly rotating cutting head being pushed forward by the hydraulic rams until there is space to assemble a new ring to the rear. The cutting head then stops whilst the ring is assembled. Depending on the ground conditions, between 10 and 20 rings are typically erected every 24 hours. The London clay is soft, but can contain hard bands of calcareous material. Deeper down, the Lambeth beds include layers of hard limestone that slow progress and can push the TBM away from its planned course, so the engineers in the on-board control room must stay alert and correct the alignment as soon as the deviation is noticed.

The TBMs make other stops as well. Behind them lie the cables that bring their electricity and the pipes supplying grout, as well as the conveyor belts removing the spoil. The pipes and cables are stored at the rear of the TBM trailer, and slowly unroll from large spools as the tunnel is bored. Every 50 m new pipe spools are added, and the power cable is extended every 200 m. Secondary power supplies are provided to keep the TBM systems (lighting, etc.) operational whilst the main cable is lengthened.

The TBMs driving westwards towards Farringdon were exposed in each station tunnel that they reached, allowing for maintenance. This allowed for the cutting teeth on the front to be renewed. The TBMs from the other direction remained in tunnel throughout, and so their teeth were replaced when necessary by stopping the TBM and accessing the cutting head via the plenum chamber behind. In order to keep the pressure on the tunnel face this work was sometimes done under compressed air.

Like the Greathead shields of old, the Herrenknecht TBMs were steered by varying the pressure on the hydraulic rams. Gone are the days of plumb-lines, theodolites, and alignment with illuminated slits though. The control cabins contained sophisticated computer systems that used inertial navigation to determine the movement of the TBM. A clear path that was maintained along its length (in the upper left quadrant in the direction of travel) allowed a 'total station' installed in the tunnel to view a prism at the front of the TBM and check its position against where it should be. A screen in the cabin showed a representation of the tunnel, with what resembled a paper aeroplane flying down it. The operator used this to correct the course of the TBM and stay within 50 mm of the intended course.

The tunnels are lined with concrete segments 300 mm thick, weighing almost 3,000 kg, and manufactured a short way to the west of the Royal Oak portal at a dedicated (and temporary) factory set up at Old Oak Common which started work in early 2012. The concrete contains steel and polypropylene fibres to give additional strength, and each complete ring weighs over 20 tonnes. Once the tunnel rings are installed the tunnels have an internal diameter of 6·2 m;[361] the external diameter is therefore 6·8 m. Two different types of ring were made: left-curving, and

Inside the eastbound running tunnel a short distance east of the Limmo peninsula shafts. The concrete tunnel lining is in place, but the construction of the track bed is still to start. The pipe on the right-hand wall is a water main for fire-fighting (with a red hose and connector visible); on the left-hand wall are electricity cables for lighting and tools. *(Author)*

right-curving.* Placing a number of identical rings consecutively allows a curved tunnel to be lined, and within straight tunnels the two ring types are alternated.[362] A complete ring comprises five 'rectangular' segments, a wedge-shaped key segment, and two segments with angled ends that fit either side of the key.

The segments were brought into the tunnel via the narrow-gauge railway laid behind the TBMs. Small locomotives pulled wagons with stacks of segments to the back of the TBM, from where they were loaded into a 'magazine'. This held the segments until they were needed. As the TBM advanced, the segments were lifted from the magazine by the segment erector, which used a vacuum to hold them until they were accurately located in the correct position.

The spoil was removed from the tunnels at the Royal Oak site by conveyors, which were extended as the TBMs progressed. The conveyors continued up the ramp at the tunnel portal and transferred the spoil into a hopper located on a gantry above a siding. Freight trains were run into the siding and loaded with spoil from the hopper, before removing it for disposal. They took a circuitous route around London in order to reach a disused cement works at Northfleet, on the south bank of the Thames. This site was used for transferring the spoil from the trains onto barges. These transported it through the Thames estuary and round to the north, to a nature reserve at Wallasea Island, on the River Crouch. Here a conveyor installed by Crossrail unloaded the spoil, whereupon it was used for constructing a new wetlands habitat and nature reserve for the Royal Society for the Protection of Birds.

Unfortunately the steel frame supporting the hopper loading system buckled after only two weeks in use, with the hopper ending up resting on a wagon beneath. Spoil had to be stockpiled on the constrained site, and as capacity for this dwindled, both TBMs were halted. *Phyllis* was restarted after a temporary spoil removal operation using lorries was introduced. A decision was made to scrap the conveyor system, and return to the original process of loading the trains using front-loading excavators. This allowed *Ada* to restart.

In September 2013 the TBM operators faced one of their most difficult challenges: threading *Ada* through Tottenham Court Road station. The site was constrained by the existing Underground station, as well as numerous piles for nearby buildings. It was a tight fit, with the tunnel passing just 85 cm above the Northern line platform tunnels, and 35 cm below the bottom of the piles for the new structure for the Crossrail escalators. The Northern line was running at the time, and station staff could hear the TBM when they stood on the platform at the start of the day. Close liaison between Crossrail and LU engineers ensured that no disruption was caused as the TBM passed through what they were calling "The Eye of the Needle". Any concerns that tiles might fall from the platform walls, or that water contained in a void in the clay might start to leak in proved to be groundless, but plans had been prepared for handling such events. Fortunately, the tunnel made through the site some months earlier by *Phyllis* was further south, and a larger path across the station had been available.

The following month, after 17 months of work, *Phyllis* arrived at Farringdon. Once through the site for the station platform tunnels, the TBM was diverted to the north

---

* Being circular, the rings could be installed to curve in any direction. The names are merely used to distinguish between the two different ring types.

of the tunnel alignment. Here the front drum, including the cutting head was disconnected and abandoned underground. The tunnels behind the cutting head were too small for it to be removed and cutting it up would have been time consuming and dangerous without massive ventilation plant being installed. As a memento of the work, a time capsule has been placed inside the drum. The trailers behind the TBM, comprising the majority of its length, were pulled backwards through the tunnels as far as a shaft at Fisher Street, in Holborn, through which they were removed to the surface using a crane. *Ada*, which arrived at Farringdon in January 2014, suffered a similar fate, but did not get a time capsule.

The advantage in removing the TBM trailers at Holborn was that the ventilation pipes installed in the tunnels to ensure the health and well-being of the tunnellers could be removed. With these out of the way, work could start on breaking out the running tunnels at Paddington, Bond Street, and Tottenham Court Road. Much of the excavation for these stations was completed in advance, as large diaphragm-walled boxes, down to a level between the tunnels. The large platform tunnels are then excavated by breaking out the concrete segments installed by the TBMs, and supporting the resulting spaces with sprayed concrete linings (SCL) to avoid the need for large and complex tunnel segments to be made and installed.

At Paddington the excavation work reached the running tunnels in August 2014, having removed 40,000 tonnes of earth from the station box. With the rear of the tunnel lining visible, the task of breaking out the 2,640 concrete segments began. Equipment with cutting claws and breakers was used to demolish the lining from the outside.

A dramatic photo showing the work at Paddington to break-out the concrete tunnel lining segments. Around the segments can be seen the layer of cement grout, with the clay beyond this. The smooth marks in the clay are from the tools used to remove it as the tunnel is enlarged. *(Crossrail)*

Work in progress within the station box at Paddington, in January 2015. This photograph is taken from the level of the future ticket hall concourse; below is the recently excavated platform level, with all traces of the tunnel rings removed. Only one in three of the steel columns on the left will remain *in situ*, the others being used to provide structural support whilst the box is constructed. The rough finish to the diaphragm wall on the right will be hidden by cladding when the station opens to the public. *(Author)*

The stations constructed in this way will be more like those of the JLE, with large open spaces through which escalators and lifts will descend to platform level, rather than earlier underground stations with their warrens of tubular passageways.

The eastern tunnels

The tunnels between Farringdon and the shaft at the Limmo were driven from the latter location. The launch of the two TBMs, called *Elizabeth* and *Victoria*, was rather different to that at Royal Oak, as there was no portal for them to be assembled against. Instead, the tunnel eyes were placed at the bottom of a shaft 30 m in diameter and 47 m deep. For each tunnel the TBM drum was lowered into the shaft and aligned with the eye, before starting to excavate. As they started to excavate their tunnels, the trailers were added behind them, so these TBMs were only fully assembled once they were below ground. Although both TBM drums were placed into the shaft side-by-side, their launch was staggered, as with the western tunnels, to reduce the risk of ground settlement if the two were run in parallel.

The cutting head of TBM *Elizabeth* being lowered into the shaft on the Limmo peninsula. The TBM was lowered in sections and assembled at tunnel level. *(Crossrail)*

The station strategy on the eastern tunnels was also different. Instead of breaking out the running tunnels to form the station platform tunnels, station boxes were constructed in advance down to platform level. At each station eyes in the ends of the boxes allowed the TBMs to break in as they joined the tunnel to the box. The pressure at the cutting face was reduced as the machines approached the break-through point, so that as they entered the box the face would be at atmospheric pressure. They would then be dragged through the station platform area, and any maintenance work could be performed at this time. After being aligned with the eyes at the far end of the platforms they would then set off for the next station.

The first station to be structurally completed was at Canary Wharf, which was built for Crossrail by the Canary Wharf Group. It is on the opposite side of the office development to the Jubilee line station, and has followed the same approach of using the old dock infrastructure, in this case the northernmost of the former West India Docks. However, rather than taking over the whole width of the dock the station has been built as a box within the dock, surrounded by water on four sides, and resembling a large moored ship.

Work on the box was started in May 2009, when 310 interlocking tubular steel piles were driven into the dock floor (which was at an average depth of 9 m) using a Japanese Giken silent piler to form a cofferdam around the site. This technique was chosen to avoid disturbing nearby offices, and works by pressing the tubular piles into the ground. As each pile was sunk to a depth of 18 m it was joined to anchor piles which had been sunk around the outside of the site, and which helped to stabilize the cofferdam structure. This avoided having supports within the cofferdam, which would have interfered with the station construction. In order to hold itself into position as the Giken piles were driven, the piling machine gripped the completed piles in turn as it progressed around the site, progressing "like a caterpillar" according to the workers,[363] and avoiding the need to use heavy machinery to be repositioned. Once complete, reinforced concrete piles were driven through the tubes to a depth of 38 m. In February 2010 pumps were switched on to remove 100,000 litres of water from within the cofferdam.[364] A construction deck was laid between the cofferdam and the anchor piles on the north side of the site, providing a platform from which machinery could work. An access bridge was provided so that equipment could be driven on directly, without the need for cranes to carry it over the narrow channel of water remaining.

Excavation then removed around 300,000 tonnes of spoil from within the coffer dam. One-third of this was reused on site, with the remainder being transported on barges to Holehaven Creek on Canvey Island, where it was used to landscape a former landfill site. Construction started on the concrete station box, which at 256 m long, 30 m wide, and 28 m deep filled the cofferdam, descending to well below the old dock floor. Further piles were required, taking their number to over 1,000, and nearly 375,000 tonnes of concrete was used.[365] Inside the box the floors and other structural details progressed until the shell was completed in late 2011. By March 2012 the contractors were ready for the arrival of the first TBM — although they had to wait until May 2013 before this happened, when *Elizabeth* broke through the carefully prepared tunnel eye.

Further west, the platform tunnels at Whitechapel and Liverpool Street stations were built in advance of the TBMs. They were excavated using the SCL technique, in which excavators mined out the tunnels in 1 m sections, and the surfaces of the exposed ground were sprayed with fast-setting concrete. The spraying was performed by robotic rigs controlled by a nearby operator. The first layer is 75 mm thick, and subsequent layers were then sprayed until the lining had a thickness of 300 mm. A waterproofing layer was then applied, which in most of the tunnels consists of 50 mm of smooth concrete covered by 20 mm of epoxy waterproofing material, but in the Farringdon area (because of the higher water permeability of the ground) sheets of waterproofing material were applied to the surface of the initial lining. The secondary lining was then sprayed over the waterproofing, except in the tunnel invert where a framework was used to cast the track slab onto which the rails will be fixed. Finally, a fire-resistant layer of concrete containing polypropylene fibres was sprayed on, taking the total thickness of the lining to 700 mm.[366] There was concern amongst the engineers that when the TBMs broke into the platform tunnels they could cause unpredictable cracking of the lining away from the entry point. To prevent this, the last 3·5 m of the platform tunnels were filled with foam concrete at the ends where the TBMs were to enter. This supported the platform tunnel structure as the break-through occurred. It also generated immense heat in the TBMs, as they were not intended to cut through concrete, and great care had to be taken by the operators.

At Liverpool Street, much of the tunnelling was carried out from a 42 m shaft located in Finsbury Circus. This little oasis of green in the City of London was taken over by Crossrail in August 2010 and turned into a work site. A shaft 42 m deep was sunk from the circus, and from this SCL tunnels were excavated in four directions. In total around 1·5 km of tunnels was dug from the Finsbury Circus shaft using this process, including the platform tunnels, concourse, and other passageways. The first to be excavated were two 4·5 m diameter tunnels 80 m and 100 m long. These were temporary structures to allow the injection of grout into the ground above the new platform tunnels in the event of any movement.[367] The platform tunnels were made by mining 6 m diameter pilot tunnels (with SCL), and then enlarging these to their full 9·5 m diameters.

The TBMs arrived in early 2015, and once through the station proceeded west for their final tunnelling to Farringdon. Here, reception chambers were constructed by enlarging the tunnels constructed by *Ada* and *Phyllis* to the east of the station, and providing a temporary concrete lining. *Elizabeth* and *Victoria* were then driven into these chambers at an angle, as if they intended to continue westwards along the tunnels. The trailers were removed back down the tunnels for removal via the shaft at Stepney Green, together with the motors. The main bearings, weighing around 50 tonnes, were hauled back through the tunnels on cradles. The cutter heads were cut up and taken away.

The original idea was for the running tunnels to be completed through the remaining cylindrical front shells of the TBMs, but there were concerns about the waterproofing of the tunnel. Instead, the plan was changed and the shells have been cut into pieces and removed. The tunnel was then completed using a sprayed concrete primary lining. Unlike the rest of the tunnels, shuttering was used for the

One of the first temporary tunnels with a sprayed concrete lining beneath Finsbury Circus. *(Crossrail)*

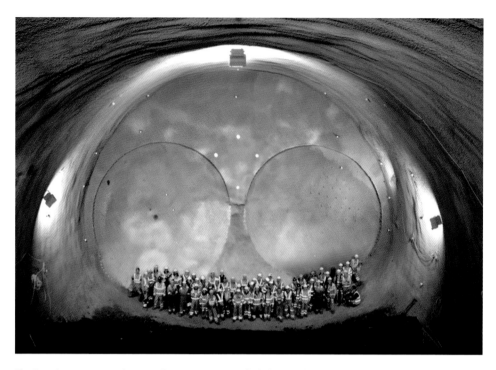

The junction caverns at Stepney Green are spectacularly large. This view, celebrating the completion of the eastern cavern, shows the two tunnel eyes for the running tunnels towards Shenfield and Abbey Wood. *(Crossrail)*

waterproofing and secondary lining for speed and to ensure the quality for this connecting section of tunnel. The shuttering (a framework around which the lining was formed) was partially collapsible, so that it could be removed from the lining and moved to the next section of tunnel very easily.[368]

The eastern tunnels bifurcate at Stepney Green, with one branch leading to the Pudding Mill Lane portal and then on to the Great Eastern main lines, and the other heading south-east via Canary Wharf to pass under the Thames and on dedicated tracks to its terminus at Abbey Wood. The construction work at Stepney Green has created a pair of caverns in which the junctions will be installed. The caverns are two of the largest SCL tunnels ever made, around 50 m long, 17 m wide, and 15 m high. They were made prior to the arrival of the TBMs, by sinking a six-storey-deep shaft from the surface and excavating out at tunnel level.

Two of the TBMs were each used for two separate tunnelling drives by the contractor Dragados / John Sisk JV, which saved having to purchase additional machines. *Jessica* was launched at the Pudding Mill Lane portal in August 2013, and arrived at the Stepney Green cavern in February 2014. The TBM was then dismantled and transported to the Limmo worksite, where it was launched on 4 June 2014 to bore the 900 m of tunnel to the Victoria Dock portal. This process was repeated after *Ellie* arrived at Stepney Green so that the remaining tunnel to Victoria Dock could be excavated,

Back at the Limmo shaft, TBM *Jessica* is reassembled for the drive west to Victoria Dock. The TBM shows clear signs of its previous underground journey. *(Crossrail)*

although unfavourable ground conditions found near the portal meant that there was a need to provide additional grouting at this location. Both of these TBMs were dismantled at the portal, with key components being returned to Herrenknecht for refurbishment and reuse on other tunnelling projects.

Spoil from the eastern tunnels emerged from the ground via the shafts at the Limmo. Here it was loaded directly into barges for transfer to Wallasea Island. The concrete tunnel segments were manufactured at a factory in Chatham, Kent, and brought by barge to the Limmo, thus avoiding the need for much road traffic.[369] Each ring on the eastern tunnels comprises seven segments and a key piece.

The record for tunnelling in a day was set by *Ellie*, at 72 m on 16 April 2014, but *Ada* set the record for a week, at 257 m. Between them the Crossrail TBMs averaged 184 m of tunnel each week.

The Thames Tunnel

Crossrail constructed another pair of tunnels beneath the Thames between North Woolwich and Plumstead, which included a station at Woolwich, adjacent to the old Woolwich Arsenal, and on a site being redeveloped with thousands of new homes. There was some dispute at the start of the project over the construction of the station, with the government initially refusing to provide extra funding despite there being a strong case for a station here. In early 2011, a deal was agreed between the Department for Transport and the owner of the site, Berkeley Homes, with the latter

The TBM *Sophia* in the station box at Woolwich, where maintenance work was carried out. *(Crossrail)*

making a substantial contribution to the cost of the work and constructing the station box. In return, Berkeley was given development rights for housing above and beside the station. Just over two years later, after more discussions, funding was agreed for the fitting out of the box to make it into an operational station. The box was constructed using diaphragm walls to a depth of 25 m, forming a space 256 m long and 26 m wide. The walls descended to below the floor of the box, which is at a depth of 18 m. A large sewer crossed the site for the box: this was diverted by constructing a 400 m tunnel using a mini-TBM 1·2 m in diameter, launched from a shaft 7 m deep on the site.* The diversion tunnel rerouted the sewer around the station box, allowing it to be constructed bottom-up.

The first of the slurry TBMs boring these tunnels, *Sophia*, was launched from the Plumstead portal site in January 2013. Unlike the launches of the EPBMs for Crossrail, where a temporary thrust ring was constructed to give the TBM something against which it could push until it was into the ground, the contractors used an innovative process in which the TBM pulled itself into the tunnel. An hydraulic system was used for this technique. It is called 'flying shield tunnelling', and had first been used for the construction of a tunnel in Cologne in 2005 by the contractors Hochtief, who were part of the joint venture (with Murphy) constructing the Thames Tunnel.

On 15 May it broke into the station box at Woolwich where it temporarily stopped work having travelled about 1,200 m. Just four days later the second TBM, called *Mary*, began to excavate from the portal, arriving at Woolwich in August. This allowed resources to be focused on one TBM at a time; the site would otherwise have required procuring twice the capacity for water and electricity at the site (each Mixshield used 1,120 KW for the cutter-head alone).[370] However, it made sense to

---

* The TBM was manufactured by Iseki Microtunnelling and was a bespoke version of their 'Unclemole' machine. The tunnelling was subcontracted to Joseph Gallagher Ltd.

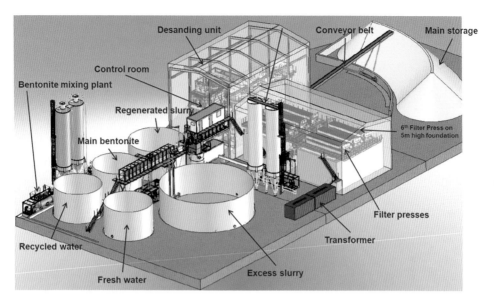

The complex chalk cake factory at Plumstead, which extracts the sand and chalk from the bentonite, recycles the cleaned bentonite back to the TBMs, and removes water from the chalk for compression into 'cakes'. *(Crossrail)*

have two separate TBMs, as it meant that the operation could switch from one to the other in a matter of days; had only one TBM used the boring of the Thames Tunnels would have taken months longer.

Both of these tunnels have the complexity of being threaded over the tunnels for the DLR where the latter are rising into Woolwich Arsenal station, with a clearance of 2 m. Extensive monitoring of the DLR commenced a year before the Crossrail tunnels approached to allow the DLR engineers to get used to what 'normal' conditions looked like from the monitoring equipment. The DLR engineers were surprised to see small amounts of movement in their tunnels, and raised concerns with the Crossrail contractors. By looking at the monitoring results it was determined that the ground movement was due to the tidal flow in the Thames; it was certainly not a cause for concern though. Once the first TBM had passed they could see that it had had less impact on the DLR than the tides.[371]

With *Mary* in the Woolwich station box undergoing maintenance, *Sophia* was restarted for the remainder of the westbound tunnel under the Thames. From the station box at Woolwich the tunnels descend to maintain around 12 m of cover beneath the river bed. They then rise up to the portal at North Woolwich. Extensive dewatering of the ground was needed in order to construct the portal structure, with 41 wells being sunk to remove water at a rate of up to 100 l/s. Removing the water from too wide an area might have caused ground settlement, so up to three-quarters of the water was pumped back into the ground further away from the portal.[372] At the end of January 2014 *Sophia* broke through at North Woolwich, and soon afterwards *Mary* began the under-river journey.

The mix of bentonite and chalk slurry was pumped back from the TBMs to the

Plumstead portal site where it was separated. The cleaned bentonite was returned to the TBMs for reuse, and the chalk was converted into 'cakes'. These cakes were transferred to Pitsea, in Essex, to help restore a landfill site, and Kingsnorth power station, in Kent, to restore contaminated land. The pair of tunnels between the Plumstead portal and Woolwich station box resulted in around 100,000 tonnes of chalk and flint being excavated.

The concrete segments for this contract were manufactured in Ireland by Shay Murtagh. One lorry transported the eight segments for a single ring, and brought them to London via the ferry.[373] Each ring is 1·6 m long.

Connaught Tunnel

Until December 2006 the North London Railway operated between Stratford and North Woolwich, running along the north side of the Royal Victoria Dock and then switching to the south side of the Royal Albert and King George V Docks. The route had been opened by the Eastern Counties and Thames Junction Railway, and originally used a swing bridge over the Connaught Passage, which was the connection between the Royal Victoria and Albert Docks. The delays that the bridge caused drove the railway to construct a cut and cover tunnel under the Connaught Passage instead, which opened in 1878. After the closure of the tunnel in 2006 it was earmarked for use by Crossrail, but with the awareness that it would need substantial refurbishment.

The tunnel, together with its approach cuttings, is about 550 m long. The cuttings are spanned by unusual arched buttresses between the side walls. The arches are made of three rings of brick supporting large concrete structures. The majority of the tunnel is a double track structure, but the section that passes under the passage between the docks was rebuilt in 1935. The larger ships that were using the docks had started to scrape the bed of the passage, and it needed to be deepened. In the tunnel beneath, two single track tunnels were formed from brickwork, allowing the crown to be lowered through this section. Cast steel segments were used to reinforce the lining of this 50 m section of tunnel.

The approach to the Connaught Tunnel is spanned by brick and concrete arched buttresses. This view is looking away from the tunnel portal, and was taken in September 2010 before Crossrail work started. The remains of the North London line tracks are rusting and overgrown with weeds. *(Crossrail)*

Looking towards the centre portion of the Connaught Tunnel and showing the single-track tunnels beneath the Connaught Passage further back. The track bed has been removed down to the tunnel invert. *(Crossrail)*

This section of the tunnel needed complete reconstruction for Crossrail, as the single bores were not large enough to accommodate the trains and the overhead power line. The original plan was to dismantle the metal lining and fill the tunnels with foam concrete. A concrete slab 1 m thick would be built in the bed of the passage to provide protection from above. New tunnels would then be bored through the brickwork and concrete. As part of the work a survey of the tunnel and dock was made, and this revealed the tunnel roof (and dock floor) to be thinner and more fragile than was expected, and consisting of a lot of broken concrete.[374] The plans needed to be changed.

It was decided to carry out the works from above. The difficulty was that the Connaught Passage is still used for boats to access the Victoria Dock for two annual events at the ExCeL exhibition centre each year: the Boat Show and the Defence Exhibition. Crossrail would not have been popular if the Boat Show had to take place without boats. Careful planning suggested that the work could be squeezed into the period between the two exhibitions, which were in January and September. Preliminary work was started with specialist contractors to survey the area around the passage for any unexploded bombs from the Second World War. The docks were heavily bombed, but some devices that hit the water did not trigger and ended up embedding themselves in the mud at the bottom of the docks. A combination of

Work taking place above the tunnels in the drained Connaught Passage. The cofferdam is to the right, and the roofs of the single-track tunnels at the far left. The metal props support the sides of the passage in the absence of water. *(Crossrail)*

magnetic surveying equipment and very careful ground probing thoroughly explored the mud in the docks. Dewatering work was also undertaken, with wells being sunk near to the central section.

A few days after the Boat Show closed in January 2013, and with the knowledge that there were no wartime explosives in the areas, coffer dams were constructed at each end of the dock passage. Large steel props were installed between the sides of the passage to provide support once the water was removed. Around 13 million litres of water were drained out of the coffer dam, exposing the tunnel crown. This was broken out and the steel lining and some of the brickwork from 1935 were removed. Precast concrete panels were installed, so that the depth of water above the tunnel could be maintained but the necessary clearance would be available for the railway. The new central part of the tunnel has been built as a double track tunnel, but with a rectangular cross-section.

Although the seven-month reconstruction of the centre section of the tunnel received much of the attention, there was extensive work carried out in the rest of the tunnel. The old track and track bed were all removed, and the foundations dug down so that a new track bed could be installed. Damage that had occurred to the tunnel on 7 September 1940 when a wartime bomb did explode was finally (and properly) repaired, having previously been patched with concrete.[375]

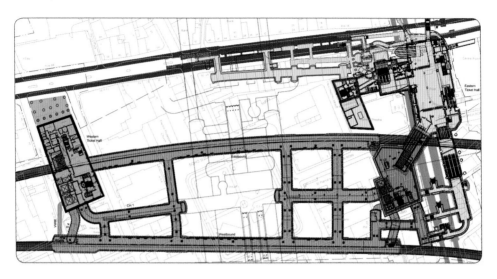

A plan of Tottenham Court Road station showing the transformation that will occur as a result of both Crossrail and the station upgrade project. Crossrail runs across the bottom, with running tunnels in blue and platforms and passageways in dark pink. The Central line is parallel to Crossrail, and shown in red along the top of the plan, with the Northern line in purple down the right-hand side. The dark orange area is for new escalators down to Crossrail, and the pale orange shows the LUL station. The current escalator bank is adjacent to the Central line. There are new access passageways to the Central line being made parallel and to the south of the platforms, and a considerable enlargement of the ticket hall with new Northern line escalators along the right-hand side of this plan. The dotted black lines running north and south across the middle of the plan indicate the location reserved for Crossrail 2. *(Crossrail)*

Platform tunnels and stations

Some of the stations have been constructed as large concrete boxes, which will have the platforms at the lowest level and ticket halls and other facilities on higher levels. Others require tunnels and passageways to be created that will fit around existing tunnels. Many of these new underground spaces are being created using the SCL process.

The shotcrete used to make the passageways and platforms at many of the stations is rather more sophisticated than standard concrete. Fibres of carbon-rich steel, 40 mm long, are blended into the mix, giving it nine times the tensile strength of ordinary concrete. The robotic delivery systems could deposit 40 tonnes of the shotcrete onto the tunnel walls every hour.

Tottenham Court Road is a particularly complex project, as it combines work to construct the Crossrail platforms and a new western ticket hall with an essential station enlargement project for the existing ticket hall and London Underground lines. In order to get sufficient access, a large worksite was formed above the eastern ticket hall area. The buildings on the south-west corner of the road junction were all purchased and carefully demolished, but even this space was insufficient. A secondary worksite was established at the foot of the Centre Point tower, on the opposite side of Charing Cross Road, and secant piling for a new escalator box 30 m deep was installed whilst the road ran between lines of blue-painted hoardings.

This box will house a new triple bank of escalators descending to the Northern line platforms, thereby removing some of the pressure from the existing escalators. At platform level several new cross-passages have been created between the platform tunnels; these will have stairs leading to the new escalators, as well as the Crossrail platforms. The cross-passages were made during an eight-month closure of the Northern line platforms that started in April 2011. Hoardings were constructed on the platform edges and plasterwork and decoration was removed from the platform where the new passageways were being built. The tunnel segments, dating back over 100 years, were unbolted and over 1,000 tonnes of new steel tunnel segments were installed. Some created the openings for the cross-passages, and others give the platforms a more vertical rear wall. This created just enough space to fit the new stairs in between the tunnels.

Once the box for the Northern line escalators was complete the project took over the section of Charing Cross Road west of Centre Point tower, rerouting traffic to the east into St Giles High Street. This allowed further shafts to be sunk, and the ticket hall construction continued as an open excavation. The alternative would have been to construct an umbrella bridge (like those used previously on the Victoria and Jubilee line works) and proceed more slowly in a cramped site.

Looking down from the Centre Point building into the worksite at Tottenham Court Road station. The original CLR building, still used to access the station, is beneath the portacabin offices on the right. Charing Cross Road has been diverted around the site; instead of curving where the bus can be seen on the left it used to continue in a straight line to the road junction on the right. The parallel concrete beams along its old course will form the roof of the enlarged ticket hall. *(Crossrail)*

A new access passageway 115 m long was excavated in parallel with the Central line platforms to provide additional capacity for passengers. This connects with new stairwells linked to the cross-passages between the platforms. A special excavator advanced this tunnel in a carefully planned sequence of work, with a primary lining of sprayed concrete 350 mm thick being applied by a robot. This has reinforcement fibres mixed in so that there is no need to install a steel mesh, which has a higher risk to the workers as it has to be done without any ground support. The tunnel is an unusual shape as well, expanding from 4·5 m diameter at the east end to 5·5 m diameter at the west. Once complete, a secondary lining of reinforced concrete was cast *in situ*. The tunnel also includes stub connections for a potential future link to Crossrail 2, which is planned to serve the station on a north-south alignment.[376] Two new footbridges were required across the westbound platform to link with new stairs leading down to the platforms. A sewer just above the tunnels caused the project to build a support raft between the two. This was made by building a series of horizontal piles 340 mm in diameter inserted from the adjacent (but disused) Post Office Railway tunnel. The passages were then excavated with SCL up to and over the Central line platform tunnel without disrupting the train service. The bridge abutments were built either side of the tunnel. The exposed crown of the platform tunnel was then broken out during two weekend closures of the Central line through Tottenham Court Road. Concrete beams were installed to form the bridge floors, and the 'cheek plates' at the sides of the footbridges were fitted. This reduced the disruption that might otherwise have occurred to the train service had the bridges been constructed conventionally.[377]

A new box has also been formed for the escalators from the ticket hall to the Crossrail concourse. This box is above the Northern line platforms, and the piling work had to proceed very carefully, with some piles passing within 1 m of the tunnels.

The grouting plan for Tottenham Court Road station, showing how all of the ground above the tunnels can be have grout injected below via seven shafts. *(Crossrail)*

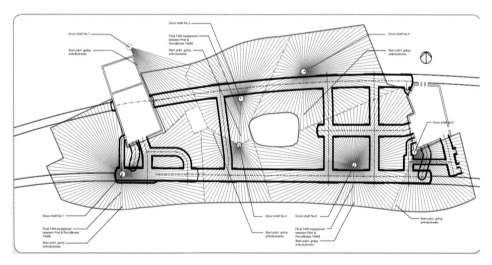

This involved the sinking of unique D-shaped piles by Bauer Technologies, the shape of which ensured that the box could fit into the extremely constrained location.[378] These descended to 44 m. Other piling at the station included seven piles to support the future development above the station and transfer the load to the subsoil without loading the tunnels. These were very large piles, up to 2·43 m in diameter, and sunk to depths of up to 64 m (down to the chalk). Four of these passed very close to the Northern line escalator box, and were fitted with slip coated liners that prevent any load from being transferred to the box.

Extensive compensation grouting arrangements were put in place around the entirety of the station site. Seven 4·5 m diameter grout shafts were sunk to a depth of around 18 m. At the bottom, smaller pipes were driven horizontally radiating out around the shafts. These steel pipes, called tubes à manchette, were 52 mm in diameter and around 50 – 90 m long, and at Tottenham Court Road their length totaled approximately 25 km. Grout could escape from these tubes every 50 cm, and was injected by computer-controlled pumps in response to monitoring that showed ground movement. Because of the difficulty of drilling the thin holes for the pipes tens of metres into the ground without being deflected, special instruments were used to check the alignment to ensure accurate positioning of the grout.[379] The pipes supplying the grout were all inserted manually into the horizontal tubes, and sealed into place using inflatable balloons whilst the pumps forced the grout in. These were all dug well in advance of the tunnelling works to ensure that they would be ready in time, and remained in place until around six months after the completion of work as settlement could occur once tunnelling is complete.

An interesting challenge arose at Whitechapel in 2014. The main escalator shaft is to connect the Crossrail platform-level concourse with the ticket hall and other interchanges at surface level. It was originally planned to wait until a temporary ticket hall facility was opened before the shaft would be dug down from the surface, but the contractor came up with an innovative solution to save time. A custom tunnelling machine, adapted from equipment used in coal mines, was built by a German company, allowing the shaft to be dug from the bottom upwards. The machine was suspended from rails fitted to the ceiling, which protected the operators from falling débris from the tunnel face. As well as the digger on the front which was used for excavating the tunnel, the machine also sprayed the concrete lining, reducing the time that the bare earth was left exposed — another important safety feature. The same process was subsequently used for the escalator shaft at Liverpool Street station.

One design feature that will make the Crossrail stations look and feel different to their London Underground forerunners, apart from their size, will be the tunnel junctions. The use of sprayed concrete linings has allowed smooth curves to be used, rather than right angled joins. This will ease passenger flows and improve visibility, as well as giving the stations their own distinctive feel. There is an engineering benefit too: it is easier to create the linings and make them waterproof. Standardization of the sizes and types of the junctions has allowed a kit of parts to be created for the architectural cladding, which in turn helps keep the cost down through economies of scale.[380]

And then there were nine

In June 2014, Crossrail announced the launch of their ninth TBM, near Westbourne Park. *Molley*, named by children from a nearby school, was rather different to the other eight TBMs. Rather than building a running tunnel, this slurry micro-tunnelling machine was used to build a 564 m length of sewer, to replace an existing sewer that needed to be demolished for Crossrail. *Molley* was therefore considerably smaller: just 1·45 m in diameter and 3·3 m long. The TBM was remotely controlled from the surface, as it was not possible to have anyone inside such a small machine. The tunnel was constructed beneath Tavistock Street, between Westbourne Park station and Basing Street, and then northwards beneath Great Western Road to terminate on the north side of the main-line railway tracks from Paddington.

Completing Crossrail

The construction of Crossrail will continue until 2018, although the tunnelling work was completed on 26 May 2015. The focus of the work switched to the electrical and mechanical fitting out of the line from this point. In 2017 the first of the new Crossrail trains should start running as the Crossrail service becomes operational — however, these will be on the surface on the existing eastern and western routes to be taken over by Crossrail.* The first trains will enter the tunnels with passengers on board in 2018.

Conclusion

The Metropolitan Railway was technologically groundbreaking only in that it took the tried and trusted concept of railway tunnel construction and applied it in an urban environment. Innovations such as smokeless locomotives largely failed, and the subsequent extensions employed open cuttings as much as possible. The ventilation issues that still plagued the MR at the end of the nineteenth century showed the wisdom of this. Only with the advent of electrification could the air be cleared in the tunnels, but by this time the age of cut and cover tunnelling beneath London's streets had come to an end.

It was the geological good fortune that London was underlain by a bed of clay, almost the perfect tunnelling medium, that allowed the development of the deep tube network. The true innovations that allowed this to be done were, in chronological order:

- the tunnelling shield – allowing tunnels to be made without the danger of unsupported and exposed soil prior to the installation of the tunnel lining.
- the cast iron tunnel lining – quicker to install than brickwork, with greater strength, thus reducing the amount of excavation required to accommodate the tunnel lining.
- the lift – allowing passengers to reach platforms at depth without having to encounter tens, if not hundreds, of steps.
- electricity generation on a large scale – making it possible to supply the energy needs of an urban railway.
- the electric motor – moving locomotives that emitted no smoke or steam.

---

*   Services between Shenfield and Liverpool Street were taken over by TfL from 31 May 2015, although they are branded as TfL Rail rather than Crossrail.

- the rotary excavator – increasing the rate at which tube tunnels could be bored, and reducing the cost of tunnelling.
- the escalator – providing a continuous means of ascending from and descending to the platforms.*
- tunnel boring machines – enabling tunnels to be constructed with larger diameters, faster, and more safely.
- compensation grouting – preventing subsidence at the surface above larger tunnels from becoming a problem that would limit tunnelling.
- sprayed concrete lining (via NATM) – providing a way of constructing underground spaces to shapes that are customized to their requirements, rather than just being cylindrical or cuboid.

With planning in progress for another major line beneath London, known as Crossrail 2, it would appear that the underground construction story will continue for many more years.

---

* At a few stations the escalators ascend to the platforms.

Appendix 1: Contractors and Engineers

This appendix lists the contractors responsible for constructing all of the major sections and extensions for the Underground, and the engineers responsible for the work. Letters in square brackets after their names show if they were recorded as the **R**esident Engineer or **C**onsulting Engineer. Also shown are the dates that the sections of lines opened to the public.

Cut and cover railways

Section of line	Year opened	Contractors	Engineer(s)
Metropolitan Railway			
Paddington (Bishop's Road) – Euston Square	1863	Smith & Knight	John Fowler Thomas Marr Johnson [R]
Euston Square – Farringdon Street	1863	John Jay	John Fowler Thomas Marr Johnson
Farringdon Street – Moorgate	1865	John Kelk	John Fowler
Praed St Junction – South Kensington	1868	Kelk, Waring and Lucas	John Fowler
Moorgate – Liverpool Street	1875	Kelk & Lucas	Edward Wilson
Liverpool Street – Aldgate	1876	Kelk & Lucas	Francis Brady
Aldgate – Tower of London	1882	Thomas Andrew Walker	Sir John Hawkshaw John Wolfe Barry Joseph Tomlinson Jr [R]
Aldgate Junction – Aldgate East	1884	Thomas Andrew Walker	Sir John Hawkshaw John Wolfe Barry
Metropolitan Railway (Metropolitan & St John's Wood Railway)			
Baker Street – Swiss Cottage	1868	Lucas Bros. and Aird & Son	John Fowler
Swiss Cottage – Willesden Green	1879	Joseph Firbank	Charles Liddell
Metropolitan Railway (City Widened Lines)			
King's Cross – Moorgate	1865	John Kelk	John Fowler
Metropolitan District Railway			
West Brompton – Mansion House	1868-71	Peto, Betts, Kelk, & Waring	John Fowler
Earl's Court – High Street Kensington	1869	Peto, Betts, Kelk, & Waring	John Fowler
Metropolitan and Metropolitan District Railway (City Lines and Extension)			
Mansion House – Tower of London	1884	Thomas Andrew Walker	Sir John Hawkshaw John Wolfe Barry
Minories Junction – Whitechapel Junction	1884	Thomas Andrew Walker	Sir John Hawkshaw John Wolfe Barry

Section of line	Year opened	Contractors	Engineer(s)
East London Railway			
Wapping – Rotherhithe (Thames Tunnel)	1843	Marc and Isambard Brunel	Marc and Isambard Brunel
Rotherhithe – Surrey Docks	1869	Brassey, Wythes, and Lucas Bros.	John Hawkshaw G.R. Stephenson
Wapping – Shoreditch	1876	Thomas Andrew Walker	
Whitechapel & Bow Railway			
Whitechapel – Campbell Road Junction	1902	John Price	Cuthbert A. Brereton A. Gibb [R] A. Pearce [R]

Tube railways

Section of line	Year opened	Contractors	Engineer(s)
City & South London Railway / Northern line			
King William Street – Elephant & Castle	1890	Edmund Gabbutt / Walter Scott & Co.	James Greathead Sir John Fowler [C]
Elephant & Castle – Stockwell	1890	Walter Scott & Co.	Sir Benjamin Baker [C] Basil Mott [R]
Borough – Moorgate	1900	John Mowlem & Co.	James Greathead Sir Benjamin Baker
Stockwell – Clapham Common	1900	W. Rigby & Co	James Greathead
Moorgate – Angel	1901	W. Rigby & Co	James Greathead Sir Benjamin Baker
Angel – Euston	1907	Walter Scott & Middleton	Sir Benjamin Baker Basil Mott David Hay H.J. Deane [R]
Moorgate – Angel (enlargement)	1924	Perry & Co.	Arthur R. Cooper Mott, Hay & Anderson [C]
Angel – Euston (enlargement)	1924	Charles Brand & Son	Gerald Curry [R]
Borough Junction – Clapham Common (enlargement)	1924	Walter Scott & Middleton	Mott, Hay & Anderson [C] Isaac J. Jones [R]
Clapham Common and Clapham Road station tunnel enlargement	1924	Metropolitan Tunnel and Public Works Co.	Mott, Hay & Anderson [C] Mark D. Mott [R]
Euston – Camden Town	1924	John Mowlem & Co.	Harley H. Dalrymple-Hay [C]
Clapham South – Tooting Broadway	1926	Charles Brand & Son	Arthur R. Cooper Mott, Hay & Anderson [C]

Section of line	Year opened	Contractors	Engineer(s)
City & South London Railway / Northern line			
Tooting Broadway – Morden	1926	The Foundation Co.	Arthur R. Cooper Mott, Hay & Anderson [C]
King's Cross loop	1927	Walter Scott & Middleton	
Waterloo & City Railway			
Waterloo – Bank	1898	John Mowlem & Co.	W.R. Galbraith James Greathead Harley H. Dalrymple-Hay [R]
Central London Railway / Central line			
Shepherd's Bush – Marble Arch	1900	John Price	Sir John Fowler Sir Benjamin Baker James Greathead Basil Mott
Marble Arch – Post Office	1900	Walter Scott & Co	
Post Office – Bank	1900	John Talbot	
Bank – Liverpool Street	1912	John Mowlem & Co.	E.P. Grove H.J. Deane [R] Mott & Hay [C]
Liverpool Street – Mile End	1946	Charles Brand & Son	V.A.M. Robinson Mott, Hay & Anderson [C]
Mile End – Leyton	1946/7	John Mowlem & Co.	
Wanstead – Gants Hill	1947	Charles Brand & Son	
Gants Hill – Newbury Park	1947	Edmund Nuttall Sons & Co.	
Great Northern & City Railway			
Moorgate – Finsbury Park	1904	S. Pearson & Son	Sir Douglas Fox & Partners D.L. Hutchinson [R] Alexander Ross [R] H.W. Sadler [R]
Baker Street & Waterloo Railway / Bakerloo line			
Lambeth North – Marylebone	1906	Perry & Co.	James R. Chapman Galbraith & Church [C] Benjamin Baker [C] Harley H. Dalrymple-Hay [R]
Lambeth North – Elephant & Castle (including depot)	1906	John Mowlem & Co.	
Marylebone – Edgware Road	1907	Perry & Co.	
Edgware Road – Paddington	1913	John Mowlem & Co.	
Paddington – Queen's Park	1915	Walter Scott & Middleton	Harley H. Dalrymple-Hay [C]
Queen's Park (incline and surface work)	1915	John Mowlem & Co.	Harley H. Dalrymple-Hay [C]

Section of line	Year opened	Contractors	Engineer(s)
Baker Street & Waterloo Railway / Bakerloo line			
Baker Street – Finchley Road	1939	Charles Brand & Son	V.A.M. Robinson Harley H. Dalrymple-Hay [C] William T. Halcrow [C] D.F.C. Fitzgerald [R]
Great Northern, Piccadilly & Brompton Railway / Piccadilly line			
Barons Court – South Kensington	1906	Walter Scott & Middleton	James R. Chapman Alexander Ross
South Kensington – Holborn	1906	Walker, Price & Reeves	James R. Chapman Sir James Szlumper W.W. Szlumper
Strand – Finsbury Park	1906/7	Walker, Price & Reeves	James R. Chapman Cuthbert A. Brereton
Finsbury Park – Southgate	1932/3	Charles Brand & Son	Harley H. Dalrymple-Hay [C]
Southgate – Cockfosters	1933	Sir Robert McAlpine & Sons	Harley H. Dalrymple-Hay [C]
Hounslow West – Hatton Cross	1975	W. & C. French (Construction) Ltd	
Hatton Cross – Heathrow Central	1977	John Mowlem & Co.	
Hatton Cross – Heathrow Terminal 4	1986	Thyssen-Taywood consortium	
Heathrow Terminals 1,2,3 – Heathrow Terminal 5	2008	Morgan Vinci	Jean-Christophe Galan [R]
Charing Cross, Euston & Hampstead Railway / Northern line			
Charing Cross – Golders Green/Highgate	1907	Walker, Price & Reeves	James R. Chapman Sir Douglas Fox & Partners [C] W.R. Galbraith [C] A.W. Donaldson [R]
Charing Cross – Embankment	1914	John Mowlem & Co.	Harley H. Dalrymple-Hay G. Blacklock [R]
Golders Green – Hendon Central (Burroughs Tunnels)	1923	Charles Brand & Son	Harley H. Dalrymple-Hay [C]
Hendon Central – Edgware	1924	The Foundation Co.	Harley H. Dalrymple-Hay [C]
Embankment – Kennington	1926	Metropolitan Tunnel and Public Works Co.	Harley H. Dalrymple-Hay [C]

Section of line	Year opened	Contractors	Engineer(s)
Charing Cross, Euston & Hampstead Railway / Northern line			
Highgate – East Finchley	1939	Charles Brand & Son	V.A.M. Robinson Sir William Halcrow & Partners [C] J. Lander [R]
Victoria line			
Finsbury Park – Netherton Road shaft	1968	Edmund Nuttall Sons & Co. Kinnear Moodie & Co.	C.E. Dunton H.G. Follenfant Sir William Halcrow & Partners [C] Mott, Hay & Anderson [C]
Walthamstow Central – Netherton Road shaft	1968	Charles Brand & Son	
Finsbury Park – King's Cross	1969	Kinnear Moodie & Co. Ltd	
King's Cross – Oxford Circus	1969	Mitchell Bros. Sons & Co. Ltd	
Oxford Circus – Victoria	1969	John Mowlem & Co.	
Oxford Circus station	1969	Kinnear Moodie & Co. Ltd	
Victoria – Vauxhall	1971	Balfour Beatty& Co. Ltd	H.G. Follenfant Sir William Halcrow & Partners [C] Mott, Hay & Anderson [C]
Vauxhall – Stockwell	1971	Mitchell Bros. Sons & Co. Ltd	
Stockwell – Brixton	1971	A. Waddington & Son Ltd	
Jubilee line			
Baker Street junctions	1979	John Mowlem & Co.	
Baker Street – Bond Street	1979	Charles Brand & Son	
Bond Street – Green Park	1979	A. Waddington & Son Ltd	
Green Park – Charing Cross	1979	Kinnear Moodie Ltd	
Green Park – Waterloo	1999	Balfour Beatty Amec JV	
Waterloo – Canada Water	1999	Aoki Soletanche JV	
Canada Water – Canning Town	1999	McAlpine Wayss & Freytag – Bachy JV	

Appendix 2: Tube tunnel ring dimensions

Once the 1892 Joint Select Committee had recommended a minimum tunnel diameter of 11 ft 6 ins, the tube railways whose Bills followed tended to adopt this size. It was based on the realization that the C&SLR had been built too small. The GN&CR, approved before the Committee reported, needed 16 ft diameter tunnels to handle the intended main-line trains. The three Yerkes tubes followed the Committee recommendation, but discovered that by reducing the size of the segment flanges slightly, and abandoning the ineffective concrete infill they could enlarge their tunnels to the strange-looking diameter of 11 ft 8¼ ins.

The length of the tunnel rings increases slightly over time. Since the tunnelling process is a strict repetition of excavation, shield advancement, and tunnel lining erection, it follows that the longer the ring, the fewer the cycles needed, and the faster the tunnel will be made. However, longer rings mean a greater length to the tail-skin of the shield, in which the next tunnel lining ring will be erected. The greater the ratio of the shield length to its diameter, the harder it will be to steer. This explains the reason that the Victoria line, with its gentle curves, was able to use longer tunnel rings.

Cast iron tunnel segments were often embossed with information such as the initials of the railway company, the size, and the manufacturer. This segment, seen in the spiral stair shaft at Old Street, shows that it was cast by Head, Wrightson, & Co, is part of a ring 16 ft in diameter, and was made for the City & South London Railway. *(Author)*

The other limiting factor is the weight of the segments, although the introduction of hydraulic segment erectors tended to make this less important. The heavier the segments, the more men were needed to lift and install them in the early tunnels; in the small, dimly lit working area this would be a problem for any more than four men working at once.

The table below summarizes the information for straight running tunnels.

Railway	Material	Internal diameter	Ring length	Segments per ring
Tower Subway	Cast iron	7 ft ¼ in	18 ins	3 + key
C&SLR	Cast iron	10 ft 2 ins	19 ins	6 + key
		10 ft 6 ins	20 ins	6 + key
W&CR	Cast iron	12 ft 1¾ ins	20 ins	7 + key
CLR	Cast iron	11 ft 6 ins	20 ins	6 + key
GN&CR	Cast iron	16 ft	20 ins	8 + 2 keys [A]
BS&WR	Cast iron	11 ft 8¼ ins	20 ins	6 + key
		12 ft (under-river)	18 ins (under-river)	6+ key
GNP&BR	Cast iron	11 ft 8¼ ins	20 ins	6 + key
CCE&HR	Cast iron	11 ft 8¼ ins	20 ins	6 + key
C&SLR (Morden extension)	Cast iron	11 ft 8¼ ins	20 ins	6 + key
Northern (Highgate extension)	Cast iron	12 ft	20 ins	6 + key
Bakerloo (Baker St – Finchley Rd)	Cast iron	12 ft	20 ins	6 + key
Central (Liverpool St – Leyton)	Cast iron	12 ft	20 ins	6 + key
Central (Leytonstone – Newbury Park)	Concrete	12 ft 3 ins	20 ins	6 + key
	Cast iron	12 ft	20 ins	6 + key
Deep shelters	Concrete	16 ft 6 ins	20 ins	8 + key
Victoria	Concrete (Halcrow)	12 ft 6 ins	24 ins	11 + 2 wedges
	Concrete (MHA)	12 ft 6 ins	24 ins	12 + 2 wedges
	Cast iron	12 ft 8 ins	20 ins	6 + key
Piccadilly (Heathrow extension)	Concrete	12 ft 6 ins	60 cm	20 + 2 wedges
Jubilee	Concrete	3·81 m	60 cm	20 + 2 wedges
	Cast iron	3·85 m	60 cm	8 + key

357

Railway	Material	Internal diameter	Ring length	Segments per ring
Piccadilly (Heathrow T4 extension)	Concrete	3·81 m	75 cm	16 + 2 wedges
	Cast iron [B]	3·85 m	60 cm	8 + key
Northern line (Old Street relining)	Stainless steel	4·68 m	60 cm	12 + key
Jubilee line extension	Bolted concrete	4·4 m	1·2 m	5 + key
	Expanded concrete	4·45 m	1·0 m	10 + 2 keys
Piccadilly (Heathrow T5 extension)	Concrete	4·5 m	1·0 m	7 + key
Crossrail	Concrete	6·2 m	1·6 m	6 + key

Note A: Lower half of lining, consisting of four segments and one key, removed and replaced by brickwork.

Note B: Segments originally ordered for Jubilee line phase 2, and reused for Heathrow Terminal 4 extension.

From the early 1900s until the advent of the Victoria line in the 1960s the standard for running tunnels was a diameter 11 ft 8¼ inches with rings 20 inches long comprising six identical segments plus a key piece, fitted at the crown of the tunnel.

The table below summarizes the information for a selection of the larger-diameter tunnels. Although tunnel diameters are generally well-recorded, details of ring lengths and the composition of each ring are less well documented, hence the table being shorter than the previous one.

Railway	Material	Internal diameter	Ring length	Segments per ring
W&CR	Cast iron	23 ft	18 ins	13 + key
CLR	Cast iron	21 ft	18 ins	12 + key
GN&CR	Cast iron	21 ft / 23 ft		12 + key
BS&WR	Cast iron	21 ft 2½ ins	20 ins [C]	12 + key
GNP&BR	Cast iron	21 ft 2½ ins	20 ins [C]	12 + key
CCE&HR	Cast iron	21 ft 2½ ins	20 ins [C]	12 + key
C&SLR	Cast iron	30 ft [D]	18 ins	16 + key
C&SLR (Morden extension)	Cast iron	21 ft 2½ ins	20 ins	12 + key
Victoria line	Cast iron	21 ft 2½ ins	20 ins	12 + key
	Cast iron	30 ft [E]	20 ins	16 + key
Jubilee line (Stage I)	Cast iron	9·50 m [E]	0·61 m	24 + key

Railway	Material	Internal diameter	Ring length	Segments per ring
Jubilee line extension	SGI [F]	7·7 m	0·6 m	14 + key
	SGI [G]	7·0 m	1·0 m	16 + key
	Expanded concrete [H]	7·0 m	1·0 m	10 + 2 keys

Note C: Length presumed based on consistent spacing of sleepers with running tunnels, sleepers fitting into every other segment.

Note D: These were the platform tunnels with an island platform between two tracks, as found at Clapham Common, Clapham North, Angel, and Euston.

Note E: These were the largest tunnels in use on these lines, for crossovers.

Note F: Figures given for London Bridge station.

Note G: Figures given for Westminster station.

Note H: Figures given for Southwark station.

The three tubes constructed by Yerkes all spaced their transverse sleepers in accordance with the tunnel segment spacing, hence the supposition that the segment length for platform tunnels was the same as for running tunnels. The CLR and GN&CR used longitudinal sleepers, and so the spacing of the segments had no relation to any track dimensions, and the C&SLR originally used brick platform tunnels. For many years the Underground standardized its station platform tunnels, and so the extensions of the 1920s, 1930s, and 1940s, as well as the Victoria line would all have used the same type of tunnel segment. It was only with the Fleet/Jubilee line and the Piccadilly line extension to Heathrow in the 1970s that LT adopted metric tunnel sizes.

A typical station on the Underground employs a large number of different tunnel sizes. As an example, the following types were used for the extension of the C&SLR extension to Morden:

Ring size	Number of rings	Purpose
25 ft	76	Lower escalator landings Platform tunnel shield chambers
22 ft 4 ins	Not stated	Tooting Broadway escalator shaft (elliptical)
21 ft 2½ ins	2,696	Platform tunnels Step-plate junction
19 ft 4 ins	Not stated	Escalator shafts Lower concourses
18 ft	32	Step-plate junction
15 ft	159	Step-plate junction
13 ft 1¾ ins	56	Step-plate junction
12 ft 6 ins	181	Running tunnels with curve of less than 20 chains Step-plate junction
11 ft 8¼ ins	26,230	Running tunnels Station cross-passages

Another C&SLR segment marking, from one of the 11 ft 6 ins diameter running tunnels. This segment is part of a tunnel ring preserved at the London Transport Museum Depot in Acton. *(Author)*

A segment from a 12 ft diameter tunnel ring, manufactured by the Stanton Ironworks, near Nottingham. This example is in the deep-level shelter at Clapham South station. *(Author)*

Appendix 3: Shield and tunnel dimensions

None of the early shields was very large, and all of them were shorter than the diameters of the tunnels that they were making. The table overleaf records the details for many (but not all) of the main shields used to construct the Underground. The internal and external sizes of the resulting tunnels are included so that the relative sizes can be compared for the shields and tunnels. The list is in chronological order.

Line	Manufacturer	Shield		Tunnel	
		Length	Ext. diameter	Ext. diameter	Int. diameter
Tower Subway	Bells, Goodman and Co.	4 ft 9 ins	7 ft 3 ins	7 ft 1¾ins	6 ft 7¾ ins
C&SLR	William Sewell	5 ft 11 ins		10 ft 10¾ ins	10 ft 2 ins
		6 ft 6 ins	11 ft 4½ ins	11 ft 3 ins	10 ft 6 ins
W&CR	Markham	7 ft 0 ins	13 ft 2 ins	13 ft	12 ft 1¾ in
CLR	Markham and others	7 ft 0 ins	12 ft 8 ins	12 ft 6 ins	11 ft 6 ins
GN&CR	Markham	8 ft 3 ins	17 ft 3 ins˙	17 ft	16 ft 0 ins
BS&WR	Markham	9 ft 8½ in		12 ft 6 ins	11 ft 8¼ ins
	Widnes Foundry Co.		13 ft 0 ins	12 ft 9¾ ins	12 ft 0 ins
GNP&BR / CCE&HR	Markham [Price rotary excavator]		12 ft 8 ins	12 ft 6 ins	11 ft 8¼ ins
C&SLR enlargement	Sir William Arrol & Co.	7 ft 5 ins	12 ft 10 ins	12 ft 5 ins	11 ft 8¼ ins
C&SLR (Morden extension)	Markham		12 ft 8 ins		11 ft 8¼ ins
Piccadilly line (Cockfosters extension)	Markham		12 ft 11 ins˙		11 ft 8¼ ins
Central line (Liverpool St – Bethnal Green) / Northern line (Archway – East Finchley portals)	Markham [rotary excavator]	9 ft 8¾ ins	13 ft 2¾ ins		12 ft 0 ins
Central line (Ilford Tube) (concrete)				13 ft ½ in	12 ft 3 ins
Victoria line (cast iron)	Kinnear Moodie		13 ft 1 in	13 ft 1 in	12 ft 8 ins
Victoria line (concrete)	Kinnear Moodie		14 ft 0 in	13 ft 6 ins	12 ft 6 ins
Victoria line (concrete)	Sir Robert McAlpine & Sons Ltd	10 ft 3 ins˙	13 ft 6¾ ins	13 ft 6 ins	12 ft 6 ins
Jubilee line (Baker St – Charing Cross) (concrete)				4·146 m	3·81 m

˙ Approximate size

References

Many original papers and documents held in The National Archives, the London Metropolitan Archives, and the Institution of Civil Engineers Library have been consulted in the writing of this book. The sections below detail the main sources that have been used.

Papers

Barlow, P., *On the Relief of London Street Traffic* (Spon 1867)

Bartlett, J.V., Biggart, A.R., and Triggs, R.L., *The bentonite tunnelling machine* (Proceedings of the Institution of Civil Engineers (Vol. 54 Issue 4) 1973)

Botelle, M., Payne, K, and Redhead, B., *Squeezing the heat out of London's Tube* (Proceedings of the Institution of Civil Engineers – Civil Engineering (Vol. 163) 2010)

Burgess, N., Fagents, J., and Paterson, J., *Northern Line tunnel reconstruction at Old Street* (Proceedings of the Institution of Civil Engineers – Transport (Vol. 153 Issue 1) 2002)

McClements, N., *The Value of Common Design – C100 Crossrail Architectural Components* (Crossrail Project: Infrastructure Design and Construction 2015)

Chrimes, M.M., *Taking the Railway Underground: The work of Benjamin Baker and his contemporaries* (Institution of Civil Engineers 1999)

Craig, R.N, and Muir Wood, A.M., *A review of tunnel lining practice in the United Kingdom* (Transport and Road Research Laboratory (Supplementary Report No. 335) 1978)

Cuthbert, E.W., Lyons, A.C., and Bubbers, B.L., *The Jubilee Line* (Proceedings of the Institution of Civil Engineers (Vol. 68) 1980)

Dare, H.H., *Preliminary Work on the Proposed Connection between Sydney and North Sydney, with some notes on Long Span Bridges and Subaqueous Tunnelling* (Sydney University Engineering Society 1909)

Darroch, N., *London's Deep Tube Railways: Visibly Invisible* (MA Thesis, University of York, 2012)

Davis, A., *The Geology of the City and South London Railway Clapham – Morden Extension* (Proceedings of the Geologists Association 39 (Part 3) 1928)

Dunton, C.E., Kell, J., and Morgan, H.D., *Victoria Line: Experimentation, design, programming, and early progress* (Proceedings of the Institution of Civil Engineers (Vol. 31) 1965)

Greathead, J., *The City and South London Railway: with some remarks upon subaqueous tunnelling by shield and compressed air* (Institution of Civil Engineers 1896)

Groves, G.L., *The Ilford Tube* (Proceedings of the Institution of Civil Engineers (Vol. 26) 1946)

Haigh, A.H., *Subaqueous Tunnelling through the Thames Gravel : Baker Street and Waterloo Railway* (Proceedings of the Institution of Civil Engineers (Vol. 150) 1902)

Hall, H., *The New Piccadilly Circus Station* (Proceedings of the Institution of Civil Engineers (Vol. 228) 1929)

Harley-Mason, John H., *Reconstruction of the Aldgate East Station* (Proceedings of the Institution of Civil Engineers (Vol. 11 Issue 6) 1939)

Hickman, C., *Transporting Tunnel Boring Machines* (Crossrail Project: Infrastructure Design and Construction 2015)

Jäger, J., and Stärk, A., *Deformation prediction for tunnels at PiccEx junction in London Heathrow – An engineering approach* (Underground Space – The 4th Dimension of Metropolises 2007)

Jobling D.G., and Lyons, A.C., *Extension of the Piccadilly line from Hounslow West to Heathrow Central* (Proceedings of the Institution of Civil Engineers (Vol. 60 Part 1) 1976)

Jones, I.J., and Curry, G., *Enlargement of City and South London Railway Tunnels* (Proceedings of the Institution of Civil Engineers (Vol. 224) 1927)

King, J., *Harding Memorial Lecture: A Century of Tunnelling and Where We Go Now* (British Tunnelling Society 2000)

Lee, Charles E., *The Tower Subway* (Institution of Mechanical Engineers 1970)

Mair, R.J., *Recent experiences of tunnelling and deep excavations in London* (Proc. 4th Intl Conf. on Case Histories in Geotechnical Engineering 1998)

Mott, B, *Presidential Address to the Institution of Civil Engineers* (1924)

Pérez Lupi, P., Lewis, E., Adetoye, J., Gonzalez, X., Gallego Ramirez, N., Munn, Z., and Campos, D., *Comparison of drilling methods used for TaM installations in London Clay* (Crossrail Project: Infrastructure Design and Construction 2015)

Pickett, A., *Crossrail Sprayed Concrete Linings* (Crossrail Project: Infrastructure Design and Construction 2015)

Rainey, T., *The adverse influence of geology and groundwater on the behaviour of London Underground railway tunnels near Old Street Station* (Proceedings of the Geologists Association 100 (Part 1) 1989)

Sabine, G.D., and Skelton, E., *Extension of the Piccadilly Line to Terminal 4, Heathrow* (Proceedings of the Institution of Civil Engineers Part 1 (Vol. 78) 1985)

Stärk, A., and Jäger, J., *London Heathrow Terminal 5 – Construction and monitoring of Piccadilly Extension Junction* (Underground Space – The 4th Dimension of Metropolises 2007)

Tabor, E.H., *The Rotherhithe Tunnel – Discussion* (Proceedings of the Institution of Civil Engineers (Vol. 175) 1909)

Thomas, J.P., *The Seven from Chicago* (London Underground Railway Society 1970)

Tupholme, C.H.S., *Excavating London's New Victoria Line* (Ground Engineering 1969)

Turner, F.S.P., *Preliminary planning for a new tube railway across London – Discussion* (Proceedings of the Institution of Civil Engineers (Vol. 13 Issue 4) 1959)

Reports

Report of the Joint Select Committee of the House of Lords and the House of Commons on the Electric and Cable Railways (Metropolis) (HMSO 1892)

Report of the Committee into the System of Ventilation of Tunnels on the Metropolitan Railway (HMSO 1897)

Requirements of the Board of Trade in regard to the precautions to be taken against the risk of Accident by Fire on Underground Electric Railways (Board of Trade 1904)

Reports by the Inspecting Officers of Railways upon Certain Accidents which have been Inquired into: City & South London Railway (Ministry of Transport 1924)

Railway (London Plan) Committee: Report to the Minister of War Transport (HMSO 21 January 1946)

London Plan Working Party Report to the Minister of Transport (HMSO 1949)

London Rail Study (GLC 1974)

Central London Rail Study (Department of Transport 1989)

London East-West Study (Shadow Strategic Rail Authority 2000)

London Transport Annual Reports (various years)

Booklets published by or with the Underground companies

Ozonair on the Central London Railway: The Story of a Wonderful Achievement (Ozonair 1923)

Re-opening of the City & South London Railway (Underground 1924)

Opening of the Morden Extension & the Kennington Loop (Underground 1926)

The New Piccadilly Circus Station (Underground 1928)

How a Tube Railway is Constructed (London Transport 1934)

Seven More Stations on the Central Line (London Transport 1947)

Central Line Extensions (London Transport 1948)

Underground Railway Construction (London Transport 1968)

The Brixton Extension of the Victoria Line (London Transport 1971)

Underground to Heathrow (London Transport 1977)

The Jubilee Line (London Transport 1979)

A brief history of the Lots Road power station and site (Circadian 2001)

Books

Badsey-Ellis, Antony, *London's Lost Tube Schemes* (Capital Transport 2005)

Badsey-Ellis, Antony, *The Hampstead Tube* (Capital Transport 2007)

Badsey-Ellis, Antony, and Horne, Mike, *The Aldwych Branch* (Capital Transport 2009)

Barker, T.C. and Robbins, M., *A History of London Transport Vol. 1 – The Nineteenth Century* (Allen & Unwin 1975)

Borley, H.V. and Kidner, R.W., *The West London Railway and the W.L.E.R.* (The Oakwood Press c.1968)

Black, Mike; Dodge, Christian; and Lawrence, Ursula (Eds.), *Crossrail Project: Infrastructure Design and Construction* (Institution of Civil Engineers 2015)

Carpenter, Barry, *Opening of the Piccadilly Line Extension: The Diamond Anniversary* (Piccadilly Line 1993)

Chapman, David, Metje, Nicole, and Stärk, Alfred, *Introduction to Tunnel Construction* (CRC Press 2010)

Coleman, Terry, *The Railway Navvies* (Pelican Books 1968)

Copperthwaite, W.C., *Tunnel Shields and the use of Compressed Air in Subaqueous Works* (Archibald Constable & Co 1906)

Croome, Desmond and Jackson, Alan A., *Rails Through the Clay* (Capital Transport 1993)

Croome Desmond, *The Circle Line* (Capital Transport 2003)

Day, John R., *The Story of the Victoria Line* (London Transport 1969)

Douglas, Hugh, *The Underground Story* (Robert Hale 1963)

Dover, A.T., *Electric Traction: A Treatise on the Application of Electric Power to Tramways and Railways* (Macmillan 1917)

Edmonds, Alexander, *History of the Metropolitan District Railway Company to June 1908* (London Transport 1973)

Emmerson, Andrew, *The Underground Pioneers* (Capital Transport 2000)

Emmerson, Andrew and Beard, Tony, *London's Secret Tubes* (Capital Transport 2004)

Follenfant, H.G., *Reconstructing London's Underground* (London Transport 1974)

Freeman, M.J., *Railways and the Victorian Imagination* (Yale University Press 1999)

Gillham, John C., *The Waterloo & City Railway* (Oakwood Press 2001)

Halden, G.M., *Setting out of Tube Railways* (Spon 1907)

Hewett, B.H.M. and Johannesson, S., *Shield and Compressed Air Tunnelling* (McGraw Hill 1922)

Holman, Printz P., *The Amazing Electric Tube* (London Transport Museum 1990)

Horne, Mike, *The Central Line* (Doug Rose 1987)

Horne, Mike, *The Victoria Line* (Doug Rose 1988)

Horne, Mike, *The Piccadilly Tube* (Capital Transport 2007)

Horne, Mike, *The Story of a station: Oxford Circus* (http://www.metadyne.co.uk/pdf_files/Oxo.pdf)

Jackson, Alan A., *London's Metropolitan Railway* (David & Charles 1986)

Lascelles, T.S., *The City & South London Railway* (Oakwood Press 1987)

Lawrence, David, *Bright Underground Spaces* (Capital Transport 2008)

Lee, Charles E., *The Metropolitan Line* (London Transport 1972)

Lee, Charles E., *The East London Line and the Thames Tunnel* (London Transport 1976)

Lunniss, R. and Baber, J., *Immersed Tunnels* (CRC Press 2013)

Mitchell, Bob, *Jubilee Line Extension: from concept to completion* (Thomas Telford 2003)

Nock, O.S., *Underground Railways of the World* (A & C Black Ltd 1973)

Pennick, Nigel, *Early Tube Railways of London* (Electric Traction 1983)

Powell, Kenneth, *The Jubilee Line Extension* (Lawrence King 2000)

Pudney, John, *Crossing London's River* (Dent & Sons 1972)

Rose, Douglas, *Tiles of the Unexpected* (Doug Rose 2007)

Sheppard, F.H.W, *Survey of London Vol. 41: Brompton* (English Heritage 1983)

Smith, Robert H., *Electric Traction* (Harper & Brothers 1905)

Soper, George A., *The Air and Ventilation of Subways* (John Wiley & Sons 1908)

Trevithick, Francis, *Life of Richard Trevithick* (Spon 1872)

Williams, F.S., *Our Iron Roads: Their history, construction and administration* (Bemrose & Son 1885)

Wilson, B.G. and Haram, V. Stewart, *The Central London Railway* (Fairseat Press 1950)

Wolmar, Christian, *The Subterranean Railway* (Atlantic Books 2004)

Wort, K.G. and Bennett, M.G., *Markham & Company of Chesterfield* (Merton Priory Press 2005)

Web sites
Crossrail: http://www.crossrail.co.uk/
District Dave's Forum: http://www.districtdavesforum.co.uk/
Engineering Timelines: http://www.engineering-timelines.com/timelines.asp
Forgotten Relics: http://www.forgottenrelics.co.uk/

Grace's Guide: http://www.gracesguide.co.uk/Main_Page
Herrenknecht: http://www.herrenknecht.com/
Iseki Microtunnelling: http://www.isekimicro.com/
London Reconnections: http://www.londonreconnections.com/
Mike Horne – Observations of a Londoner: http://machorne.wordpress.com/
Old Maps: http://old-maps.co.uk/
Subterranea Britannica: http://www.subbrit.org.uk/
Underground History: http://underground-history.co.uk/front.php

Endnotes

1   http://www.forgottenrelics.co.uk/tunnels/gallery/fritchley.html
2   Trevithick, p252.
3   Pudney, p99.
4   http://www.engineering-timelines.com/scripts/engineeringItem.asp?id=1187
5   Lunniss & Baber, p5.
6   Williams, p158.
7   Jackson, p15.
8   Darroch, p31
9   *The Land Clauses Consolidation Act 1845*, Chapter 18 Section 92.
10 Jackson, p108.
11 Nock, p27.
12 *Report of the Joint Select Committee on the Electric and Cable Railways (Metropolis).*
13 *The Examiner*, 17 December 1859.
14 *The Builder*, 10 January 1863.
15 *The Railway News*, 15 January 1916.
16 *The Standard*, 21 March 1860.
17 *The Examiner*, 31 March 1860.
18 *The Morning Post*, 3 May 1860.
19 *The Morning Chronicle*, 14 May 1860.
20 Williams, p166.
21 *Ibid.*
22 Wolmar, p35.
23 Douglas, p49.
24 *The Daily News*, 18 May 1860.
25 *The Daily News*, 10 August 1860.
26 *Lloyd's Weekly Newspaper*, 14 October 1860.
27 Report by the Railway Department of the Board of Trade into the boiler explosion at King's Cross.
28 *The Engineer*, 31 May 1861.
29 *The Engineer*, 20 September 1861.
30 *Illustrated Times*, 19 October 1861.
31 Williams, p165.
32 *The Guardian*, 20 June 1862.
33 *The Standard*, 18 July 1862.
34 *The Railway Gazette*, 28 June 1935.
35 Freeman, p131.
36 Borley & Kidner, p13.
37 *Engineering*, 20 December 1867.
38 *Engineering*, 25 December 1868.
39 Edmonds, p16.
40 *Engineering*, 24 June 1870.
41 *Engineering*, 20 December 1867.
42 Lee (*East London Line*), p14.
43 *The Engineer*, 27 January 1865.
44 Lee (*Metropolitan Line*), p17.
45 *The Engineer*, 20 June 1879.
46 Reported in *The Engineer*, 1 November 1867.
47 *The Engineer*, 8 January, 1875.
48 Soper, p74.
49 *Report of the Committee into the System of Ventilation of Tunnels on the Metropolitan Railway*, p vi.
50 Jackson, p71.
51 Jackson, p108.
52 *The Engineer*, 9 March 1883.
53 *The Daily News*, 16 November 1863.
54 *Evening News*, 28 August 1962.
55 *The Engineer*, 9 April 1869, p255.
56 Douglas, p131.
57 *The Pall Mall Gazette*, 19 March 1870.
58 Copperthwaite, p9.
59 *Engineering*, 1 April 1870.
60 *Ibid.*
61 For example, *The Pall Mall Gazette* of 14 April 1870.
62 *The Times*, 1 April 1870.
63 *Illustrated London News*, 9 April 1870.
64 *The Times*, 21 April 1870.
65 *The Standard*, 16 April 1870.
66 *The Times*, 2 July 1870.

67   *The Standard*, 16 January 1871.
68   *The Pall Mall Gazette*, 10 January 1871.
69   *The Standard*, 20 January 1871.
70   Edmondo de Amicis, *Jottings about London* (translated), 1883
71   *Evening News*, 28 August 1962.
72   *The Illustrated Police News*, 17 May 1879.
73   *The Dundee Courier*, 11 May 1888, as well as other newspapers.
74   Pudney, p117.
75   *The Morning Post*, 18 January 1896.
76   Holman, p20.
77   *The Daily News*, 19 May 1888.
78   Pennick, p13, and Greathead, p54.
79   Dare, p84.
80   Nock, p43.
81   Greathead, p28.
82   *The Daily News*, 8 Feb 1887.
83   *The Engineer*, 7 October 1887.
84   *The Engineer*, 22 November 1895.
85   Holman, p19.
86   Greathead, p73.
87   Greathead, p13.
88   *The Morning Post*, 10 October 1888.
89   *The Morning Post*, 16 October 1888.
90   Greathead, p10.
91   Halden, p1.
92   Hewett & Johannesson, p68.
93   Mott, p10.
94   Smith, p243.
95   Hewett & Johannesson, p64.
96   Smith, p242.
97   *The Engineer*, 27 January 1899.
98   *The Engineer*, 9 November 1894.
99   The description of these comes from *The Engineer*, 2 August 1895.
100 *The Railway Magazine*, August 1898.
101 *The Graphic*, 16 November 1895.
102 *The Times*, 31 January 1896.
103 *The Engineer*, 11 November 1898.
104 Wilson and Haram, p11.
105 *The Times*, 15 October 1896.
106 *The Engineer*, 15 October 1897.
107 Groves, Discussion, p45.
108 *The Engineer*, 11 November 1898.
109 Haigh, Discussion p73.
110 *The Daily News*, 24 October 1898.
111 *The Engineer*, 18 November 1898.
112 Wort & Bennett.
113 Copperthwaite, p109.
114 Smith, p241.
115 Horne (*Central Line*), p8.
116 Copperthwaite, p78.
117 *The Engineer*, 4 August 1899.
118 Wilson and Haram, p12-13.
119 GN&CR Engineer's reports 1899-1903.
120 *Transport*, 5 February 1904.
121 GN&CR Inspection Report, Board of Trade, 26 February 1904.
122 Thomas, p122.
123 *Buffalo Courier Express*, 12 January 1934.
124 Haigh, Discussion p43.
125 *The Railway Gazette*, 27 September 1946.
126 Haigh, p28
127 Pennick, p21.
128 *The Engineer*, 4 April 1902.
129 *The Lancet*, 22 December 1900.
130 Croome & Jackson, p69, and Pennick, p21.
131 Haigh, p37.
132 Haigh, Discussion p76.
133 *The Engineer*, 27 March 1903.
134 *Page's Magazine*, July 1903.
135 *The Times*, 2 May 1900.
136 Smith, p245.
137 Badsey-Ellis & Horne, p8.
138 Smith, p242.
139 *The Railway Times*, 15 June 1907.
140 Groves, Discussion, p57.
141 *The Times*, 29 September 1903.
142 *The Railway Times*, 15 June 1907.
143 Badsey-Ellis (*Hampstead Tube*), p22.
144 See Jackson, Alastair A., *The Development of Steel Framed Buildings in Britain 1880 – 1905* (Construction History Vol. 14 1998) for more details.
145 *A Brief History of the Lots Road Power Station and site*.
146 *The Tramway & Railway World*, 12 November 1903.
147 Sheppard, p117.
148 Jackson, p24.
149 *Train Omnibus Tram* (Staff Magazine), February 1927.
150 *Underground News*, November 2012.
151 Lascelles, p18.
152 *Requirements of the Board of Trade in regard to the precautions to be taken against the risk of Accident by Fire on*

Underground Electric Railways, Draft – 22 September 1903.

153 GN&CR Inspection Report, Board of Trade, 26 February 1904.

154 *The Engineer*, 8 January 1915.

155 See Rose for more information on the UERL tiling.

156 *Requirements of the Board of Trade in regard to the precautions to be taken against the risk of Accident by Fire on Underground Electric Railways*, May 1904.

157 BoT Inspection Report for GN&CR, 26 February 1904.

158 *The Railway Magazine*, December 1936.

159 Horne (*Oxford Circus*), p4.

160 *The Engineer*, 17 October 1902.

161 *The Engineer*, 9 March 1906.

162 *The Engineer*, 5 June 1914.

163 *The Tramway & Railway World*, 6 December 1906.

164 Memorandum to BoT, 28 January 1904.

165 *The Railway Times* 27 May 1911.

166 *The Times*, 10 May 1911.

167 *Electrical Review*, 17 May 1912.

168 Ozonair brochure.

169 *The Engineer*, 17 May 1912.

170 *Operating Manager's Personal Letter No. 7*, 6 April 1929.

171 *The Daily News*, 11 May 1897.

172 *The Daily News*, 30 July 1897.

173 *The Times*, 20 January 1898.

174 *The Tramway & Railway World*, 2 May 1907.

175 Jones & Curry, Discussion p219.

176 *The Railway Times*, 4 May 1907.

177 http://machorne.blogspot.co.uk/2013/05/escalators-inclined-elevators-and-myths.html

178 Board of Trade: Inspection Report, 5 October 1911.

179 National Archives file MT6/8135

180 *The Tramway & Railway World*, 8 August 1912.

181 *Train Omnibus Tram* (Staff Magazine), 28 March 1914.

182 *The Railway Gazette*, 3 April 1914.

183 *Train Omnibus Tram* (Staff Magazine), 28 March 1914.

184 *The Times*, 5 February 1913.

185 *The Engineer*, 18 November 1921.

186 Jones & Curry, Discussion p212.

187 Jones & Curry, p186.

188 *The Times*, 26 September 1922.

189 *Re-opening of the City & South London Railway*, 1924.

190 Jones & Curry, Discussion p222.

191 Follenfant, p11.

192 *The Engineer*, 19 January 1923.

193 Jones & Curry, p180.

194 Jones & Curry, Discussion p214.

195 *The Times*, 29 November 1923.

196 *Reopening of the City and South London Railway*, p18.

197 Jones & Curry, p185.

198 *Ibid.*, p191.

199 Jones & Curry, Discussion p215.

200 Report by the Inspecting Officers of Railways: City & South London Railway, 20 February 1924.

201 Lascelles, p40.

202 Quoted in *The Times*, 29 November 1923.

203 Jones & Curry, p195.

204 Badsey-Ellis (*Hampstead Tube*), p60.

205 *The Tramway & Railway World*, 20 December 1923.

206 Jones & Curry, p198.

207 *The Tramway & Railway World*, 18 September 1924.

208 Davis, p340-3.

209 *The Engineer*, 17 September 1926.

210 *The Engineer*, 13 August 1926.

211 Badsey-Ellis (*Hampstead Tube*), p93.

212 *The Railway Magazine*, December 1956.

213 *The Times*, 5 February 1913.

214 *The Railway Times*, 4 November 1911.

215 Hall, Discussion, p182 and p189.

216 Hall, Discussion, p186.

217 *The Railway Times*, 5 December 1908.

218 *The Times*, 23 May 1933.

219 Follenfant, p36.

220 *The Railway Gazette*, 2 February 1940.

221 *Engineering*, 17 November 1933.

222 *The Railway Gazette*, 3 May 1935.

223 Horne (*Piccadilly Tube*), p69, 74.

224 *The London Railway Record*, April 2002.

225 Carpenter, p11.

226 *The Railway Gazette*, supplement 18 November 1932.

227 Follenfant, p138.

228 *The Railway Gazette*, supplement 18

November 1932.

229 *The London Railway Record*, April 2002 and July 2002.

230 *Train Omnibus Tram* (Staff Magazine), October 1932.

231 Lawrence, p43.

232 Croome & Jackson, p198.

233 *The Engineer*, 14 August 1936.

234 *The Engineer*, 19 August 1938.

235 *Pennyfare*, July 1937.

236 *Railways*, June 1940.

237 *The Times*, 3 February 1938.

238 *The Engineer*, 4 November 1938.

239 *The Railway Gazette: Improving London's Transport*, 15 May 1946.

240 Groves, p12.

241 *The Engineer*, 15 June 1951.

242 *Meccano Magazine*, June 1939.

243 *Meccano Magazine*, March 1947.

244 *Meccano Magazine*, June 1939.

245 Groves, p18.

246 Craig & Muir Wood, p136.

247 Craig & Muir Wood, p135.

248 *Pennyfare*, May 1938.

249 *The Railway Magazine*, January 1964.

250 *The Engineer*, 4 March 1949.

251 *Seven More Stations*, p13.

252 *The Railway Magazine*, December 1936.

253 *Underground News*, October 2007.

254 *The Engineer*, 26 November 1937.

255 *The Railway Gazette: Improving London's Transport*, 15 May 1946.

256 Harley-Mason, p503.

257 *The Engineer*, 1 December 1939.

258 *Meccano Magazine*, April 1940.

259 *Underground News*, February 2004.

260 *The Times*, 6 October 1939.

261 *Underground News*, November 2003.

262 Emmerson & Beard, p174.

263 *The Engineer*, 4 December 1942.

264 Darroch, p118.

265 *London Plan Working Party Report*, §22.

266 Turner, Discussion, p578.

267 King, p11.

268 Craig & Muir Wood, p15.

269 Dunton, Kell & Morgan, p7.

270 *Underground*, September 1962.

271 Dunton, Kell & Morgan, p8.

272 King, p15.

273 *The Railway Magazine*, June 1963.

274 Dunton, Kell & Morgan, Discussion, p447.

275 *Underground*, July 1965.

276 *Illustrated London News*, 7 August 1965.

277 Day, p60.

278 *Concrete Quarterly*, October 1966.

279 London Transport Museum and London Irish Centre: oral history.

280 http://tonyconboy.blogspot.co.uk/2009/12/victoria-line-pony-boy.html

281 Turner, Discussion, p570.

282 Day, p72.

283 Dunton, Kell & Morgan, Discussion, p452.

284 Powell, p188.

285 London Transport Annual Report 1960.

286 *Underground*, October 1963.

287 *Underground*, Vol XIV No.3 , June 1976.

288 Jobling & Lyons, Discussion, p719.

289 *Ibid*, p719 and p732.

290 King, p24.

291 Mitchell, p190, and Jobling & Lyons, Discussion, p728.

292 Jobling & Lyons, Discussion, p721.

293 Craig & Muir Wood, p25.

294 King, p24.

295 Jobling & Lyons, Discussion, p723.

296 *Concrete Quarterly*, October 1966.

297 Cuthbert, Lyons & Bubbers, Discussion, p136.

298 *LT Magazine*, December 1972.

299 Wort & Bennett, p46.

300 *Underground News*, 13 October 1978.

301 Sabine & Skelton, p1262.

302 *Underground News*, December 1983 and June 1984.

303 Sabine & Skelton, p1269.

304 *Ibid.*, p1266.

305 http://underground-history.co.uk/heathrow.php

306 *The Railway Magazine*, March 1962.

307 *Underground*, September 1964, and Follenfant, p85.

308 *Tunnel & Bridge Assessments: LUL Bakerloo line tunnels (Waterloo to Embankment)*, Thames Tideway Tunnel Application for Development Consent (Doc. Ref. 9.15.70), September 2013.

309 *London Lines*, Summer 1997.

310 *Daily Telegraph*, 5 March 1997.

311 *New Civil Engineer*, 10 April 1997.
312 Jones & Curry, p178.
313 Burgess, Fagents & Paterson, p1.
314 Follenfant, p157.
315 Rainey, p129.
316 *Old Street Remedial Works*, Morgan Est project profile.
317 *Underground News*, June 1997.
318 Burgess, Fagents & Paterson, p7.
319 *Underground News*, November 1996.
320 *New Civil Engineer*, 30 May 2013.
321 Tube Lines HSE Alert 172, 14 August 2012.
322 *On the Move* (LU in-house magazine), June 2014.
323 TfL Investment Programme Report 2014/15 Q1.
324 Craig & Muir Wood, p14.
325 *New Civil Engineer*, 11 November 1999.
326 Bartlett, Biggart & Triggs, Discussion, p351.
327 *The London Railway Record*, Early Jubilee Line extension plans, April 1999.
328 Bartlett, Biggart & Triggs, p611.
329 Bartlett, Biggart & Triggs, Discussion, p358.
330 *New Scientist*, 21 September 1972.
331 *One Hundred Years of Transportation*, Mott MacDonald, 2002.
332 *Underground News*, January 1987.
333 *Underground News*, September 1987.
334 *The Times*, 5 August 1938.
335 Botelle, Payne & Redhead, p115.
336 Mitchell. p5.
337 *Building*, 7 April 1995.
338 Mitchell, p222.
339 *Building*, 7 April 1995.
340 *World Tunnelling*, Jubilee Line Extension supplement, February 1996.
341 Mitchell, p196.
342 *World Tunnelling*, Jubilee Line Extension supplement, February 1996.
343 *New Civil Engineer*, 8 November 2012.
344 Chapman, Metje, and Stärk, p189.
345 *New Civil Engineer*, Jubilee Line Extension supplement, February 1994.
346 *New Civil Engineer*, 1 August 1999.
347 *New Civil Engineer*, Jubilee Line Extension supplement, September 1996.
348 Mitchell, p164.
349 *New Civil Engineer*, Jubilee Line Extension supplement, September 1996.
350 London Bridge Station overall modernisation works: Briefing November 1995 (LUL)
351 *New Civil Engineer*, Jubilee Line Extension supplement, September 1996.
352 *T5 inform*, Spring 2005.
353 Chapman, Metje, and Stärk, p135.
354 *New Civil Engineer*, 1 February 2004.
355 Jäger and Stärk, p44.
356 *Tunnels and Tunnelling International*, October 2005.
357 Chapman, Metje, and Stärk, p319.
358 *London East-West Study*, p11.
359 Hickman, p94.
360 *Modern Railways*, December 2013.
361 *Modern Railways*, February 2012.
362 *The Engineer*, 2 April 2012.
363 *New Civil Engineer*, 30 June 2011.
364 *Transport Briefing*, 11 February 2010.
365 *New Civil Engineer*, Crossrail Major Project Report, June 2012.
366 Pickett, and *New Civil Engineer*, Crossrail Half Way Major Project Report, June 2014.
367 *New Civil Engineer*, 17 May 2012.
368 *The Railway Engineer*, September 2015, and site visit to Eastern Ticket Hall, September 2015.
369 *New Civil Engineer*, Crossrail Major Project Report, June 2012.
370 *New Civil Engineer*, 12 September 2013.
371 *The Rail Engineer*, August 2013.
372 *New Civil Engineer*, 12 December 2013.
373 *The Rail Engineer*, August 2013.
374 *New Civil Engineer*, Crossrail Major Project Report, June 2012.
375 *Rail*, 18 April 2012.
376 *New Civil Engineer*, 1 March 2012.
377 *The Rail Engineer*, January 2013.
378 *New Civil Engineer*, 2 June 2011.
379 *New Civil Engineer*, 23 August 2012, and Pérez Lupi *et al.*, p190.
380 McClements, p46.

Index

Notes:
There may be more than one reference on the page indicated. Entries in italics include an illustration.